PRIMATE EVOLUTION

The Evolution of Primate Behavior
Alison Jolly

The Ascent of Man
David Pilbeam

The Macmillan Series in Physical Anthropology
Elwyn L. Simons and David Pilbeam, editors
other volumes in preparation

Elwyn L. Simons

YALE UNIVERSITY

PRIMATE EVOLUTION

AN INTRODUCTION TO MAN'S PLACE IN NATURE

The Macmillan Series in Physical Anthropology

Macmillan Publishing Co., Inc.
NEW YORK
Collier Macmillan Publishers
LONDON

This book is dedicated to my parents,
Verne and Verna (Cuddeback) Simons, and
to my children, Katherine and David.

Macmillan Publishing Co., Inc.
866 Third Avenue, New York, New York 10022

Collier-Macmillan Canada, Ltd.
Toronto, Ontario

Library of Congress catalog card number: 70-156980

Printing: Year:
  3 4 5 6 7 8 9   4 5 6 7 8 9

Preface

Man in his innate curiosity has throughout many ages and cultures often raised the question of the relation of humanity to the natural world. Many solutions to this perplexing problem have been put forward in myth and legend, primitive religion and classical philosophy, science and literature, each solution adapted to the levels of understanding prevailing in a particular time and place but each essentially an attempt to find answers to the eternal riddles: Why are we? Where did we come from? What is our purpose and our future? Paleontological science gives answers to the part of these questions dealing with the history of vertebrate life and eventually of the primates and man. Nevertheless, much of what appears to be a basic human need, that of understanding the place of man in the universe, lies outside the area of descriptive and interpretive science. These other parts have traditionally been dealt with by theologians and philosophers. Consequently, this book will deal with what happened in the history of the close relatives of man and of man himself. Why this happened remains a matter of individual belief.

Until about a hundred years ago, the mute fossil testament of our past lay unknown or unrecognized in the deep places of the earth. Men, too, were slumbering, being either unable or unwilling to read the difficult but fascinating story of vertebrate evolution that the earth had to tell. As is well known, the development of the concepts of organic evolution and natural selection originating in publications by the great British naturalists Darwin and Wallace in 1858 and 1859 left man's world a radically different place than it had been before. Since then, ideas of organic evolution and constant change in culture and language have influenced not only the natural sciences but the humanities as well.

How did these concepts affect the study and discovery of the evolutionary record of man and other primates? In 1859, the science of paleontology was already an ancient subject, with roots in the writings of Pliny and Lucretius, that, after the slow reawakening during the High Renaissance, had languished for two centuries under the odium of propounding the existence of extinct or "lost" species. Until as late as the end of the eighteenth century, it was widely believed even among the learned that the structure or economy of nature was such that species could not become extinct. The pious felt also that extinction of species was untenable because it implied an imperfection in God as creator. Nevertheless, there had been flashes of light. In the sixteenth century, Leonardo da Vinci observed cogently that fossil shells recovered during construction of canals in Northern Italy were not like existing types and that their inland occurrence indicated that the sea had once covered the area where they were found. Later, Gesner in Switzerland and Andreas Seucher in Germany played their part in bringing attention to the existence of "lost species" in the surface deposits of the earth.

Coincident with the French Revolution began the great contributions of Baron Georges Cuvier in Paris, which by the end of the first half of the nineteenth century had copiously demonstrated the existence of vast numbers of extinct species, not only of plants, invertebrates, and lower vertebrates, but of mammals as well. Even so, the beginnings of our knowledge of primate evolution were indeed faint. When Darwin published *Origin of Species* in 1859, only five extinct nonhuman primate species had been recovered from ancient sediments and described. The most ancient of these, *Adapis*, a lemur-like form from French Eocene deposits, had been described by Cuvier himself in 1822, but it had not yet been generally recognized as a member of the Primates. Cuvier took it to be a primitive ungulate or pachyderm. Somewhat later (1837), the brilliant French lawyer and paleontologist Édouard Lartet reported from the Miocene deposits at Sansan (Gers), France, the mandible of an apelike creature he thought ancestral to the living gibbons. This he called *Pliopithecus antiquus*. In 1839, Wagner described the first known fossil monkey, *Mesopithecus*, from Pliocene deposits near Athens. In 1846, the British geologist Wood described the dentition of a fossil prosimian from freshwater Eocene deposits at Hordwell, Hampshire; this he named *Microchoerus erineceous*. However, as the name (meaning "hedgehog-like tiny hog") implies, Wood did not recognize the primate affinities of this species. Over 20 years after Lartet's find of *Pliopithecus* was announced (in 1856), he secured most of the mandible of another larger ape from Miocene limy sands, similar to those of Sansan, at Saint Gaudens, France. This he named *Dryopithecus*—the famous "oak ape." Lartet believed this animal to be a close relative of man. Discovery of a form so clearly related to man had the effect of reminding mid-nineteenth-century geologists and paleontologists that human remains might occur also in fossil form and be associated with extinct animals. Indeed, although their significance was not widely understood, stone age human remains had also been discovered by this time. Among these was the so-called Red Lady of Paviland reported in 1823 by Professor Buckland of Oxford. This find from Goat's Hole, Paviland, South Wales, is now recognized as truly ancient. The body is painted with red ochre, a late stone age practice seen in numerous Upper Paleolithic burials in France and elsewhere in Europe, and artifacts of mammoth ivory also suggestive of its antiquity were in contact with this skeleton. Buckland himself did not believe that the artifacts had been carved from fresh ivory, and he suggested that the "lady," subsequently shown to be a man, dated from about the time of the Roman Conquest of Britain. Perhaps more significant than the Paviland discovery were the fossils (one at least of which later proved to be a neandertal child) reported in 1833–1834 by Schmerling, anatomist at the University of Liège, from the cave of Engis about 8 miles southwest of Liège. The antiquity of these fossils was also doubted by many, although Schmerling presented adequate evidence of their association with extinct species of rhinoceroses and mammoths. Eventually, Sir Charles Lyell, the eminent British geologist, recognized and published the antiquity of the Engis finds, but Schmerling's discoveries were not initially given much credence.

The description of *Dryopithecus fontani* from Saint Gaudens was widely heralded, for Lartet and his associate at the Paris Museum, Albert Gaudry, stated that *Dryopithecus* was more closely related to man than any other known primate, living or fossil, an opinion from which Gaudry (1890) later retreated with the discovery of more material. More than a hundred years ago, these few primate and human fossils set the stage for the unfolding of our knowledge of the evolutionary history of our own order of Mammalia. Recovery of fossil nonhuman and human remains was accelerated in the 1860s and 1870s, and growth of scientific understanding of their meaning has continued with greater and greater depth up to the present. We may, therefore, hope that within the next few decades the major details of our evolutionary development from more primitive forms will become available. The present volume is an attempt to report progress to date.

The study of primate evolution is now proceeding on a worldwide basis that ignores nearly all political and cultural boundaries. I should like to take this opportunity to credit the following scientists interested in the study of evolution and of vertebrate or primate history. They have either given their time in discussion or correspondence on this subject or have allowed me to examine fossil members of this order in their respective collections (or both) in the course of gathering the background data for this book: K. D. Adam, P. Andrews, R. Andrews, the late Camille Arambourg, D. Baird, Josef Biegert, Emil Breitinger, John and Vina Buettner-Janusch, Eduard Casier, M. M. Chow, J. Clark, E. S. Colbert, C. S. Coon, A. W. Crompton, Raymond Dart, the late W. O. Dietrich, Theodosius Dobzhansky, the late T. Edinger, L. Eiseley, G. Erickson, J. Frisch, C. L. Gazin, J. T. Gregory, D. A. Hooijer, the late A. T. Hopwood, F. C. Howell, J. Hürzeler, G. E. Hutchinson, G. L. Jepsen, C. J. Jolly, H.-D. Kahlke, the late J. Kälin, G. Krumbiegel, René Lavocat, W. E. Le Gros Clark, L. S. B. Leakey, R. E. F. Leakey, J.-P. Lehman, G. E. Lewis, H. W. Matthes, Ernst Mayr, D. G. MacInnes, M. C. McKenna, J. R. Napier, K. P. Oakley, J. H. Ostrom, Bryan Patterson, D. R. Pilbeam, K. N. Prasad, Leonard Radinsky, C. L. Remington, J. T. Robinson, A. S. Romer, D. E. Russell, D. E. Savage, A. H. Schultz, G. G. Simpson, Ronald Singer, T. D. Stewart, W. S. Straus, F. S. Szalay, I. M. Tattersall, Heinz Tobien, W. D. Turnbull, R. L. Tuttle, G. H. R. von Koenigswald, S. L. Washburn, J. S. Weiner, R. W. Wilson, T. Whitworth, Ju-Kang Woo, and Helmut Zapfe.

I should particularly like to thank my students for much stimulating discussion and for material assistance in putting together parts of the text. I must also thank all those who have over the years devoted their enthusiasm and energies to the field researches, on three continents, that it has been my privilege to direct. These friends are far too numerous to list here by name, but a special acknowledgment is due Grant E. Meyer, to whom much of the credit for the success of these expeditions belongs. He has himself discovered many fossils important to the understanding of primate evolution.

Students and staff who have been of particular assistance in putting together this book, apart from those already listed, are Friderun Ankel, Thomas Bown, Glenn Conroy, Peter Ettel, John Fleagle, Richard Kay, Fredericka Oakley, David Roberts, Kenneth Rose, and Yale illustrators Rosanne Rowen and Carl Wester. Many of the excellent photographs were taken by A. H. Coleman, and much of the manuscript typing was done by Louise Holtzinger, both of the Peabody Museum, Yale University.

Essential parts of my own research summarized in this book were funded by generous grants from the National Science Foundation (four from the earth sciences section and one from the anthropology section) and from the Smithsonian Foreign Currency Program (two grants), the Wenner-Gren Foundation (two), and the Boise Fund of Oxford University (two).

E. L. S.

Contents

Geologic Setting

HISTORY OF STUDY AND DISTRIBUTION

The initial reports of fossil primates that came out in the nineteenth century consisted almost entirely of descriptions of specific new fossil types. The sites of these finds were scattered over a wide area but were principally located in the Northern Hemisphere. The ages of the deposits from which these fossils came ranged across the successive Tertiary epochs. As a consequence, it was hardly possible for anyone to attempt a general synthesis of primate history during the first hundred years of their recovery as fossils (1821–1921), and indeed no one did so. Moreover, with the typical taxonomic enthusiasms of the last century, many of the earliest described primates were more than once published as new kinds of animals when they were not. For instance, specimens of the North American Eocene lemuroid primate *Notharctus*, described initially by Leidy in 1870, were subsequently named as the types of several synonymous genera: *Hypposyus* Leidy, 1872; *Tomitherium* Cope, 1872a; *Thinolestes, Telmalestes,* and *Telmatolestes* all Marsh, 1872; and *Prosinopa* Trouessart, 1891.

Schlosser (1887) published the first long review of the phylogeny of lemurs and apes, after early studies at Yale. This dealt principally with European fossils. Branco (1898) concerned himself with fossil apes from Tertiary fissure fills in Germany but included comments on finds from other regions. Jacob Wortman (1903, 1904) reported in detail on the early primates in the Marsh collection of Tertiary fossils at Yale. His review was the first extensive account in English of primate fossils. Several earlier publications had come out on the subject, including those of Cope (1872a,b, 1873, 1881, 1883), Leidy (1869, 1870, 1873), Marsh (1872), Lartet (1837, 1856), Gervais (1852, 1872, 1877), Rütimeyer (1862, 1891), and Lemoine (1878). The Argentine paleontologist Florentino Ameghino, in a series of papers (1891, 1892, 1898, 1902, 1904), described several Tertiary primates from South America, but also attributed primate status to other fossils that actually do not belong in the order.

In 1911, Schlosser produced his monographic account of mammals of the Fayum Oligocene of Egypt in which were included the initial descriptions of the oldest then known catarrhines, *Parapithecus* and *Propliopithecus.* Meanwhile, Osborn (1908) added another Egyptian Oligocene primate, *Apidium.* Soon after this, Professor Stehlin (1912, 1916) of Basel published two important accounts in German included in a critical catalogue of the mammals of the Swiss Eocene. Stehlin commented extensively on the various fossil genera and species belonging to the primate subfamilies Microchoerinae and Adapinae. By the time Scott (1913) had published his classic *A history of land mammals in the Western Hemisphere,* interpretation of New World fossil primates seemed so formidable that he entirely omitted a discussion of the order from his otherwise comprehensive study. Beginning with short publications, Gregory (1915, 1916, 1918) of the American Museum reviewed the relationships of *Notharctus* and the classification of lemurs generally. These studies were climaxed in 1920 with the publication of his memoir on *Notharctus,* which is the most exhaustive treatment ever afforded a single genus of prosimians, living or fossil. In 1922, in *The origin and evolution of the human dentition,* Gregory set forth his initial analysis of higher primate evolution, a matter he dealt with later in more detail (Gregory and Hellman, 1926; Gregory, Hellman, and Lewis, 1938). Grandidier (1904) and Teilhard de Chardin (1916, 1921, 1927) added to the knowledge of European Eocene primates. Remane (1921) presented a classic study of the dental variability of apes, although its pertinence to the classification of fossil apes was little recognized for many years. In the meantime, Gidley (1923) at the Smithsonian Institution had published his pioneering study of Paleocene primates. In this paper, he made the first explicit attempt to summarize the common features thought to be typical of basal primates. In 1925, Dart announced the discovery of the early Pleistocene hominid of South Africa, *Australopithecus*. Pilgrim (1915, 1927) reviewed the known material of Indian fossil apes and described several forms he thought to be new.

Abel (1931) contributed the first extensive and critically composed study of the whole range of extinct primates under the title *Die Stellung des Menschen im Rahmen der Wirbeltiere*, although Schlosser (1923) had previously produced a fairly extensive comment on fossil primates for the fourth German edition of von Zittel's well-known paleontology text. The taxonomic scheme of Abel's work is now long outdated, but otherwise the study still provides much useful information.

During the 1930s and 1940s a considerable number of new names for past primates were published. These were included in reports by Broom (1936, 1939), Heller (1935), Hopwood (1933, 1934), Jepsen (1930a,b, 1934), Lamberton (1934), Lewis (1934, 1937), MacInnes (1943), Simpson (1935a,b, 1937a, 1940), Stock (1933), and Weigelt (1933). Weidenreich (1945) dealt with Peking man and *Gigantopithecus*. Von Koenigswald (1935, 1940, 1952) also contributed to the knowledge of *Gigantopithecus* and Java man. Le Gros Clark (1934a,b, 1946, 1950) produced a series of important papers and books on primate history and on fossils related to man.

Hürzeler (1946, 1948, 1949, 1954, 1958) dealt with Eocene *Necrolemur* and its allies, with *Oreopithecus*, and with *Pliopithecus* in Europe. After 1950, the number of studies of living and fossil primates increased to the point that only a few of the longer works of this period can be mentioned. Studies that dealt either with particular groups of primates or with primates from particular parts of the Tertiary include Simpson (1955) on *Phenacolemur*; Le Gros Clark and Leakey (1951), Le Gros Clark and Thomas (1952), and Le Gros Clark (1956) on the fossil Hominoidea of East Africa; Gazin (1958) on North American early Eocene primates; Napier and Davis (1959) on the forelimb skeleton of *Dryopithecus* (= *Proconsul*)* *africanus*; Zapfe (1960) on the Czechoslovakian finds of *Pliopithecus*; Simons (1961a, 1962a) on European Eocene primates; Russell (1964) in a review of European Paleocene mammals with descriptions of new primates; Simons and Pilbeam (1965) on the dryopithecines. Russell, Louis, and Savage (1967) reassessed and described new primate species of the French early Eocene.

Freedman (1957) on the fossil monkeys of South Africa and Robinson (1956) on the dentition of *Australopithecus* are also important sources of information. General surveys of fossil primates were produced by Heberer (1956), Remane (1956, 1965), and Simons (1963a). A current long account (in German) of fossil primates is that of Thenius (1969). The most useful reviews of fossil and living

---

*Enclosing a generic name in parentheses and preceding it by an equal sign (=) means that it is a junior synonym of the name immediately in front of it. Parentheses around a generic name without an equal sign mean that it is a subgenus of the name preceding it. A generic name that is in quotes or that is not set in italics is an invalid name. A "cf." before a name means that the particular find concerned should be compared with specimens of the name following it.

primates (in French) are those of Piveteau (1957) and Genet-Varcin (1963, 1969). Gregory's (1951) *Evolution emerging* provides interesting summary statements of his views on primate evolution. General revisions or surveys of fossil members of the group include McKenna (1963a, 1966) on the earliest primates and Simons (1962a, 1963a,b, 1964a,b, 1965a, 1968) on various Fayum Oligocene forms, on primate taxonomy, and on *Ramapithecus*. Szalay (1967) presents some novel points of view on the earliest primates.

The literature on living primates and on middle and late Pleistocene fossil men is too extensive to be covered in full here, but it seems worthwhile to mention a few more interesting studies. Elliot's (1913) *A review of the primates* was one of the most comprehensive early studies. Wood-Jones' (1916) *Arboreal man* and Gregory's (1910) *The orders of mammals* present a number of early points of discussion. Pocock (1925, 1926) reviewed external characters of the living primates; the series on primates by Hill begun in 1953 and still in process of publication deals principally with the taxonomy and anatomy of the living primates and is the most exhaustive, if somewhat heterogeneous, coverage of the primate literature currently available. Fiedler (1956) has written a well-organized short review of living forms. James (1960) on the jaws and teeth of primates and Napier and Napier (1967) in *A handbook of living primates* provide useful current references on the dentition anatomy and ecology of living primates.

In the area of human paleontology alone, Boule (1921), writing in French, produced one of the earliest accounts of the record of fossil man. Because of many new finds, as well as new dates for previously known fossils, most books on this subject published before the 1960s are now out of date. Of interest are Weidenreich's (1945) *Apes, giants, and man* and Hooton's (1932) *Up from the ape.* Other texts of value have been written by Le Gros Clark (1955, 1959). The most useful current books in English on human paleontology are those by Howells (1965), Buettner-Janusch (1966), Campbell (1966), Pfeiffer (1969), Pilbeam (1970), and Tattersall (1970). Le Gros Clark's (1967) recent book *Man-apes or ape-men?* is the best account of personalities and the course of discoveries that contributed to our developing understanding of *Australopithecus* in Africa. Day (1965) presents a useful photographic guide to the more important fossil hominids now known.

DATING METHODS AND GEOLOGIC TIME

According to estimates, the earth is more than $4\frac{1}{2}$ billion years old, a calculation that has recently received dramatic confirmation by the dates of moon rocks. Although the surface of the moon has changed relatively little since its original formation, that of the earth has been repeatedly subjected to the processes of mountain building, erosion, and deep burial of sediments. For this reason, the earth's surface does not now contain any remnants of the original rocks, so far as we know. Apparently, the oldest rocks now surviving on the earth are the Montevedes and Morton granites of the Minnesota River Valley, which date back to 3,300 million years ago.

As is the case for the dating of the whole history of life on the earth, there are two basic approaches to the dating of primate history. These are the "relative" time scale method, in which the sequences of fossils from successive layers of rock are determined, and the "absolute" or atomic dating method, which derives its dates from calculations based on the natural radioactive breakdown that takes place in certain sedimentary and volcanic rocks after they are formed.

In the late eighteenth century, the Scottish geologist James Hutton first propounded two principles which have proven basic to geologic studies. These were the principles of "superposition" and "uniformitarianism." He recognized that where rocks are found in relatively undistorted layered form the oldest is the lowermost and proceeding upward each deposit is successively younger. His idea of uniformitarianism was that the processes whereby rocks are built and subsequently buried or eroded away must have always gone on in a manner and at a rate similar to that obtaining today.

Just before 1800, the British surveyor William Smith pointed out that almost every sedimentary rock formation contains a characteristic suite of fossils and that these groups of characteristic fossil types succeed each other in a regular manner. He also grasped the facts that such characteristic combinations of fossils can be found again in sites far from the place of their original discovery, and that wherever a distinctive group of animals or fauna occurs it represents the same time period. Early paleontologists, such as Baron Cuvier, began to discover successive faunas of vertebrate fossils. One of the first of these successive series was collected from rocks of the basin surrounding Paris. These included a series of faunas originally deposited on land and coming from the early part of the age of mammals. Lamarck noticed that each succeeding stage contains a different group of mammals, and he first put forth the idea that floods or other catastrophes destroyed the animals of the Paris Basin and that then a new suite of animals entered the region from elsewhere. Actually, we now know that such faunal changes take place through a complex combination of phenomena: some species evolve into different, more advanced forms, other species migrate to distant areas or become extinct, and species from other regions come into an area for the first time.

Study of the fossils of land vertebrates contained in a sedimentary rock series provides a relative method for dating the age of such deposits. This is because certain animal species achieve broad ranges; but because of continuous change during their evolution, they do not exist very long before they evolve into something else. Such animals are often referred to as "index fossils." Wherever such a form occurs, it indicates a particular time or small segment of earth history when and only when that particular form existed.

Wide-ranging oceanic fossil protozoans are the best index fossils because they may occur throughout oceans of the entire world. Nevertheless, some mammal and even primate fossils are useful in indicating particular time zones. For instance, the dawn horse *Hyracotherium* and the earliest notharctine lemuroid *Pelycodus* are abundant in Western North America in early Eocene deposits. The fact that they also turn up in Eocene sediments of the Paris Basin and in the London clay shows that these latter deposits are of the same approximate age as are such American early Eocene deposits as the Willwood Formation of the Bighorn Basin, Wyoming. Such fossils "relatively" date the rocks in which they occur. However, for more precise dating, one must turn to geochemistry.

All the geologic clocks work on the same principle, that of natural radioactive decay of unstable forms or isotopes of reasonably common elements occurring in sedimentary rocks. In this process the "parent" atom loses particles from its nucleus spontaneously to form a "daughter" atom of a different element. The rate of decay is unalterable by outside factors such as pressure, temperature, or lapse of time. In consequence, if the amount of the original unstable isotope remaining in a rock sample and the amount of the "daughter" element produced by decay can be isolated from the same sample, then the ratio between them will tell how long it has been since that particular rock formed. The rate of decay is expressed by convention as the "half-life," that is, the amount of time it takes for half of the original "parent" atoms contained to have decayed to the "daughter" form. Unlike conventional depletion, in this process the amount of unstable isotope declines to an infinitely small amount (see Figure 1). As far as Tertiary and human events are concerned, there are three such decay sequences that are of principal value: potassium–argon, uranium–lead, and carbon–nitrogen.

Currently accepted half-lives are

Element	Half-Life
Potassium^{40}-Argon^{40}	1.3 billion years
Uranium^{235}-Lead^{207}	713 million years
Carbon^{14}-Nitrogen^{14}	5,000 years

Carbon-14 is produced at a constant rate through the action of cosmic rays in the upper atmosphere. By means of the cycle of biological processes, it eventually finds its way into all living things. At death, input of C^{14} ceases. Consequently, if a buried log has only three fourths as much C^{14} as a fresh log it would be about 2,000 years old, if only one half as much it would be 5,000 years old, and so forth. However, this process is useful for dating only the very latest stages of human evolution, for by the time that a plant or bone is as much as 40,000 years old essentially all measurable traces of C^{14} are gone. In consequence, plant remains used to date cave dwellings or living floors older than that upper limit only indicate an age of 40,000 + B.P. (before present).

Most of the history of man, the nonhuman primates, and Creta-

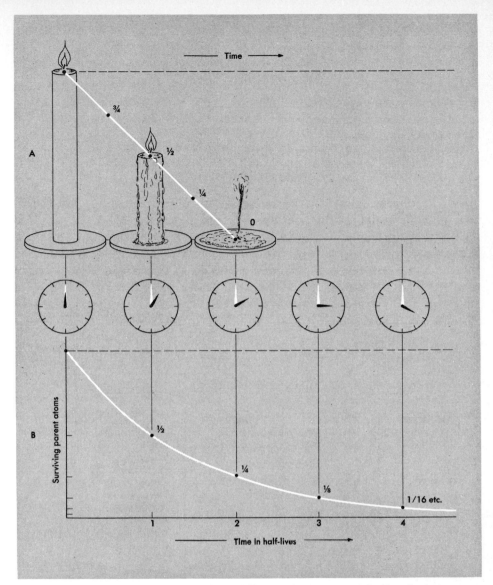

Figure 1 Diagram of the difference between straight-line depletion and radioactive decay. *A:* Uniform straight-line depletion of most everyday processes. *B:* By contrast, the radioactive decay curve approaches zero line asymptotically. The end of one half-life interval is the beginning of a new one. (From Eicher, 1968. © 1968. Reproduced by permission of Prentice-Hall, Inc.)

ceous–Tertiary placental mammals draws its absolute dates from the potassium–argon and the uranium–lead methods. Fortunately, the objective of dating Tertiary land mammals is facilitated by the fact that the unstable isotopes of uranium and potassium are often laid down in sufficient amounts to be measured subsequently in

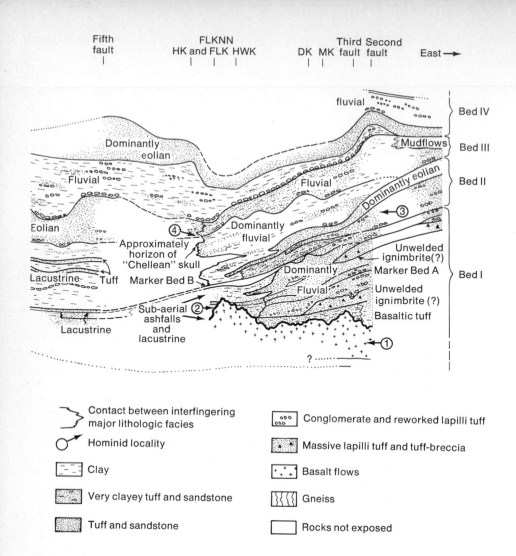

Figure 2 Varied sediments at Olduvai Gorge, Tanzania, have conventionally been divided into five beds from bottom to top. K/Ar ages have been obtained from repeated datings of the basalt and other sediments. Numbered horizons have been dated, and they show that several successive parts of the Pleistocene Epoch are represented there. Ages of the four sites are

1. Basalt at base of Bed I: 1.92 ± .06 million years.
2. Twelve inches above *"Zinjanthropus"* living floor, Bed I: 1.86 ± .06 million years.
3. Middle or lower Bed II: approximately 1.5 million years.
4. Overlies Chellean II, top of Bed II: approximately 1.0 million years.

(After Hay, 1963. Copyright 1963 by the American Association for the Advancement of Science.)

ash falls and lava flows. In practice, this is more often the case with the potassium isotope. The method of dating a rock sample by the potassium–argon method (K/Ar dating) involves several factors. First, the lava or tuff must be examined to determine its porosity, for if it is very porous at least some of the argon gas formed by the radioactive decay will have leaked out of the rock, and to the extent that this has happened the date calculated will be too old. If suitable, the rock sample is heated to over 2,000 °F and the argon is trapped by a charcoal filter. Then the electrochemically charged argon atoms are fired by a mass spectrometer into a counting device that records their frequency. Because the half-life of K/Ar decay is so great (1.3 billion years), a difference of 100,000 to 300,000 years is only barely perceptible (if at all), because approximately only one billionth of the amount of potassium in a rock or mineral decays to Ar^{40} in 100,000 years. Thus, dates less than half a million years or so are meaningless because the margin of error is generally regarded as ±300,000 years. Most K/Ar dates have been determined only during the last 8 to 10 years; before then, the durations of successive subdivisions of the age of mammals were much less certainly known.

The most useful reviews of dates that relate to fossil primates are those of Evernden et al. (1964) and Evernden and Curtis (1965). One of the most interesting localities where K/Ar dating has been of interest to students of human evolution is Olduvai Gorge, Tanzania, which has produced about thirty early hominids, some of which are surely in or near the line of human ancestry. Figure 2 shows an idealized cross section of the Gorge, indicating sites of some of the hominid finds and some of the levels that have been geochemically dated. It was K/Ar dates determined from rock samples found in Olduvai Gorge that, in 1960, first established the antiquity of *Australopithecus* at more than $1\frac{3}{4}$ million years. This dramatic dating, which was more than twice most previous estimates for the age of *Australopithecus*, set the stage for much important geochemical dating of fossil primates during the past decade.

TERTIARY EPOCHS AND FAUNAL SUCCESSION

The fossil record of the primates, as we know it, is essentially synchronous with the Cenozoic Era, the age of mammals. This part of geologic history is commonly divided into two periods, the Tertiary and Quaternary, names that go back to the earliest days of geologic studies, when it was thought that the sedimentary rocks of the world precipitated out of the ocean in four principal phases. Long ago, it was recognized that the primary and secondary stages represented numerous periods of geologic time, now divided up into the many subdivisions of the Azoic, Proterozoic, Paleozoic, and Mesozoic Eras.

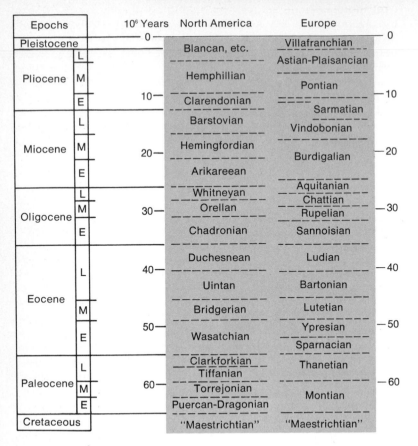

Epochs		10^6 Years	North America	Europe	
Pleistocene		0	Blancan, etc.	Villafranchian	0
Pliocene	L			Astian-Plaisancian	
	M		Hemphillian	Pontian	
	E	10	Clarendonian	Sarmatian	10
Miocene	L		Barstovian	Vindobonian	
	M	20	Hemingfordian	Burdigalian	20
	E		Arikareean		
Oligocene	L		Whitneyan	Aquitanian	
	M	30	Orellan	Chattian	30
				Rupelian	
	E		Chadronian	Sannoisian	
Eocene	L	40	Duchesnean	Ludian	40
			Uintan	Bartonian	
	M		Bridgerian	Lutetian	
	E	50	Wasatchian	Ypresian	50
				Sparnacian	
Paleocene	L		Clarkforkian	Thanetian	
			Tiffanian		
	M	60	Torrejonian	Montian	60
	E		Puercan-Dragonian		
Cretaceous			"Maestrichtian"	"Maestrichtian"	

Figure 3 Provincial ages and their absolute time correlations for the North American and European Tertiary, as determined by K/Ar dating. "E," "M," and "L" within epochs refer to the early, middle, and late third of each epoch, respectively. (After Evernden and Curtis, 1965.)

From fossils found principally in Eastern Asia and in North America we know that at the close of the last period of the Mesozoic Era, the Cretaceous, extensive changes in climate and topography of the land occurred and that primitive plants were increasingly replaced by the flowering plants or angiosperms. Even among the lower vertebrates, the formerly dominant forms such as the dinosaurs were on the wane, and reptiles of present-day sorts such as snakes, crocodiles, and lizards were becoming more abundant. The earliest placental mammals had made their appearance, but they were still competing on a nearly equal basis with pouched mammals and with even more primitive groups such as the multituberculate mammals. At this approximate period of time, the continents assumed outlines rather more similar to those of the present day than had been the case previously. This came about with the elevation and drying up of a number of inland seas in the Old World and in North America. However, we know that North America and Europe were then very close together, probably connected.

Throughout the nineteenth century, geologists were busy identifying and naming those sequences of rock that today are considered to make up the successive epochs of the Tertiary Period. These are the rocks from which comes essentially all our knowledge of the nature and course of evolution of our own order, Primates.

In the 1830s, the British geologist Sir Charles Lyell divided the Tertiary Period into three epochs: the Eocene (meaning "dawn" + "recent"), the Miocene (meaning "minor" + "recent"), and the Pliocene (meaning "major" + "recent"). Of course, Pliocene rock contains more ("major") modern ("recent") species, Miocene rock less, and Eocene rock the least. He then divided the Pliocene into a newer and an older half, finally coining the name Pleistocene for the newer half, a term now generally regarded as equivalent to the Quaternary Period of earlier geologists. Subsequent to this, it was recognized that sediments existed that preserved a historical record of two further time periods since the Cretaceous: one, the Paleocene, between Cretaceous and Eocene times (this was formerly called the Lower Eocene), and another, the Oligocene, between Eocene and Miocene times. Only in the past decade, with the determination of geochemical dates on an extensive basis, have the times of the beginning and ending of these last six epochs of earth history, and their subdivisions, been determined with considerable accuracy (see Figure 3). During these time periods the evolutionary development of the primates occurred and these animals played their initial role on the stage of mammalian events. A detailed record of all the exotic variety of land vertebrates that have appeared on the earth during the history of placental mammals would require a long book in itself, much longer than the present one. Nevertheless, it may be useful to set the background of the evolving primates, with a brief outline of each of these epochs, giving particular emphasis to the general sorts of environments that the primates successively occupied throughout the world.

Paleocene Epoch
(Duration: from about 65 million to about 58 million years ago)

Sediments of this age first delivered fossil mammals into the hands of the determined collector David Baldwin, then working for Professor Marsh at Yale, in the 1870s, but more than half a century elapsed before the Paleocene Epoch was generally recognized as a significant portion of the earth's history. Radioactive date determinations now indicate that it began some 65 million to 70 million years ago and ended 58 million or 59 million years ago. During the course of this epoch, mammalian evolution and diversification were very rapid, as if there had been some new breakthrough in what placental mammals were able to do. Primary theories as to the reason for this speed-up in mammalian diversification alternate between the idea that the placentals had by then evolved a more sophisticated metabolism that allowed for greater diversification and the idea that, with only the last dinosaurs as competing predators, larger size and radiation into numerous stocks were for the first time possible. Our most complete knowledge of Paleocene life comes from rocks in our western states, principally New Mexico, Colorado, Wyoming, and Montana. Much more is known about the earliest phases of the placental radiation in North America, but there are a few fossil sites in Europe and Asia that show that some of the animals were the same throughout the Northern Hemisphere. No land animals of the Paleocene are known from Africa, Australia, or Southern Asia, and what we do know of later Paleocene animals in South America shows a very different assortment of animals there and then. However, just at the end of the Paleocene, one species, *Arctostylops steini*, representing the notoungulates (a characteristic South American order) occurred in Wyoming. Its presence there indicates that there had to have been a transitory connection between the New World continents. During the middle Paleocene several different genera of primates made their appearance. Species of *Plesiadapis* ranged from France to Wyoming in the late Paleocene. The French prosimian *Berruvius*, a tiny animal no larger than a shrew, may be fairly closely related to *Navajovius* of the Colorado late Paleocene. All the evidence favors the view that primates arose in the Northern Hemisphere, but because of the close faunal association between Europe and North America we do not know whether this happened in the Eastern or the Western Hemisphere.

Plants indicate that Paleocene climates were mild, with floras similar to those of the Southern states of today ranging north into Canada and Alaska. The dominant mammalian herbivores were the condylarths, of which the sheep-sized *Phenacodus* was typical. In the latter third of this epoch the first mammals of large size— as large as cattle or tapirs—evolved. These were of two different orders: the pantodonts and the uintatheres. Toward the end of this epoch the marsupials, the multituberculates, and several of the archaic ungulate groups faded toward extinction and the first rodents and the ancestors of the fissiped (or "modern" carnivores) appeared. No present-day mammalian families had as yet differentiated.

Eocene Epoch
(Duration: from about 58 million to about 34 million years ago)

Fossil mammals of the Eocene Epoch are abundantly known in Western North America and in Europe and Asia. Only a handful of African Eocene mammals are preserved. Those occurring abundantly in South America are diversified but show little general resemblance to placentals elsewhere. At this time apparently all of the southern continents were separated from the northern. It is presently thought that at the beginning of this epoch Europe and North America were not much separated in the north and there were available cross-migration routes. Very recently published information would suggest that some of these routes were overland. Early Eocene faunas of the London-Paris regions are extraordinarily similar to those collected from the intermontane basins of the American West. At least two dozen genera and many species of mammals appear indistinguishable in the two regions. Moreover, the character of associated plants suggests a much warmer, wetter climate. Conditions of frost seldom occurred. Prosimians of more modern aspect were abundant, some resembling the living lower primates and others showing progressive features such as fusion of the two halves of the lower jaw at the symphysis, which is more characteristic of the higher primates. By this time essentially all the modern orders of mammals had differentiated. All the Paleocene groups of primates died out, but rodents and adapid and tarsioid prosimians became more common. The first bats and whales are found in rocks of this epoch. Uintatheres, some condylarths, and archaic carnivores (creodonts) persisted up to the end of the Eocene, by which time the radiations of the even-toed ungulates (Artiodactyla) and the odd-toed ungulates (Perissodactyla) were well underway.

Oligocene Epoch
(Duration: from about 34 million to about 25 million years ago)

In North America the percentage of plants indicating temperate climate increased during the Oligocene. With the general cooling, primates all but disappeared from the northern continents, being represented only by the two American genera *Macrotarsius* and *Rooneyia*, known from a single specimen each. The temperate forests of Northern Europe were rich in conifers, resin from which was fossilized on a grand scale in the Baltic Sea area, to become one of the greatest single sources of present-day amber. Farther south, the ancestral Mediterranean Sea ("Tethys") shrank in size and land bridges were opened across to Africa. However, these must have been very transitory, for the number of kinds of animals that passed back and forth to Europe was very small. The Fayum badlands of Egypt reveal that in the Oligocene the area supported a tropical rainforest laced by sluggish rivers. Here the first mastodons, hyraxes, and elephant-shrews were to be found, as also were the earliest known apes and monkeys. Large creodont carnivores, a few species of anthracothere artiodactyls, and one novel family of rodents appear to have been recent migrants into Africa from the north. In North America and Asia some of the richest fossil beds of the entire Tertiary are known in the White River badlands of the Dakotas and the badlands of Mongolia and Baluchistan. From these and other holarctic Oligocene deposits come a variety of striking mammals: the gigantic titanotheres, the numerous oreodonts or "ruminating swine," and in Asia the gigantic *Indracotherium*—a rhinoceros that apparently stood 18 feet high at the shoulders. The first mouselike rodents and beavers appeared, as well as hares, the first saber-toothed cats, and more modern types of carnivores. Rodents and the oldest New World monkeys reached South America in the early Oligocene. Since no other northern types got there at that time, they may have spread across a chain of islands, rather than across an isthmus.

Miocene Epoch

(Duration: from about 25 million to about 12 million years ago)

In the Miocene there seems to have been a gradual expansion of grasslands, coupled with great diversification of grazing mammals in North America as the denser forests shifted southward. In the Old World a broad belt of forests extended from Spain across Southern Europe and on through Turkey into Northern India and even China. During the second half of the Miocene, apes wandered out of Africa, where they had become very abundant, and were subsequently found throughout the southern forest of Eurasia, ranging as far north as the present-day region of the Rhine Valley. About the middle Miocene there was also increased faunal interchange between North America and Asia across an Alaskan–Siberian land bridge. In North America a variety of camels and rhinoceroses existed together with primitive foxes, bear-dogs, peccaries, rodents, and hosts of other forms including primitive pronghorn antilocaprids and a variety of equids. In Eurasia the first giraffids, hyenas, deer, and bovids appeared. Mastodons and their relatives the deinotheres spread out of Africa, and eventually the mastodons reached nearly all parts of the world except Australia. In the Old World the families represented by pigs, cats, civets, dogs, and tapirs were diversified. In East Africa great apes, *Dryopithecus*, and lesser apes, *Limnopithecus*, were common, and monkeys and bushbabies were present but rare.

Pliocene Epoch

(Duration: from about 12 million to about 3 million years ago)

In the Northern Hemisphere climates seem to have become somewhat cooler and dryer, and large areas, particularly in the Old World, gave way to grasslands with restricted stream-margin forests. These regions were populated by a typical open-country fauna, named after a characteristic equid, *Hipparion*. This type of horse had evolved from more primitive equids of the genus *Merychippus* in North America during the close of Miocene times, and the seemingly rapid spread of its savanna-dwelling species throughout the Old World is generally taken as signaling the beginning of Pliocene times. Together with *Hipparion* roamed great herds of bovids including antelopes, particularly *Gazella* and the ancestors of cattle, large, short-necked giraffids, and in the more wooded areas canids, felids, civets, otters, deer, pigs, and ancestral beavers and porcupines. Following long after the arrival of the apes, monkeys of the genus *Mesopithecus* appeared in Greece and during the course of the Pliocene seem to have spread slowly across Asia, reaching China only at the close of the epoch. Some of the largest species of *Dryopithecus* were still present in the early Pliocene of Turkey and West Pakistan, but by middle Pliocene times with the further dwindling of forests they became rare. It was just about this time that the more open-country adapted giant apes of the genus *Giganto-pithecus* appeared in India. Also at the end of the Miocene and in the early Pliocene *Ramapithecus*, the earliest hominid, emerged in East Africa, West Pakistan, and Northern India. Little is known of the Pliocene of Africa, but toward the close of that period in the Turkana region of Northern Kenya and in the Omo Basin of Ethiopia extensive faunas extending back beyond 3 million to 5 million years into the latest Pliocene have recently been found. These appear to contain at least two kinds of *Australopithecus*—the earliest tool-using forebear of man.

Pleistocene Epoch
(Duration: from about 3 million to about 10,000 years ago)

Being closer to the present, the Pleistocene rocks of the world and their contained faunas have been studied much more extensively than has any epoch of the Tertiary. It would be impossible in a few lines to summarize in any adequate way what is known of the Pleistocene. Briefly, it was a time of great climatic fluctuation, and although there are traces of cold periods all the way back to Miocene times, the Pleistocene had maximum peaks of continental glaciation. In the Northern Hemisphere the mammals had come to be more and more like their descendants that survive today, but there were also a number of exotic forms that have since died out. These include the giant ground sloths, mammoths, mastodons, saber-toothed cats and, in the Old World, huge chalicotheres and deinotheres, as well as a variety of giant pigs, giant sheep, giant giraffids, giant buffalo, and even giant baboons. The latter giant forms were commonest in East and South Africa in the early Pleistocene, where they are found together with *Australopithecus*. Interestingly, the carnivores associated with these particular giants were not unusually large. During the Pleistocene there were successive advances and retreats of the continental ice, such that in the north there were several alternations of warm-climate and cold-climate faunas. A large number of cold-adapted mammalian species seem to have had their origin about this time. Africa was less affected by the cold, but even there the Pleistocene was a time of extinction of many forms. Scientists still debate whether man or climatic fluctuation was the principal causative agent in these extinctions.

PHYLOGENETIC TREES

Phylogenetic trees, or diagrams that represent the postulated relationships between groups of past organisms, are the stock in trade of paleontologists. However useful they may be by succinctly indicating, in diagram, hypotheses about evolutionary relationships of given groups, they have their limits. Anyone studying evolutionary history, including that of the primates, should be aware that to-gether with the information that phylogenies convey there are cer-tain inherent deficiencies in their construction, some of which will be outlined here. Basically, these inadequacies derive from the fact that representations of the radiating lines of a particular group of organisms are essentially three-dimensional and do not adapt well to the limitations of a printed page. Secondly, most phylogenies show fossil forms resting on a system of branching lines or limbs, when actually it is populations, not individuals, that evolve. There-fore, it would be better to think of given individual fossils dif-ferently. Such a single find can be likened to one molecule of H_2O in a stream where all such molecules in a given straight line across its banks are considered to represent all the individuals of a spec-ies existing at a particular instant in time. This sort of model is also less amenable to two-dimensional representation than are the typical tree diagrams. By its very shape the tree with branching limbs also plays on another facet of human nature: caution. Faced with the necessity of placing given past organisms in relation to others, scholars tend to take conservative positions. In this case, caution takes the form of putting each named species out on a separate twig of its own. This gets around facing the more de-manding challenge of deciding whether any of the fossil material under consideration might actually stand in the mainstream of the evolution of the group concerned, that is, on the trunk of the dia-gram, as a direct ancestor.

Another similar sort of problem often encountered is that end members of the order Primates living today represent a sort of graded series running from the lowly lemurs up to man. Somehow from this there has been inferred the widely held belief that man's ancestors passed through all the grades of evolution found in living groups. Such is clearly not the case. In fact, most orders of mammals have both present-day members that are considered "primitive" and those that are thought to be "advanced," but living forms are not the ancestors or descendants of each other. In consequence, the two latter terms are misleading and almost meaningless. In spite of all this, diagrams are still sometimes drawn as phylogenies and yet contain only living forms. Another misleading element of such diagrams is that they lead to the logical misstep that monkeys were ancestral to apes and that monkeys in turn were derived from tarsiers. We do not have any proof for such steps in primate evolu-tion. It is true that Hominidae was derived from animals that we have to call apes, but beyond this we do not know how the earlier stages should be described. For instance, the Eocene forebears of the "dawn apes" of North Africa may have looked more like lemurs than like monkeys, and there may never have been tarsier-like forms in this lineage. Structural resemblance to monkeys seen in a few features of the limb skeleton of Miocene apes could just as well be described as resemblance to lemurs or to lorises.

Another point is that many fossil finds will not be in the actual, direct ancestry of a living form, but even so the various fossils found may be more or less close to the mainstream of evolution of the group. Thus recovery of primates approximating more or less closely the actual ancestral stages makes it possible to draw the broad picture of successive grades of advance within a group (reasonably well documented from fossils) even when the specimens concerned cannot be proven as direct ancestors. Another somewhat misleading feature of phylogenetic trees is that they often tend to imply that there was a purposive direction in the evolution of the group simply by the positioning of the branches. Many diagrams in books on human evolution give the distinct impression that the whole course of evolution of the primates leads directly toward man. Had one middle Miocene species of mammal become extinct, this would not be the case. Representation of primate phylogeny would come out entirely differently in the annals of the tarsiers.

Figure 4, constituting an attempt to show the phylogeny of early hominids and redrawn from Tobias (1967), demonstrates further

Figure 4 Proposed phylogenetic relationships of early hominids of Africa and Eurasia, as arranged by P. V. Tobias. Tr—Trinil Beds; Dj—Djetis Beds; Old. Hom.—Olduvai hominid. (After Tobias, 1967b.)

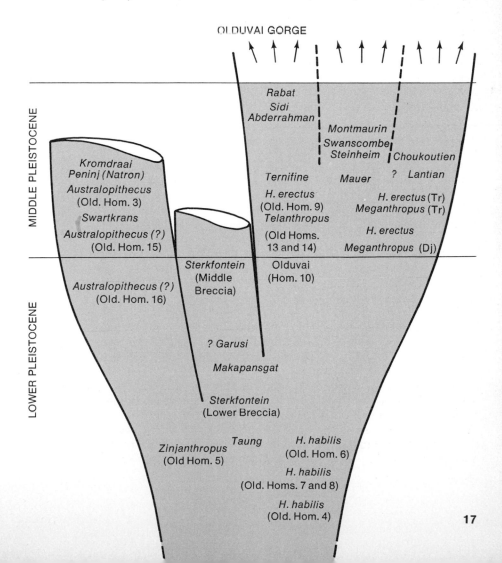

17

pitfalls for the unwary phylogenist. In this illustration three degrees of relatedness are indicated: complete separation, as with the branches for the Kromdraai and Sterkfontein hominids; dashed separation, as between Steinheim and Choukoutien man; and no indicated separation, as between "*Zinjanthropus*" and the Taung child. Actually, we have no conclusive evidence as to whether any or all of the populations represented by the individual finds of this diagram could have successfully interbred or not. In consequence, showing differing degrees of relatedness is misleading. Tobias further indicated in his text the view that Olduvai Hominid 5, Taung, and Olduvai Hominid 6 constitute three different genera and species, *Zinjanthropus boisei*, *Australopithecus africanus*, and *Homo habilis*. These three "species" contain some of the greatest individual extremes of morphology known for the early Pleistocene. Either these lineages should have been drawn as separate branches down into the Pliocene or most of these "species" should be placed in one lineage. Figure 4 (page 17) does show the advantage of placement of fossil forms within the branches, indicating that the finds are members of groups and not terminal entities to be placed on twiglike side lines.

The simplest phylogenetic arrangement is a Y, but even this three-way relationship produces a problem for paleontological interpretation, sometimes called the Y-problem. The two divergent branches may be recognized by different species (or generic and species) names. If their common ancestor is found, what should it be called? Several alternative arrangements all of which could be suggested for Hominidae are listed below:

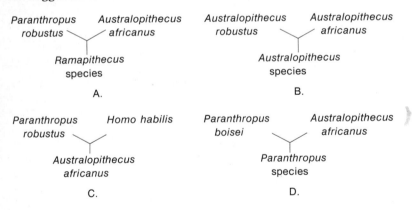

In cases A and C the three branches are all considered to represent different genera and species. In case B all are placed in the same genus, and in case D only the progressive (most like later man) species is put in a different genus.

One final element that has often affected the construction of phylogenetic diagrams is discoverer's bias, well illustrated in many phylogenies of Hominoidea. For example, among many extinct apes shown in such a tree, Pilgrim (1915) placed *Sivapithecus* closest to undoubted hominids, and Abel (1931) in a similar diagram of all fossil apes gave this position to *Dryopithecus darwini*. Neither *Siva-pithecus* nor *D. darwini* had anything to do with the origin of Hominidae, but Pilgrim had coined the name *Sivapithecus* and Abel had named *D. darwini*. Because of closeness to their material, each placed his candidate near the main line to man.

PRIMATES AND PALEOGEOGRAPHY

The present-day and past distribution of primates presents several questions of interest in relation to paleogeography and former distribution of animal groups. There are several reasons for this situation. Contrary to the case with the historical record of most mammalian orders, even more extinct genera and species of primates have been described than of the ubiquitous living forms.

Moreover, primates are an unusual order in that they are, in general, restricted to warmer climates. Naturally, any plant or animal species has a range or area to which it is restricted, and none occurs in every environment, but many mammal groups seem comparatively unaffected by the north–south temperature gradient and have members that live in cool or cold regions. Mammals as different as bears and shrews range from arctic to tropical climates.

On the other hand, among primates those forms such as man, mountain gorilla, and Japanese macaque that can survive even when temperatures fall below freezing are among the most advanced or divergent members of the order. They are the least like the basal prosimians in outward structure. Apparently, they have also more recently evolved the physiological mechanisms to cope with colder climates.

In addition to climatic restriction, the deployment of Primates as an order has been affected by various geographic factors limiting their distribution. Since the primates of latest Cretaceous and Paleocene times represent one of the oldest identifiable orders of placental mammals, it seems likely that their occurrence then in Western North America and almost as early in Europe, documents the origin of the order in the Northern Hemisphere. There is only a very low probability that there was time enough in the early stages of the placental radiation for the first primates to have arisen in the Southern Hemisphere and later migrated north. In fact, all evidence suggests the reverse. Recent studies by McKenna and Szalay (personal communication) indicate that continental drift played an important role in the early history of the primates, because there is now impressive evidence that the final rifting of the North Atlantic between Greenland and Spitzbergen probably did not come until mid-Eocene times and that the land bridge there then lay in more southern latitudes than these areas occupy today. This discovery would explain the phenomenon originally noted by Cope (1872a) that the early Eocene faunas of England found in the London Clay contain many of the same mammal (and other vertebrate) genera that occur in the North American Wasatch, and in some cases both have probably identical species. The provincial ages concerned are the Wasatchian in North America and the Sparnacian in Europe. We know now that in Wasatchian–Sparnacian times several primate genera, *Plesiadapis, Phenacolemur,* and *Pelycodus,* occurred in both continents. Other pairs of genera such as *Teilhardina* from Belgium and *Loveina* from the Western states are closely similar.

McKenna (1967) posits lemuroid stocks in Africa in late Cretaceous through middle Paleocene times. To me, this conjecture seems unlikely. Had primates reached Africa then, one would expect more diversity later. In fact, diversification to the ordinal level should have occurred as happened with the early-arriving presumed condylarth placentals that by the end of Eocene times had produced several separate orders: Embrithopoda, Hyracoidea, and Proboscidea. One can safely question whether it is advisable to support Africa as the center of dispersal of lemuroids when in fact no fossil lemuroids have ever been found there. The first problem is how to explain the entry into Madagascar of the basal lemur stock unless lemurs once spread across Africa from the north. This in turn has to be coupled with the fact that no lemurs or lorises occur in the African Oligocene. Moreover, there are in the European Eocene faunas, primates such as *Protoadapis, Anchomomys,* and *Pronycticebus* that are sufficiently like subsequent lemurs and lorises to at least admit the possibility of these being in or near the ancestry of the later groups. In spite of a few doubting Thomases, *Oligopithecus* of the North African Oligocene does constitute a connecting link between Eocene prosimians and the Anthropoidea. It has loss of P_1^1 and P_2^2* characteristic of all catarrhines together with the canine

---

*There are various dental designations in this book. *"Permanent teeth"* are given capital-letter designations: I, C, P, and M are respectively incisor, canine, premolar, and molar. Deciduous or milk teeth ("impermanent teeth") are prefixed by a lower-case "d": dI, dC, dP, and dM.

The following designations are used to identify particular teeth: M_1, M_2, M_3, M^1, M^2, M^3. The subscript indicates a tooth of the lower jaw. The superscript indicates a tooth of the upper jaw. These designations refer to either side of the jaw unless a particular side is indicated. The number sequence is from the front of the jaw backward (e.g., M_1 is the molar of the lower jaw that is farthest forward in the mouth; M_2 is the next molar backward). However, bear in mind that many animals have lost teeth. For example, many primates such as the catarrhines have lost some front premolars. Man is one of these. He has no P_1, P^1, P_2, or P^2; his most forward premolar is P_3 or P^3.

The designation M_1^1, P_1^1, etc., indicates "M^1 and M_1," "P^1 and P_1," etc.

A "dental formula" gives one side of both jaws. For example, the dental formula for man is I_1^1, I_2^2, C_1^1, P_3^3, P_4^4, M_1^1, M_2^2, M_3^3. Another way of indicating this is $\frac{2 \cdot 1 \cdot 2 \cdot 3}{2 \cdot 1 \cdot 2 \cdot 3}$. Since this indicates one side of both jaws, if we add all the numbers and multiply by 2, we get the total number of teeth in the mouth (32 in this case). Yet another way of indicating the dental formula is to use a fraction bar and to indicate the total number of incisors, premolars, etc. For example, man would be I_2^2, C_1^1, P_2^2, M_3^3.

The designation P_4–M_3 means all the teeth beginning with P_4 through M_3. The designation M^{1-3} means all the upper molars beginning with M^1 through M^3.

to P_3 honing wear that sharpens the back side of the canine and that is characterized by the large, anterolaterally extended P_3 found only in catarrhines. The molars are more primitive, with a trace of a paraconid cusp on M_1 but not on M_2. The molars of *Oligopithecus* resemble the Fayum apes on the one hand and the European Eocene prosimians on the other. It seems likely to me that sometime during the Eocene, perhaps when or before species of creodont carnivore genera *Pterodon, Apterodon,* and *Brachyodus* (an artiodactyl) reached North Africa, the forerunners of the Malagasy lemurs and the African catarrhines migrated into Africa from Southern Europe. If it should prove the lorises came to Africa later, during the Miocene, then the initial introduction of primates into Africa need have involved no more than two or three species. Since the Mozambique Channel appears to have been in existence even in late Cretaceous times, it seems probable that whenever the lemurs reached Madagascar they came by sea, presumably by rafting on floating vegetation. Their diversity today does not belie the probability that only a sole species population served to colonize that island. Some Madagascan plants suggest floral ties in the past with Southern Asia, but it seems almost impossible to believe that lemurs could have gotten to that island from Asia across the Indian Ocean, although the possibility has been suggested. The introduction of the ceboid primates into South America by at least early Oligocene times, probably also by rafting, has been mentioned earlier in this chapter, as has the fact that the apes appear to have spread out of Africa into Eurasia in middle Miocene times whereas the monkeys appear to have emigrated later, at the beginning of the Pliocene. Oreopithecines have now been reported from Maboko Island and from Fort Ternan, Kenya. These sites being a little older than the Tuscan lignites that have yielded *Oreopithecus* in such abundance in Northern Italy also suggests that the group represented by this primate, too, left Africa in the Miocene.

The later history of primate dispersal in the Old World will be covered in more detail in the sections to follow on the various extinct primate genera. In the New World the story is simple. *Ekgmowechàshala,* recently named by MacDonald (1963) from Miocene deposits in North America, may represent a surviving omomyid that temporarily moved northward during a warm climatic fluctuation, but its exact affinities are certainly not clear at present. Apart from this occurrence, primates* in the New World have been restricted to South and Central America since the end of the early Oligocene.

*The common noun "primates," referring to any members of the order Primates, is not capitalized. If the order specifically is meant, the word is capitalized, as are the formal English nouns "Higher Primates" and "Lower Primates," which are equivalent respectively to the two suborders of Primates, Anthropoidea and Prosimii.

2 Evolutionary Biology

EVOLUTIONARY THEORY

From the time of production of the herbals and bestiaries of the late Middle Ages, it became increasingly apparent that the natural world contained an enormous diversity of living forms, practically all of which were easily distinguished from anything else. In the western world, at least, each of these was considered to be specially made by the Creator. In such a system intergradations between species or groups of similarly designed species were hard to explain, since each had been specially created.

The pre-Darwinian paleontologist Sir Richard Owen was a gifted anatomist, who—even though he outlived Darwin—was never able to accept organic evolution. He early recognized that vertebrates, for instance, were made up of the same basic parts with the same general plan. If the animals with backbones had all been specially created as separate species and their similarities of plan were not due to relatedness, why had the Creator seen fit to produce nearly endless variations on the basic theme of vertebrate anatomy, when, being omnipotent, he could just as easily have created each organism as a completely novel composition of parts? Owen finally had to fall back on the idea that the deity had used certain basic templates over and over again. A possibly apocryphal story of a visit by clerics to Charles Darwin turns on this theme. The divines are said to have reasoned that someone as knowledgeable about the natural world as Darwin was might have special insights into the character of its creator. They therefore inquired whether any inferences could be drawn as to the nature of the Divine Providence from the character of his creation? After a pause, Darwin is said to have replied: "Yes, an inordinate fondness for beetles"—these being the most diversified land animals, with more than 300,000 species now in existence. The special creation of so many must certainly reveal a dedicated interest! The correct solution to the problem of groups of similar-structured animals such as the Galapagos Island finches was hit upon by Darwin in the 1830s during the famous voyage of the *Beagle*, but he took a whole generation to write up and substantiate his views. He reasoned that the similarities must be because the Galapagos finches all descend from a common ancestor originally blown out to the island arc by storms. If groups descend from common ancestors, what is the process that makes for change and the production of two or more subsequent species from what was once one species? Clearly, one factor is isolation of two or more groups of individuals by some sort of barrier that allows for separate differentiation of the inheritance of each group; this is called "allopatric" speciation. Such separations can be effected by rivers, mountains, or oceans, such as surround the Galapagos.

The more important active principle enunciated by Darwin he called "natural selection"—a process (he considered) of differential survival before, during, and after reproduction and favoring the fittest individuals. This he called "survival of the fittest." Although the principles of inheritance were not then well understood, and the science of genetics was far from its birth, Darwin was aware that variations in structure and color could somehow be passed on by animals to their descendants and that some of these variations were more advantageous for survival than others. With individuals of a species ranging from adaptively superior to adaptively inferior, it was clear to Darwin that the best-constituted individuals would presumably be healthiest, live longest, and have more offspring— many of which might be expected to share some of the felicitous characteristics of their adaptively superior parent, or parents. This system can operate either to differentiate a species toward a better adaptation to its environment or to stabilize it toward uniformity in a well-adapted species. We now know that this is because the units of inheritance are stable entities, the "genes," that can combine in different ways to produce unusual or blended expression of their effects but that are not altered basically from generation to generation except by "mutation"—the formation of a new structure for a gene. Moreover, in most species there are several different gene alternatives for each unit of inheritance, called "alleles." No one individual has more than a small fraction of all the alternative alleles existing in the total population of a species. Consequently, no two individuals of a species (other than identical twins) can be expected to be exactly alike genetically. All the genes, including mutants and alternative alleles, existing at one time in a species are called the "gene pool" of that species. Since all of the earth's history has been one of changing environments, the surroundings of nearly all past and present species have changed with time in such aspects as temperature, amount of rainfall, and composition of competing or preyed-on species of organisms. Natural selection operating on the gene pool of a species will act to shift it to a better composition for the survival of member individuals. Industrial melanism is an example of this. Near certain factory cities in Northern England, tree trunks have become increasingly darkened by soot and other chemicals since the industrial revolution. The lighter variants of certain insect species that commonly rest on the bark of trunks, particularly one kind of moth, are thus exposed to greater predation by birds. Being lighter, they stand out where their ancestors would not have on clean trunks (Figure 5). Thus dark, melanistic moths are more fit, because they are less easily seen. A noticeable shift away from the light color pattern toward

Figure 5 Industrial melanism, an example of natural selection in action. Before the Industrial Revolution in England, camouflaged light-colored moths were predominant on tree bark covered with lighter lichens. With the spread of air pollution from industrial centers, dark moths came to predominate on soot-darkened trees. Light and dark moths are shown here on a tree trunk in polluted woodland near Birmingham, England. (Photograph from the experiments of Dr. H. B. D. Kettlewell.)

a dark norm for populations of these moths took place in less than a century. This was because of the continuous removal of the light forms due to the disadvantage of being light in a sooty environment. This is an example of changing with the environment. If the animal is well adapted, then most genetic changes or mutations are likely to move the member of a species away from the norm and to be nonadaptive. In such cases selection acts to stabilize or to select for a standard composition of genes.

In a final case a species may move into a new environment either by chance, by choice, or by being crowded out of another. In this case the species may be in an unstable adjustment to the new environment. Usually those individuals that adapt well to such a new environment are few, and therefore selection may change the population composition rather rapidly. It should thus be remembered that the unit of evolution is not the individual but the population. The quality most favored in individuals is fecundity of the sort that has the greatest chance of being ongoing—as one scientist put it, "the highest probability of having grandchildren." All genetic reshuffling by natural selection has this ongoing survival of the species as its principal end. In fact, it should not be forgotten that each and every species that survives today is the product of a continuous stream of life extending back in unbroken continuum hundreds of millions of years to the first living things.

Two other terms which find frequent use in paleontology are "parallelism" and "convergence." Both refer to the aquisition through time of similar structures, but from different sorts of origin. Parallelisms are structural developments within a particular group, such as one order, occurring independently in more than one branch of the group that are thought to be brought about by the same basic conditions. For instance, being arboreal mammals, primates species have more than once evolved long forearms, useful in hanging-feeding, from ancestors with shorter forelimbs. These are cases of parallelism. Convergence occurs when structures in only remotely related forms come to look alike, such as the similar flipper-like fins of whales, ichthyosaurs, seals, and sea cows.

PRINCIPLES OF TAXONOMY

The naming of fossil primates has largely been carried out by authors who were, in varying degrees, unaware of the newer concepts of biospecies or paleospecies. Consequently, particularly among fossil Hominoidea, the literature has become cluttered with numerous unnecessary or invalid names. Because of such proliferation of names, it seems useful to outline some of the reasons that have brought about this situation and to discuss briefly the correct procedures for naming animals.

In the particular case of Pleistocene hominids, at least sixty different specimens have been made the types* of new hominid taxa. Because many of these are based on fragments that are not even comparable with the others, it is obvious that these sixty species and the numerous genera proposed for them certainly constitute far too large a group of recently existing relatives of man. Almost every important find of a Pleistocene hominid has been made a species or genus and species type. This practice has in turn created the impression that in the recent past there were living on the earth many branches of the family tree of man all but one of which (ancestral to present-day *Homo sapiens*) were exterminated by various imagined conflicts and catastrophies. Indeed, the literature on fossil man gives the definite impression that the pattern of an advanced hominid type invading a region and competing with the previous occupants, leading to their extinction, was the prevalent one. An example would be the seemingly abrupt replacement of neandertal man by modern man in France. However, the actual evidence for diverse types of humans in conflict with each other at any one time is extremely slender. The examination of all these "types" of fossil humans in the eyes of a zoologically trained taxonomist produces a very different picture that will only allow for a much smaller number of species. Clearly, there has been a trend among those studying fossils of the higher catarrhine primates to use the Linnean binomial names, or "nomina," as a series of labels and not to denote a representative of a species. Such, if similar to other mammalian species, would have contained hundreds of thousands, perhaps tens of millions, of other individuals distributed throughout space and through a considerable period of time. Among fossil hominids, where coining of names as labels for individual specimens has been rife, the tendency arose for several different reasons. The Pleistocene fossil hominids are often fragmentary or distorted and they come from various parts of the Old World distant from each other. All three of these factors combine to make comparison between them difficult. In addition, many of the sixty-odd "named" Pleistocene hominid fossils have come into the hands of anatomists or archeologists for description. Such scholars, however well informed in their own field, may not have much acquaintance with the principles of animal taxonomy—a rather specialized field of zoology. Moreover, it is one little practiced by neontologists, because the names for the genera and species of living mammals have almost entirely been coined by now. Today it is unlikely that anyone will have a further opportunity of naming another new genus and species of modern mammal. However, for paleontologists this kind of consideration continues to come up frequently, because new fossil taxa are discovered all the time. Species concepts as they apply to fossils are discussed further on in this chapter, but at this point it seems advisable to stress that if a new fossil species or genus is to be named, it is the obligation

---

*The word "type" in this book means the particular individual specimen to which the scientific name was first given.

of the namer to tabulate the attributes or characteristics that are distinctive of the species or higher taxonomic category being named. Of course, these should not be minor features of difference of the sort that separate individuals within one species but should be more distinctive differences of the sort that can be shown to separate species or genera of living animals related to the particular type of fossil concerned.

The Linnean hierarchy

The Linnean hierarchy, first developed in the eighteenth century by Carl von Linné (or Linnaeus) (1758, 10th edition), was initially a means of allocating living organisms into a natural system of order. Post-Darwinian biologists have come increasingly to regard it as a taxonomy that is basically a description of animal and plant phylogenies.

The basic feature of the system is its series of seven levels:

Kingdom
  Phylum
    Class
      Order
        Family
          Genus
            Species

No animal is considered to be completely classified unless it is referred to each of these levels.

Simpson (1961) defines a "taxon" as a group of real organisms recognized as a formal unit at any level of a hierarchic classification. Primates (an order), Hominoidea (a superfamily), and *Australopithecus* (a genus) are all taxa. Most of the taxa discussed in this book will be of family rank or lower.

The international code of zoological nomenclature

Prior to the advent of Darwinian theory, Linnean binomials were regarded as the names for discrete species or groups of species that could be diagnosed on the basis of such things as distinctions in morphology or, among vertebrates, differences in color patterns on skin, scales, feathers, or hair. Although the biospecies concepts formulated in the 1930s had not been worked out when the first international groups began to devise a code of rules for naming animals, there were foreshadowings long before Darwin that a true species represented a viably interbreeding group (see Mayr, 1968). For instance, mammals and birds with sexually dimorphic color patterns were more than once diagnosed as two different species in the eighteenth and early nineteenth centuries, but, as Mayr points out, whenever it became known that the two pelage or feather patterns were only sex differences, the unnecessary species name was dropped. Thus it was recognized to some extent in the first hundred years or so of Linnean taxonomy that species were to be characterized by more than distinctions of form or color.

However, by the 1880s, it had become clear that an internationally agreed-on code governing the procedures for naming animals should be drawn up. This was done, beginning in 1889, and the articles of the code have been enlarged and modified at most of the subsequent international zoological congresses since that time. In order to cope with the various inconsistencies and doubtful practices in the naming of animals, the initial rules have grown in complexity to the extent that no one should try to name a fossil animal without gaining complete familiarity with these rules. At least since Mayr (1950) cautioned against unnecessary coining of new names for fossil hominids, anthropologists have been frequently reminded of the many violations of the code that have been produced among higher primates, but the practice of coining unnecessary names has continued right up to the present time, the most recent superfluities being *Tchadanthropus* (1965) and *Paraustralopithecus* (1968). Fortunately, a complete revised edition of the code was published in 1964. All students of extinct human and nonhuman primates would do well to understand the principal articles it contains.

Binominal names

The system of naming animals now universally employed by zoologists dates back to the classification presented in 1758 by Linnaeus in the tenth edition of his book *Systema naturae*. Although his system was pre-evolutionary and the species of animals he recognized were generally thought of as specially created and discrete, or nonintergrading, kinds of organisms that could be identified by the unique morphological features of each, it has been adapted with little modification to fit the modern concept of biospecies. In most cases the classical taxonomists correctly recognized the discrete modern species and named them. Moreover, most of their generic groupings proved workable, although the genus has remained less amenable to precise definition than the species has.

The species

Briefly, the "species" to the modern taxonomist is any group of animals existing now that are fully interfertile in the sense that two members of "different" subpopulations that may exist within the species are able on mating to produce offspring that are equally fertile to the offspring produced by matings "within" particular subgroups of a species. Such subgroups are variously called "demes," "local populations," "varieties," or "races." Since information derived from matings between animals that existed in the past cannot now be obtained, extinct species are of necessity more indefinitely defined. In the best practice, past species are coined only when fossils have been found that differ from any other species, extinct or extant, to the same degree as do modern species related to them. In other words, the yardsticks or measures of morphological difference contained within given related, living species can be extended to past mammals in order to sustain a system of naming past animals that is consistent with that applied to those now living.

One major difference separates biospecies and paleospecies: all the morphological variation contained in a species now existing represents that to be found throughout a space in the world existing at essentially one time in history, the present day. Paleospecies are often considered to deserve a breadth of definition that would allow for a spread throughout time as well. Consider a measure of allowable intraspecific morphological variation comparable with that contained in a given species at a point of time (the present day) in the horizontal plane of a phylogenetic diagram. If this be extended into the vertical dimension as well, in order to represent a paleospecies that existed through time, then using a standard measure of the variation within a species typical of the group today the paleospecies would contain approximately twice the variation of a modern one. Although naming of past species will remain more inexact than naming the living, following the above procedures will certainly give a consistent system comparable with the classification of living organisms. In contrast, the wholesale naming of each and every new fossil found as a new species that has obtained in the study of extinct apes and humans bears no resemblance to the taxonomy of living forms. It should also be stressed that dividing up a lineage of animals documented through a time succession is ultimately arbitrary, because if we had each generation represented by fossil finds, then such species groups as were defined would ultimately have their divisions fall between one generation and its parents. However, this arbitrariness should not be an excuse for the abandonment of naming fossils, as has been suggested. If for no other reason than in order to discuss them, we need designated, successive names for past organisms.

In taxonomy each species is basically identified by one individual specimen that has been designated by a competent scientist as the "type" of the species to which it belongs. This specimen should be housed in a museum or other collection where it is freely available to scientists who might wish to question or confirm its validity. If the type (or holotype) has been lost, a later student of the group can designate another specimen as type, but this can only be done successfully if the original type was described in sufficient detail to leave little doubt in identifying with it other individuals of its species. The type specimen of a species, being an individual, may not even be typical of the species it represents, although chances are that it will be. Aberrant or atypical individuals are known to be rare among most living species. In consequence, it should be remembered that type specimens of species are the real entities to which species names are attached, but in no sense can they represent or even typify the range of variation contained within the species for which they stand. When naming a fossil species, the author must make clear which single individual is to be considered the type. If there are other finds of the same species made at the same time, these should be listed as referred specimens within the species "hypodigm"—a list of all known contained individuals. For modern species, hypodigm lists would ultimately be impossible to assemble because of the large number of presently existing individuals, but since extinct species are usually known from only a few specimens, it is useful to have them tabulated by scholars following the designated type of their species.

The genus

This taxonomic level is less amenable to definition than the species but is generally intended to include groups of relatively closely related species. Where biological information is available, it seems that (at least among mammals, and including primates) any two contained species of one genus can usually be hybridized successfully. The offspring of such crosses typically show varying degrees of sterility, such that descendants of the interspecific crosses, if there are any, could never survive long in competition with their much more fertile parent species. Seemingly closely related species such as sheep and goat, fox and dog, or cheetah and leopard that cannot produce hybrids were, on morphological grounds and on equal grounds of their genetic incompatibility, rightly placed in different genera. In taxonomy the type of a genus is not a specimen but a type species that in turn has a type specimen.

Priority of names

According to the international code, the proper name of a particular species or genus is the oldest available name that has been applied to it. However, there are several conditions to this proposition. The name must have been correctly set forth in the first place according to procedures stipulated in the code. Names for the same animal produced after the first are considered synonyms. In a sense, such subsequent names are not truly invalid, but they are clearly superfluous and are usually dropped after their synonymy has become known. One major provision of the code is that after a name of an animal has been in common use for fifty years, if a taxonomist should discover a little-known prior name for it, the later, commonly used name can be sustained by request to the International Commission of Nomenclature.

Invalid names

Apart from the case where the type does not possess any features really distinctive from members of a previously named species, there are several other reasons why a name may be not valid. Some of these reasons are as follows:

1. A generic name becomes a "nomen nudum" if it is not accompanied by a published indication as to the nature of the type material concerned, such as a specimen number, and a definition or description. Since 1930, the author of a species must also list characteristics that he believes are distinctive for the taxon. A new genus must have a type species indicated by name.

2. A generic name will be invalid if it is an unintentional homo-

nym for an earlier-named animal. For example, *Arrhinolemur* is a fossil fish, and because this name is occupied it cannot be used again for any primate. A species homonym occurs only if the same species name is proposed for different species of the same genus or if two species with the same name and formerly placed in different genera are transferred to the same genus by a revisor. When this happens, a new name must be found for the younger of the homonyms. An actual example discussed later in this book occurs with the fossil apes. Since the species *Proconsul africanus* and "*Kenyapithecus*" (formerly "*Sivapithecus*") *africanus* are both properly transferred to genus *Dryopithecus*, the latter "*africanus*" becomes a species homonym and coining of a new species name will become necessary for it, if indeed it is a real, separate species at all.

3. A generic name becomes a nomen nudum if the type specimen of the type species is so insubstantial a part of the animal species it represents as to be nondiagnostic or unrelatable to other subsequently discovered specimens.

4. Another reason why a genus or species may be invalid, since 1960 at least, is if it was proposed conditionally by its author—that is, if the author introduced an element of uncertainty by saying, for example, that the new name might represent a new species or might only be a new subspecies.

THE SPECIES PROBLEM

Paleontologists have long been involved with the problem of how one should apply Linnean binomina to time-successive ancestor-descendant sequences of animals. As was mentioned above, the basic problem is that were a group of animals well known from several individuals of each generation across millions of years, there could be no apparent distinctions between any two given generations anywhere throughout the sequence. Thus subdivision into time-successive named segments—species and genera—would have to be wholly arbitrary. Situations close to this have actually occurred with marine fossil invertebrates (see Kermack, 1954), and a considerable literature on the problem is contained in various studies relating to extinct marine organisms. Among the most informative of these studies are those of Sylvester-Bradley (1956), Imbrie (1957), Weller (1961), and McAlester (1962).

In the case of land vertebrates, and specifically fossil primates, this theoretical problem has not often arisen, because many of the Tertiary sites from which fossil primates have been discovered are spaced at intervals across a period of about 70 million years with considerable unrecorded gaps between them. For instance, any new kind of fossil primate that might yet be found in the Oligocene badlands on the north side of the Fayum depression, Egypt, U.A.R., if not the same as those previously named from there, is likely to be a new species. This is because no other African primate fossil sites of Oligocene age are known. The Fayum primates are unlike penecontemporaneous Eurasian and New World forms, and the next oldest sample of African primates comes from East African localities in Kenya and Uganda, nearly all of which are at least 10 million years younger than these Fayum primates. In addition to all this, there is no known mammal fauna of Oligocene age anywhere else in Africa. Thus if a Fayum primate is clearly distinct at the species and generic level from its contemporaries in the Egyptian sites, it is most unlikely for the foregoing reasons that anything like it has been found and named elsewhere.

Recently, awareness has been growing that this sort of situation is not the case for other groups of primates, particularly the hominids during the last 5 million to 10 million years. The climbing rate of recovery of new fossil hominids is filling in the connecting links in the chain leading from Miocene apes to modern man. This is particularly true of the record of late Pliocene and Pleistocene African hominids (see Tobias, 1966).

Various solutions have been discussed for recognizing the exact taxonomic position of a given fossil. As a model let us assume, for the moment at least, that *Australopithecus africanus* and *Homo erectus* were ancestor and direct descendant. What would one do with an animal that was exactly intermediate between them and that also existed at the midpoint between them in time? The recent recommendation of Tobias (1966, 1969) that bigeneric and bi-specific nomina be used to indicate intermediate stages does not seem particularly useful and has practically never been applied to fossil vertebrates—Tobias gives only two examples. Actually, it is not the business of Linnean taxonomy to be so devised as to reflect increasingly subtle shades of taxonomic difference among fossils. In addition to that is the fact that some living mammal species, particularly certain rodents (Misonne, personal communication), are indistinguishable in dentition and skeleton. The implication of this is that it is possible that two extinct species could not be distinguished skeletally; if so, they would necessarily be placed under one name. Moreover, since we also know that two races or subspecies that are of one species often can be distinguished dentally and skeletally, then for practical purposes the use of subspecific nomina for fossils cannot be made rigorous on the basis of skeletal evidence (see Simons, 1963b).

These problems also demonstrate that fossil species, time-successive species, or paleospecies never can be as accurately delimited as can living forms that belong to what has been defined as "biospecies" (see Mayr, 1963; Simpson, 1961). Some students have even advocated dropping Linnean terminology for fossils and referring to them by numbers or some other type of identification. In my view, this seems wholly inappropriate, and certainly at present even neontologists, for instance, have not really learned much about the actual degrees of interfertility between various subgroups of living primates.

This leads us to an analysis of how biospecies are defined. Consider that two populations A and B exist about which the question is raised: Are these the same species or not? It is necessary also to suppose that populations A and B differ in some slight but identifiable feature, either in color or proportions, or are far removed geographically such that we can call them segregates A and B. Let us further suppose that the two have come into geographic contact recently due to removal of some ecological barrier. Such a contact is called a "suture zone." If no hybrids are ever found in such an area, A and B are evidently incapable of interbreeding and can be assumed to represent different species. It is known that in many such cases where two populations come in contact and hybrids do occur such cross-breeds are either wholly or partially sterile. In this case reproductive isolation of A and B is clearly sufficient to consider them separate species. What of the case where individuals that are hybrids are only slightly less fertile than A or B? Even here species distinction is warranted, because we may consider that population A includes two kinds of individuals: those (A^1) who notice the subtle differences of B and tend to avoid mating with B-type animals, and those (A^2) who see no difference and mate indiscriminantly. Similarly, let B contain B^1 (discriminating) and B^2 (nondiscriminating) types. If hybrids between A^2 and B^2 (which we can call type C) were only as little as 2 per cent less fertile than A^1 or B^1, their ability to maintain their population size would be at a differential disadvantage with A^1 and B^1 individuals who avoided cross-mating. The phenomena that follow such situations in the contact, hybrid, or suture zone are called "sequelae." They usually consist of selection for sharper recognition of the species differences. With birds, song or color differences may be emphasized. Among primates, Struhsaker (1970) has recently observed that behavior such as vocalizations can influence whether or not populations will interbreed. Many valid *Cercopithecus* species exist, but there are also many races for which distinct species have been proposed. How could races and species be distinguished? In one case the repertoire of vocalizations was the same although pelage differences were known (*Cercopithecus erythrotus* and *Cercopithecus cephus*). Where these two varieties overlapped near Edea, Cameroon, Struhsaker saw many wild individuals with intermediate color patterns. In other *Cercopithecus* species (*C. aethiops, C. cambelli, C. mona*), close associations such as feeding in the same trees take place but the vocal repertoire and the coloration of these species differ. He found no hybrids between these latter species. Finally, if hybrids between A^2 and B^2 show no fertility drop or even a gain in fecundity (hybrid vigor), the hybrid zone may gradually expand until populations A and B completely intergrade into a series of demes, forming what is called a "clinal species." Clearly, such discriminations into species types cannot be applied to fossils, but with them in mind we can turn to a consideration of how to deal with the problem of dividing up sequences of fossil species.

Time-successive species

It seems to me that the most reasonable method for dividing up series of time-successive ancestor–descendant species is to work by analogy from the extant to the extinct. Briefly, one should examine the amount of within-species variation and the amount of variation contained within various genera with multiple species. The groups chosen should be the closest living relatives of the fossil groups concerned—they presumably being the best indicators of the amounts of intraspecific and intrageneric variation to expect

Figure 6 Diagrammatic representation of how past, time-successive species could be divided on the basis of the present-day intraspecific and intrageneric variation exhibited in a given group and of how a monophyletic lineage of one genus with several time-successive species evolving at a constant rate could be divided taxonomically after it had given rise to a subsequent genus with many contained species, only two of which survive. (Drawing by Carl Wester, Yale Peabody Museum.)

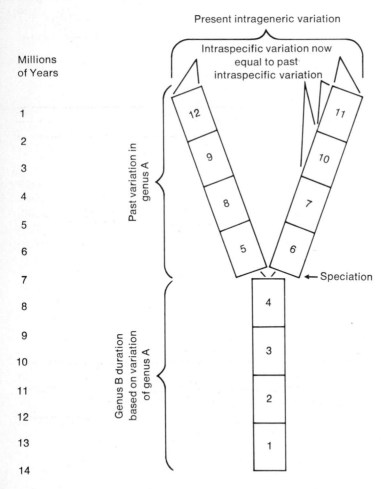

in the group. Not all mammals vary to the same degree. For instance, bears, of genus *Ursus*, have few presently accepted species, but individuals within these (just as with *Homo sapiens*) show enormous ranges of variation of size, of skull, skeletal, and dental proportions, and of color. As an opposite extreme, individuals of various species of the sparrows are remarkably uniform in color and proportions within species, but there are an enormous number of species of this genus, which gives the genus itself great breadth of variation. Once one knows something of the intrageneric and specific variation of groups related to fossil finds, then one is in a much better position to consider the proper approach to take in naming them.

Conventionally, one determines what the total range of variation is in a species now existing at this point in time and then, as it were, turns the variation scale in time's dimension much as in Figure 6.

In actual practice such arrangements of fossil primates or other fossil mammals are hardly possible, but the two following models can be given. One (Figure 7) is an interpretation of an archaic group of mammals, the Coryphodontidae, and the second (Figure 8) represents a somewhat hypothetical construct of pongid–hominid phylogeny.

If one were to find a species of *Coryphodon* between about 50 million to 58 million years old, the probability that it is a new species would be very, very low because *Coryphodon molestus* and *Coryphodon eocaenus* together have twenty-five junior species synonyms already proposed and because hundreds of specimens of *Coryphodon* have been found during that time period without revealing a variety of radically different types. If a specimen of *Eudinoceras*, which is 48 million years old, was found, it would, according to the above scheme, surely be a new species. Throughout the whole lineage it is only twice (at about 58 million and again at about 54 million years) that animals might turn up that would be transitional between *Coryphodon*, *C. proterus* and *C. eocaenus*, and later *C. eocaenus* and *C. molestus*. These could be allocated either to the earlier or the later species depending on whether they as individuals showed a greater number of "new" characters or a greater number of "old" characters retained. Apart from this sort of fairly arbitrary allocation, a more definite placement seems inadvisable for transitional forms. One could argue that this is putting contemporaneous animals (likely to belong to one interbreeding population) in different species, but in actual practice the limitations in dating fossils (already discussed) usually make it impossible to prove exact contemporaniety anyway.

Species durations of 4 million years and generic of 12 million seem rather long compared with what is accepted in other mammalian groups, but the coryphodons are known to have evolved very slowly and to have changed little throughout their history except generally to get bigger. This slow type of evolution, which has been called "bradytely," also characterizes tapirs. Another group of mammals such as the hominids might well evolve at a

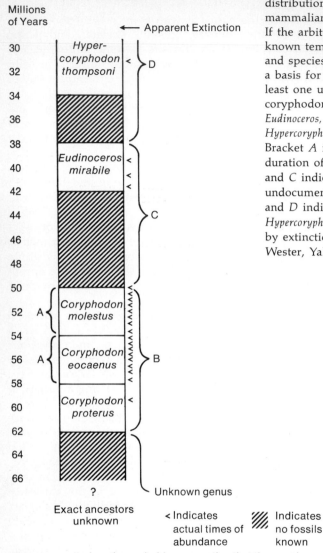

PHYLOGENY OF CORYPHODONTIDAE

Figure 7 Names and temporal distribution of members of the mammalian family Coryphondontidae. If the arbitrary spacings bracketing the known temporal duration of genera and species of this group are taken as a basis for subsequent taxonomy, at least one unknown ancestral coryphodont genus, two species of *Eudinoceros,* and one species of *Hypercoryphodon* are yet to be found. Bracket *A* indicates approximate time duration of a species in this group, *B* and *C* indicate documented and undocumented generic time duration, and *D* indicates possible duration of *Hypercoryphodon,* apparently truncated by extinction. (Drawing by Carl Wester, Yale Peabody Museum.)

Figure compiled on the probable assumption that the species listed form a single ancestor-descendant series

different rate—we think rapidly—which is called "tachytelic" evolution. It seems clear, then, that the taxonomic subdivisions into which one divides a group should bear some relationship to the rate of evolution that typifies the particular group concerned.

Figure 8 plots the approximate time durations of various hominoid species related to man. From this, it can be seen that in the probable lineage leading to modern man those species now recognized by most researchers as valid have longer time durations as

Figure 8 A phylogeny of some Hominoidea, indicating the approximate time ranges involved for various subgroups during the past 25 million years. Numbered species are (1) *Homo erectus*, (2) *Australopithecus boisei*, (3) *Australopithecus habilis*, (4) *Australopithecus robustus*, (5) *Australopithecus africanus*, (6) *Ramapithecus punjabicus*; *A, B, C,* and *D* are unknown, hypothetical intermediate species. (Drawing by Carl Wester, Yale Peabody Museum.)

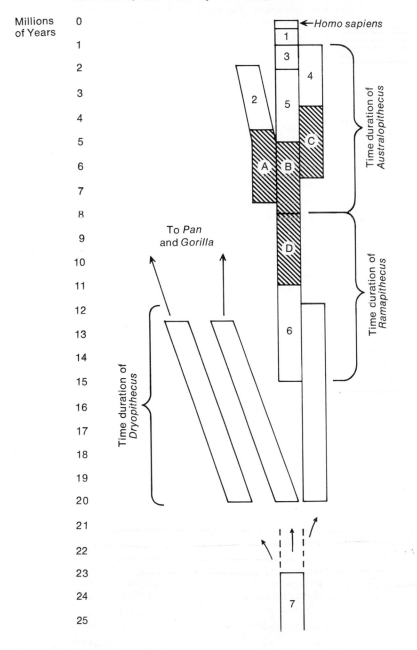

one proceeds farther back. This is usually said to be the result of an accelerated rate of evolution, and consequent morphological change, in this particular group. Nevertheless, it could alternatively be because the species closest to man have been too finely divided, or because at the time levels of the earlier species more species should be recognized. It is also clear that if one accepted the same approximate time durations indicated for species 2, 4, 5, and 6, then it would require, at a minimum, the existence of four unknown species A, B, C, and D to complete the phylogeny of Hominidae back to its earliest stages. If other branches of this family, requiring the coining of species additional to these four, ever existed, they have not been clearly demonstrated to date from the fossil record.

Primate examples

Some of the reasons why the discovery of a fossil primate can be taken to represent a new species have already been touched on in the comment on African Oligocene primates. These relate to the uniqueness of their occurrence. The North African Oligocene primate faunas differ in another significant regard from those of the middle Miocene through early Pliocene in East Africa. The percentage of fossil mammals in the latter faunas that are also found in Eurasia is much higher. This gives evidence of much broader distribution of given mammals not only inside but outside Africa as well between about 18 million to 10 million years ago. Supposed new genera or species in such faunas should be very critically reviewed before description, for when a fauna is extended across more than one continent there is a much higher possibility that such a possible "new" taxon will have already been described by another scientist working elsewhere.

In another case with modern species one argument that is often used to bolster the separateness of a species is its removal geographically from other possibly related or conspecific forms or its separation by long-standing impenetrable ecological barriers. Paleontologists differ as to the significance of the geographic distance between fossil finds, and this is also affected by whether or not such finds are associated with similar faunas. Some species have admittedly been described not because they showed any actual morphological difference from species named earlier but because they were found so far away from the sites of recovery of the earlier proposed species that their author judged that they must have been different. Other paleontologists more correctly take the view that a fossil species is not shown to be distinct and valid unless it has morphological distinction from any other species of a degree comparable with the degree of form difference found between closely related but distinctly separate living primate species. This is the principal way in which the modern concept of biospecies can be extended into the past. It also is a procedure that avoids naming species of extinct animals typologically—just because someone can find a trivial anatomical difference in a new specimen at hand for possible description. In other words, judgment about whether a particular, seemingly distinct or unique structure carried on a fossil is taxonomically significant or not must be tempered by practiced knowledge of the degree of structural distinction that correlates with species distinction among living mammals generally and modern primates specifically. In such cases geographic removal of two forms suspected of being the same is a factor that should be considered. However, even the significance of this is in turn dependent on the ecology of the particular group concerned. For example, the highly arboreal colobine monkeys are today limited from obtaining wide species ranges entirely by the distribution of forest habitat where they occur, because they do not normally cross open stretches of grassland. Animals that lived like this in the past might be expected to break up into many ecologically isolated species populations. Terrestrial hominids and baboons are not so restricted by occurrence of forest, so that far-flung distribution of the same species is much more probable among such kinds of primates, and, in fact, large ground-dwelling mammals of the size of hominids are known typically to establish broad ranges. An example of how one applies taxonomic knowledge of biospecies to past species can be given in the case of the fossil great apes of genus *Dryopithecus*. On grounds of thoroughgoing similiarities in teeth, jaws, face, and skull, species of this genus have long been plausibly considered closely related to the ancestry of modern apes and man (for instance, see Gregory, 1922). The surviving African apes appear to belong to two genera, with three species: *Pan paniscus, Pan troglodytes,* and *Gorilla gorilla.* Each of the last two species is said to contain three races or varieties, so that we can compare dental, facial, and cranial variations as they occur among given races, species, and genera in the African apes. Study of degrees of taxonomic difference between fossil and living great apes varies in one principal respect. The extinct forms cannot be obtained as whole skeletons but are usually recovered only as partial upper and lower jaws with contained teeth. For strictly comparative purposes then, we could consider only segments or parts of jaws of the living African apes, such as might be found as fossils—for instance, take only the three upper molars of one side, or the canine and lower premolars, as a set. It is not very difficult in most cases to distinguish quickly between mountain and lowland gorillas (different races) or between common and pygmy chimpanzees (different species). With a little practice only a glance at separated sets of premolars or molars is sufficient to segregate chimpanzee and gorilla teeth (different genera). With such experience acquired, one can turn to the known fossils of genus *Dryopithecus*. The fossil great ape jaw fragments do not segregate at a glance into separate groups in the way similar small parts of chimpanzee and gorilla jaws can be sorted out. For instance, gorilla molars when unworn have high conical cusps that tip outward from the body of the tooth. Chimpanzee molar cusps relative to the size of the tooth as a whole are lower and less tilted. In contrast, when various *Dryopithecus* molars are compared there are not two such sorts of teeth. In consequence, there is no need at present to utilize several different genera for Miocene dryopithecines as some authors have done. The sorts of differences that can be found among *Dryopithecus* molars are variations in the degree of expression of minor features such as the shelves rimming their bases (lingual and labial cingula). Degree of expression of the cingulum has been shown to vary among individuals and among different populations of the same species of existing ape. Therefore, it is more compatible with accepted biospecies ranking of the African apes to consider the varieties of *Dryopithecus* as no more than species of one genus, in spite of the fact that 28 different genera have been proposed for specimens of *Dryopithecus* (see Simons and Pilbeam, 1965, for the synonymies).

Interpretation of Fossils

The interpretation of fossils is often done poorly because they are seldom very complete parts of the animals whose existence they indicate. Even so, the same procedures for interpretation apply to living as well as fossil forms. Beyond simple morphological description lies the much more interesting interpretation of functional and adaptive meaning of structures. Traditionally, paleontologists tended to lean heavily in publications on the descriptive element. Because teeth set in jaw fragments of varying degrees of completeness are the commonest-found parts of fossil tetrapods, for mammals generally and for the primates in particular, the bulk of the earlier literature on fossil primates consisted largely of descriptions of the structural details of such skulls, jaws, and limb bones as were found. Generally, the principal emphasis was on description of teeth. Although this latter predilection has been the object of slightly satirical comment, it is clear that teeth are often extremely good (or the best) indicators of the feeding habits and degree of relatedness to other mammals of the animals that bear them.

More recently, and particularly during the decade of the 1960s, primate paleontologists and primatologists have increasingly stressed that fuller understanding of fossils can be gained by functional analysis of the locomotor and masticatory mechanisms in particular. Differences in the skeletal anatomy of face, jaw, and cranium or of feet, limbs, and girdles may reflect profound behavioral differences between given fossil species.

However, studies of this sort had to wait, for field-observed data on feeding and locomotor habits of wild primates, information that before the 1960s had been very limited in extent. More recently even than data from the field has come the introduction of X-ray cinematographic techniques that are just beginning to clarify further the complex chewing movements of primates.

FUNCTIONAL ANALYSIS: DENTAL MECHANISMS

Turning to teeth and jaws in particular, some examples should make clear how all-important the relative size and shape differences among teeth and their supporting structures are in different regions of the primate dentition. It is a common and probably correct belief that anthropologists can find, without much searching, upper and lower molars in given modern ape skulls so similar to those of *Homo sapiens* that considered alone they probably could not be distinguished from molars of the latter species. This point is often presented as an example of the futility of trying to segregate known fossil hominoids into manlike and apelike groups from teeth alone. What is missed by this reaction is that there are radically different proportionate relationships between the four different kinds of teeth in the two species *Homo sapiens* and *Pongo pygmaeus*. Figure 9 makes clear that in the orangutan the incisors have a much larger surface area than in man. Should two similar hominoids (known only as extinct species) have exhibited similar intradental proportions, we would already have a suggestion that in one, a "manlike" species, chewing emphasis might have been on the grinding and crushing function of the cheek teeth, whereas in another with large incisors these might have been used to husk fruits or strip off bark, suggesting a more "apelike" frugivorous diet. Thus the paleoecological interpretation must be derived from the study of living forms that are closely related phylogenetically and adaptively. As actual examples of this model, species of *Australopithecus* resemble later hominids in their incisal reduction and cheek-tooth expansion, whereas in the African Miocene ape *Dryopithecus africanus* the long and moderately broad upper central incisors, considered in conjunction with the relatively unexpanded molars that it also exhibits, suggest a trend more in the direction of the chimpanzee. Recently, Jolly (1970) has described a similar contrast of extremes in adaptive function of the dental mechanism among the large African mon-

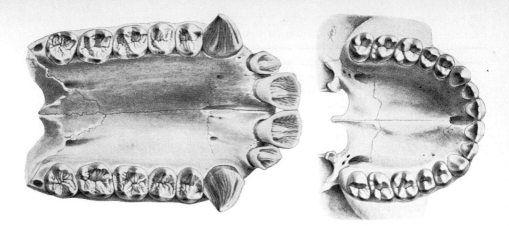

Figure 9 An occlusal view of the palatal dentitions of *Homo sapiens* (right) and a great ape, the orangutan (*Pongo pygmaeus*) (left). See text for discussion. (From Selenka, 1898.)

keys. He points out that among these monkeys the dentition can be considered as composed of three broad functional regions, two principally concerned with the preparation of food items and a third more related to agonistic displays and actual fighting. These three groups of teeth are

1. *Incisors*—food preparation, husking, stripping.
2. *Cheek teeth*—grinding and finer mastication.
3. *Canines and lower front premolar*—agonistic display, fighting.

He points out that in the ground-dwelling gelada baboons, which are adapted to grass and seed feeding in the treeless "high semyen" country of Ethiopia, feeding habits require very little incisal preparation of food. In spite of this, the small object size of the common foods—grass corms, roots, budding blades, and seeds—requires prolonged chewing. Thus food material tends to distribute posteriorly on the molars, and selection would tend to favor enlargement and elaboration of the posterior dentition. Just such structural changes characterize geladas, which more than any other Old World monkeys show molar complexity including deep enamel infoldings, thicker enamel, high columnar cusps, and large high-crowned teeth. In the similar-sized and fairly closely related forest-dwelling mandrills, which are much more habituated to eating fruits and other soft items from the forest vegetation, the predominant dental region is the anterior incisal area. These animals possess broad high-crowned incisors combined with relatively small molars and low uncomplicated cusps. Just as the relative sizes of the teeth in the two regions contrast markedly (as between geladas and mandrills) so do the degrees of wear obtained with age. In the mandrills in spite of the initial large size of incisors these wear down rapidly and are often reduced to stumps or are lost altogether. In geladas heavy incisor wear is seldom seen, but instead the molars show marked attrition, so much that the first molars often are so worn down that they have already lost contact by the time the third molars have only just completed eruption.

Such contrasts are also to be found in the primate fossil record. *Gigantopithecus* from Pliocene and Pleistocene deposits in Asia has only been found in association with open-country or open-forest faunas. Unlike the forest-dwelling African and Asian great apes of today, *Gigantopithecus* had relatively dimunitive incisors and enormous, elongate, and high-crowned cheek teeth. Both by analogy with the geladas and by indication of the habitat preferences of associated faunal elements, *Gigantopithecus* can be interpreted as an enormous ground-feeding ape that foraged on relatively small or durable objects in open or semi-open country. In this light, its perplexing similarities to the early hominids can be understood as parallel adaptations within a basically similar environment.

Where natural selection has put, or is putting, emphasis on dental evolution can be revealed not only by relative size differences in teeth but also by differential degrees of wear on teeth, by differences in eruption sequence, by whether teeth pack together or are spaced out, by differences in mandibular morphology, and by variation in the location of muscle origin and insertion, as well as by the angle of emplacement of the front teeth in particular.

To return to the contrast between dentitions of man and chimpanzee to exemplify these points, differential tooth wear is clearly indicated in the two. Study of large series of dentitions of primitive peoples and of wild-observed or wild-shot chimpanzees shows clearly that it is the incisors of chimpanzees (and perhaps also the adjacent canines) that suffer the greatest wear with age. In modern human populations presumed to have the most primitive dietary habits now surviving, the converse, heavy cheek-tooth wear, is seen.

In studies of teeth of living and fossil primates there has been considerable attention given to differential wear on the crowns of teeth. For instance, Mann (1968) has recently shown that in *Australopithecus* (as in middle Pleistocene and later hominids) the gradient of wear on the three molars decreases markedly to the rear (presumably an indicator of a long adolescence, with staged-out eruption of M_2 and M_3), whereas in living and fossil apes three successive sets of molars follow each other in time of eruption much more closely and the gradient of decreasing wear on them posteriorly is not so steep. In Chapter 9 we will see that this phenomenon also characterized *Ramapithecus*.

Another type of wear that has both functionally adaptive (and phylogenetic) meaning is the interstitial or interproximal wear seen between adjacent teeth among several distantly related groups of mammals. This sort of wear, in which nearly constant chewing or heavy compressive forces cause the teeth to "chatter" or abrade against each other as one tooth moves a microscopic distance relative to its partners, shortens the length of the teeth and eventually the entire tooth row. Interstitial, interproximal, or "contact" wear, is common in herbivorous mammals but need not always be present in such plant-feeding species. This phenomenon perhaps reaches its greatest expression in some rhinoceroses, in which teeth may be shortened by 20 per cent of their original length.

A high degree of interstitial wear, achieved early in life, characterizes both *Ramapithecus* and *Australopithecus* and is therefore, of interest as an important basal component of the hominid dental mechanism, for it is clearly an indicator of powerful stresses on the teeth during chewing. Incidentally, this is a phenomenon whose presence or absence can be observed on a single tooth, and an example of how the presence of an important functional feature can be detected in a trivially small fragment of an animal. This feature of hominid teeth may also correlate with their more nearly circular outlines. In living and fossil apes, the lower molars are more elongate or egg-shaped in outline, and consequently adjacent teeth develop contact facets more slowly if at all. In *Gigantopithecus*, where the canines wore down rapidly as they erupted, chewing motions may also have had a high transverse component. In any case their jaws are deep and very thick, and the teeth of *Gigantopithecus blacki* are the highest-crowned (hypsodont) teeth to be found among hominoid primates. This is also presumably an adaptation to resisting heavy abrasive wear from food for as long as possible.

EFFECTS OF FOSSILIZATION

A number of things happen with fossilization that call for higher levels of caution in the interpretation of morphology in extinct animals than in living forms. Basically, the problems associated with crushing, breaking, scattering, and disassociation of parts must be recognized.

Because fossil primates are virtually never found as complete skeletons with full dentition preserved, a considerable amount of attention needs to be given to the questions that surround the interpretation of parts of animals. In fact, many misinterpretations of the nature and historical or phylogenetic relationships of fossils come from a lack of adequate understanding of this general set of problems.

Perhaps the simplest factor of this sort is the phenomenon of crushing common to many fossils. The compaction of sediments both in caves and in open sites often causes crushing that has been mistakenly or unconvincingly attributed to human or protohuman agency when fossils of Miocene, Pliocene, or Pleistocene age are concerned. In some cases criminologists have been brought in and have concluded that fractures, particularly in skulls and jaws, were brought about as the result of human violence, when they are actually the same sorts of fractures one can find in fossils from the Eocene Epoch, when there is no possibility of human agency being involved.

Of course, a further effect of crushing in fossils is that in many cases measurements that would be desirable cannot be taken accurately. A good example of this situation is seen in the nearly com-

Figure 10 Crushed skeleton of *Oreopithecus bambolii*, discovered in 1958 in the late Miocene or early Pliocene Grosseto lignites of Tuscany, Italy, about 12 million years old. Scale $\times \frac{1}{8}$. (Courtesy Basle Natural History Museum.)

plete skeleton of *Oreopithecus* (Figure 10) discovered by Hürzeler in Tuscany, Italy, in 1958. That skeleton—recovered 300 feet down in a coal mine—is extensively crushed, so that, for instance, accurate estimation of brain volume is almost impossible. Other bones such as those of the pelvis, which are relatively flat, initially suffered less during the compaction of this individual. The forelimbs of this find of *Oreopithecus* seemed clearly longer than the hindlimbs, and because this did not suit the prior notions of its discoverer, who had supposed *Oreopithecus* to be a direct ancestor of man, Hürzeler suggested to me that the forelimb bones had been elongated by crushing. Because the three long bones of the forelimb are basically elongate cylinders, it is clear that crushing can greatly increase the apparent breadth of such a bone but would not substantially increase its length. The effects of crushing or flattening on fossil vertebrates can perhaps be seen most dramatically among the Mesozoic flying reptiles and particularly among the largest of these, *Pteranodon* from the Cretaceous chalks of Kansas, in which it is clear that crushing increases the breadth and not the length.

Among fossil primates, estimates of the absolute volume of the endocranium or brain case are of interest, when they can be obtained, for understanding the emergency of man's mental capacities. Nevertheless, principally because of damage, estimates of brain volume for early Pleistocene African *Australopithecus* specimens vary widely even though most of the same crania were the bases for estimate. As can be seen from the discrepancies in Table 1, the methods various scientists used to reach these figures must have varied widely against the background of their imperfection and distortion as fossils.

Another misleading feature resulting from predation, dismemberment, and breakage of bones before burial is that long bones of mammals in particular tend to break spirally or split up into angular bladelike fragments. Such fragments may then become water worn or otherwise abraded at their ends, thus simulating crude bone tools. This phenomenon renders suspect many bone fragments supposedly worn down by human agency in tool use. Dr. G. L. Jepsen has reported to me that while working in Pliocene deposits in Nebraska at a time in the 1920s when the supposed fossil ape *"Hesperopithecus harold-cookei"* had recently been described from these beds, many curious bone fragments were recovered. In some cases the shaft of a small bone was jammed into the marrow cavity of a larger fragment, and other splintered pieces showed terminal wear suggesting tool use. When *"Hesperopithecus"* was shown to consist of no more than a worn upper molar of a fossil peccary, interest in the Pliocene "tools" of Nebraska waned. Because it now seems most improbable that hominids were in North America in Pliocene times, these supposed tools are strong evidence against the necessity that such "artifacts" need be man-made. Paleontologists collecting in even earlier sediments such as those of the early Eocene of Wyoming often find similar bone fragments

Australopithecus	Dart (1926, 1962)	Schepers (1946)	Broom (1950)	Broom and Robinson (1948)	Le Gros Clark (1947)	Robinson (1961 and personal communication)	Tobias (1965, 1967)	Holloway (1970)
1. Taung (type)								
as juvenile	500–520	500–520			500–520			407
as adult					570–625		562	440
2. Sts. type		435	440–460			415		
T.M. 1511 (I)								
(Sts. 60)								
3. Sts. 5 type		480	480 and			480		485
("Mrs. Ples")			482					
4. Sts. 71 (VII)		480–520	480–520					428 est.
5. Sts. 19/58 (VIII)			550–570	530		370 est.–450		436 est.
Sts. 25								
6. MLD 37/38	480					480 est.		435 est.
7. Old. Hominid 5							530	530
8. SK 1585								530
9. SK 48				750		450–550		
10. SK 46				800		450–550		

Abbreviations refer to localities and specimen numbers of *Australopithecus* individuals; e.g., *Sts.* is Sterkfontein, South Africa; *T.M.*, Transvaal Museum; *MLD*, Makapansgat, South Africa; *Old.*, Olduvai Gorge, Tanzania; *SK*, Swartkrans, South Africa. "Mrs. Ples" is a nickname for Sts. 5.

from a time when no hominids could have existed. Finally, Brain (1967) has recently shown that near a South African Hottentot village bone pseudotools were formed when bone fragments scattered in the sandy soil acquired polish resembling wear on bone tools because of abrasion caused by long-term shifting and disturbance by the feet of animals and people. However, in this instance, the area of the worn ends or edges of the bone was more extensive than is typical of genuine bone tools, where areas worn by utilization tend to be more restricted.

Because interpretation of fossils is largely a matter of studying form, several subjective factors relating to size enter into their interpretation. For one, the absolute size of a fossil will often seem smaller than it actually is because parts are broken away. Equally, two-dimensional illustrations and photographs tend to suggest a slightly smaller size than the actual.

Another problem presented by damage to fossils that is seldom mentioned is that because of such alteration (lost parts, breaks, discoloration, distortion, etc.) two fossils of the same species—for

Figure 11 Comparison of two *Dryopithecus* jaws (*A* and *B*) from Rusinga Island, Lake Victoria, Kenya, with two individual orangutan mandibles (*C* and *D*) showing that the living apes are at least as different as the two Miocene fossils. *A* is the 1942 mandible of *Dryopithecus nyanzae*. *B* is the 1968 mandible attributed to *"Kenyapithecus africanus"* and is alleged to be the earliest homonid mandible but is actually that of an ape. (Photo by A. H. Coleman, Yale Peabody Museum.)

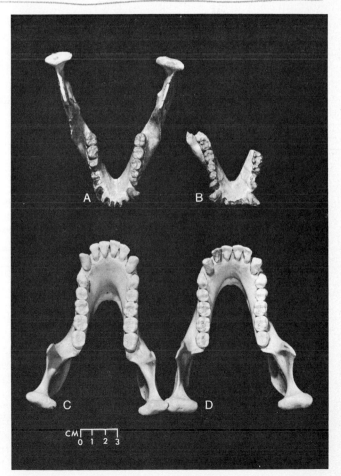

instance, two lower jaws—will often look more different than would two jaws of a modern species, which would be complete (see Figure 11, page 49). The two mandibles of Miocene apes A and B in Figure 11 have been placed in different genera and species, "*Kenyapithecus africanus*" and "*Proconsul*" *nyanzae*. Actually, both genera have proven to be invalid (see Simons and Pilbeam, 1965, and Simons, 1967, 1969a). Both of these mandibles belong to *Dryopithecus*, and each was found in the same area (deposits on Rusinga Island in Lake Victoria, Kenya). They are of the same approximate age, about 18 million years. Mandible A has been misrepresented as belonging to the earliest hominid (see Leakey, 1967), whereas mandible B has always been considered that of a typical fossil ape (see Leakey, 1943, and Le Gros Clark and Leakey, 1951). Actually, the two jaws are similar in comparable measurements. They probably both belong to the same species of fossil ape, *Dryopithecus nyanzae*. In order to illustrate the intraspecific nature of their differences they are compared in Figure 11 with two not very dissimilar mandibles of the orangutan, *Pongo pygmaeus*. In most measurements and outlines, the two orangutan mandibles (members of one species) differ more than do the two *Dryopithecus* jaws. Clearly, far too much has been made of the slight dissimilarities of the two fossil ape jaws. They are probably of the same species. Neither is a hominid and neither shows hominid features.

PHYLOGENY AND DISCOVERER'S BIAS

One result of the study of fossils has been the drawing of phylogenetic trees, as is discussed in Chapter 1. Although such trees are useful summaries, they clearly do not constitute the principal objective in studying past animals, which is to learn how and in what environmental context they lived and moved. Nevertheless, some of the practices that can be misleading in the process of identifying ancestors and descendants seem worth discussion.

It is clear that no extinct mammal can be categorically shown to be the direct ancestor of something now living, because (after the fact) there is no way to show that it ever had any offspring. When we look for ancestors we are looking for fossil finds representative of past species, although the first find or two could be of individuals not even typical of their species. In the same way, a member of a different species of the same genus could tell us something about the general construction or grade of development at a particular stage in evolution even if it were not in the direct ancestral line. A good example of this is the case of *Australopithecus* at Olduvai Gorge, Tanzania. There, at an age of $1\frac{3}{4}$ million years, two kinds of hominids have been found: *Australopithecus boisei*—a large, robust form with enormous molars—and *Australopithecus habilis*—a smaller, more gracile species. Most scholars think that

A. habilis from Bed I (where the type and "name-bearing" individual was found) is a much more likely candidate for direct ancestry of later (as well as present-day) man than is *A. boisei*. In addition, all the other hominids so far found in Africa that have been dated to between 1 million and 5 million years strongly resemble either one or the other of these Oldowan species, or are in some manner intermediate between them. Even supposing that *A. habilis* had not been found and also that scholars had reason to suspect that *A. boisei* was not our direct ancestor, what could we conclude about animals related to or ancestral to modern man in the period of 1 million to 5 million years ago if we looked only at our uncle "Zinj" (*A. boisei*)? The following points would emerge:

1. The brain was much smaller, at the most not even half the modern norm.
2. The lower jaws were very thick but not particularly deep. At the inside of the front of the mandible both a simian shelf and a superior transverse torus separated by a deep genioglossal pit were present (mandibular conclusions are based on the *A. boisei* mandible from Omo, Ethiopia).
3. Before the third molars had even come into full functional occlusion the first molars had been worn flat. This suggests a delayed and staggered molar eruption sequence and, in turn, a longer childhood. In both man and apes, full eruption of third molars correlates with full skeletal maturity.
4. There was no chin (Omo mandible).
5. The molar teeth were much larger than is typical of middle Pleistocene and later man.
6. The front teeth (canines and incisors) were about the same size as in modern man.

Further, although there are no direct associations of limb bones with the cranium of *A. boisei* at Olduvai, all known postcranial bones from Olduvai Gorge, regardless of whether they belong to *A. boisei* or to *A. habilis* (which cannot be determined because there are no direct associations), are all different from both those of modern man and the living African apes. The discovery and naming of *A. habilis* have changed none of these generalizations, which are based on a find that most scholars believe is not in our direct ancestry. Thus fossils that can be thought of as "uncles" or "cousins" can indeed be instructive as representing the general grade of advance obtaining in the group they belong to at the time they lived. As a consequence of this, phylogenies or phylogenetic trees are best considered as broad—not specific—representations of evolutionary stages. As such, their construction is useful, but they do not constitute categorically accurate relationships.

The Belgian paleontologist Dollo was one of the first to stress another important factor in assessing phylogenetic relationships: that in the course of evolution of a particular group of organisms, lost structures, as such, are never regained. Consequently, in interpreting ancestor–descendant relationships it is particularly important not to choose as a putatative ancestor a species that has already lost a structure retained in the supposed descendant. This is the error Van Valen (1963) fell into in presenting the archaic mammal *Neoclaenodon* as an ancestor or near-ancestor of the group of the North American Eocene tillodonts. The paraconid cusp of Paleocene *Neoclaenodon* is already lost, but is still present in the younger tillodonts.

One of the most amusing phenomena in primate evolution is what might be called "discoverer's bias." Because of closeness to their own material, paleontologists and paleoanthropologists often lose objectivity and tend to overestimate the value or the taxonomic distinctiveness of the particular finds they make. This often results in the animal's receiving an unnecessary name or being considered so valuable that it winds up in a safe. In the latter case the avail-ability of the particular fossil to the world of scholarship can some-times be overly limited. One classic example among fossil primates is the famous jaw and skull fragments of so-called Piltdown man. For decades the original pieces were kept locked up in a safe in the museum where they were housed. Although qualified scholars could arrange to see them, few went to the trouble to get them out. Had these pieces of fossil bones reported as coming from Piltdown been more physically accessible to scholars the fact that Piltdown man was a hoax might have emerged years earlier than it did.

Inasmuch as Carlo Ameghino of Argentina was the first paleon-tologist to show discoverer's bias in exaggerated form, this phe-nomenon could be termed the "Ameghino complex." Briefly stated, it can be formulated: "The animals or prehumans that I find are the direct ancestors of important present-day forms or of modern man, whereas the fossil animals that others find all represent un-important extinct side branches that led nowhere." This phenome-non is presumably a result of the often enthusiastic motivation that causes some to seek out the history of the past. Ameghino thought that most of the major groups of mammals had their ultimate origin in his native Argentina. Consequently, he had a strong desire to promote local study of fossils. This is also often a factor in attempts to gain adequate financial support for expensive paleontological fieldwork.

Living Primates

INTRODUCTION

The living primates are usually divided into six or seven groups, depending on whether or not the tree shrews, tupaias or technically Tupaiaoidea, are placed in the order. Following Van Valen (1965) and several other authors, there has been a growing tendency to transfer the tupaias to Insectivora, as a highly divergent group that branched away from other mammals before the Tertiary.

The most primitive undoubted primates are the lemurs, which today are entirely restricted to the island of Madagascar. These animals can be divided into three distinct families, the Lemuridae, the Indriidae, and the Daubentoniidae. Outside Madagascar, prosimians are represented by two other families, the Lorisidae and the Tarsiidae, which are usually classified in infraorders separate from each other and from Lemuriformes.

The Higher Primates of suborder Anthropoidea represent the advanced or progressive division of animals related to man and including man himself. The New World monkeys or Ceboidea that occur today in South and Central America apparently represent a separate radiation of the neotropical region. They have probably been separate from the Old World Higher Primates since at least early Eocene times. These New World forms are usually ranked in infraorder Platyrrhini, a term referring to the flat nose and laterally directed nostrils and opposed to the infraordinal term Catarrhini, which includes the Old World monkeys, apes, and man, in which forms the nostrils are directed downward. Taken together, all these Higher Primates share a number of readily identified features that are the basis of their association together in one suborder. In these primates the brain is large, eye sockets are fully formed, and the jaw rami and frontal bones fuse together in embryonic or early juvenile stages.

Locomotor categories

Just as primates range through a broad spectrum of size and belong to diversified taxonomic categories, so their locomotor capabilities are diversified. In fact, the variety of patterns of movement and behavior among Primates perhaps exceeds that to be found in any other order of mammals. Locomotor behavior and feeding, resting, and sitting postures are a complex reflection of the manner in which an animal species has adjusted to its environment. In most cases selection operates intensely to maintain or improve the adaptations that fit a given animal species for successful survival. Clearly, maintenance of high levels of agility is necessary for arboreal animals. Equally, on the ground, repeated foraging and flight through open country select for running skills quite different from those needed by an arboreal primate. In short, the various types of weight bearing, particularly of head, limbs, and feet, required in the daily course of life have evoked different kinds of limb proportions, differing orientation of articular facets and condyles, as well as quite distinct differences in entire bones. Of course, such differences are of greatest interest to students of history, because structures in fossils often specifically resemble those of living forms. Analogies with the living can show that the past form may have had a similar way of life. It is fair to conclude that if a fossil species has thoroughgoing resemblance in the skeleton to a particular modern form, then it functioned under similar environmental conditions.

For example, one can contrast the differing forelimb adaptations that separate arboreally and terrestrially adjusted primates. Quadrupedal locomotion in primates began as a branch-walking adaptation where all the limbs were used in running, walking, and climbing over an uncertainly developed substrate—the complexly or randomly distributed pattern of branches in the tropical forest. Quadrupedal primates may also leap and clamber up vines or hang and swing by their arms at times. Particularly when on the ground an unusual but typical quadrupedal gait is practiced by Anthropoidea. Perhaps it is basically misleading to give the impression that primate movements clearly fall into convenient "pigeonhole" categories. Nevertheless, the necessities of ground living select for change that, accumulated for millions of years, leaves clear-cut evidence in the limb skeleton. Because of the very diversity of primates, several types of quadrupedal locomotion on the ground are known to exist, and others may once have existed.

The most successful ground-adapted groups, apart from man and other hominids, are the knuckle-walking African apes and the ground-living baboons and patas monkeys. Because of the stance of their forelimb, the patas monkeys show retroflection of the ulna, coupled with other features related to digitigrade walking. Specifically, there is a strong angulation between the ulnar shaft and the olecranon process. This apparently correlates with a backward location of the inner distal condyle of the humerus. Studies by Crook (1966) and Jolly (1970) indicate that the highly terrestrially adapted gelada baboons of the genus *Theropithecus* share with hominids short fingers. In fact, the lengths of the finger bones of the almost gorilla-sized extinct gelada baboons of East Africa (subgenus *Simopithecus*) are the same as those of a typical male *Papio ursinus*. This is despite the fact that the latter might be only a tenth the weight of the former. One major distinction between the two

Figure 12 Two types of quadrupedal locomotion in primates. Quadrupedal monkeys commonly use walking trots or diagonal-sequence gaits, rare in other mammals. The African apes have developed a secondary quadrupedalism called "knuckle walking." *A:* An individual *Cercopithecus diana* in a lateral-sequence walk. *B:* A chimpanzee (*Pan troglodytes*) in secondary quadrupedal locomotion on the ground. In the chimpanzee, the knuckles alternatively carry the weight of the forebody, and the hind feet often pass on the same side of the respective hands. (After M. Hildebrand, 1968.)

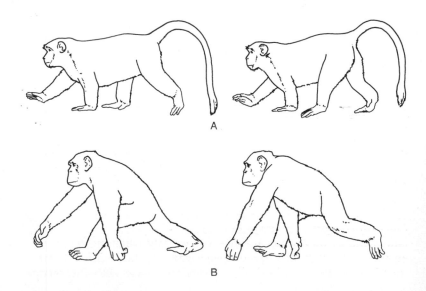

A

B

exists that explains the difference in finger length. *Papio* species often return to the trees to feed; they sleep there at night, and some populations of *Papio cynocephalus* are almost exclusively forest dwelling. For such animals, unlike *Theropithecus* (*Simopithecus*), comparatively long fingers are needed in climbing. The much more terrestrially adapted geladas no longer use the trees; this was particularly true of the giant, now extinct geladas. Among quadrupedal primates we can observe three types: (a) arboreal, (b) terrestrial, and, in the African apes, (c) secondary quadrupedalism or knuckle walking (see Figure 12, page 55).

It was once widely accepted that the forebears of man and the great apes were strict quadrupeds, category (a) above, but there is growing evidence that this was not the case. There are several other locomotor categories among living primates, listed, according to Napier and Walker (1967), as follows:

1. Quadrupedalism.
2. Bipedal walking.
3. Slow climbing.
4. Brachiation or arm swinging.
5. Vertical clinging and leaping.

To these groupings I would add another category:

6. Suspensory locomotion or quadrumanal clambering.

This last category is especially applicable to the orangutan and probably to certain extinct forms such as *Oreopithecus* and possibly to *Palaeopropithecus*. The following descriptions of primate locomotor categories are derived principally from Napier and Walker (1967) and Walker (1967b).

In addition to typical quadrupedalism of monkeys, the next three categories are rather special cases and can be dealt with briefly.

Bipedal walking

Bipedal walking is unique to man. Napier (1963b) has suggested that man is the only animal that "strides." This type of locomotion involves only the legs; the arms have no function in support but swing in alternation to the strides in the same way they are moved among quadrupedal forms (Figure 13).

A characteristic feature of bipedalism is that the knee reaches full extension before the foot touches the ground. Unlike any other primate, in man the center of gravity of the trunk and upper body is positioned directly above the hips, and during walking the spine hardly rotates around the central axis. Compared to man, other primates that occasionally walk on their hind legs actually totter, as far as their upper bodies are concerned. In man, the joint of the hip is also extended during the stride, and for an instant in each stride the full weight of the body is taken through the big toe, where the push-off for the next step originates. As a consequence of this, the big toe of man is unlike that of any other primate. The first metatarsal is brought into line with the other toes and shares a large contact facet at its base with the second

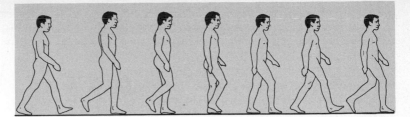

Figure 13 Human bipedal walking. In this type of locomotion the free foot comes to the ground heel first, and the body's weight is carried forward along the lateral side of the foot and crosses the ball toward the base of the big toe while the opposite leg lifts off and comes forward. In the last phase, the heel of the weight-carrying foot rises and the final contact with the ground is supported through the big toe.

metatarsal. The proximal and distal hallucal phalanges are also enlarged. The system is so unique that no more than the ungual phalanx of the big toe is needed to demonstrate that it comes from a bipedal strider (for instance, see Day, 1969).

Slow climbing

Slow climbing is the type of locomotion evolved by some of the lorisiform prosimians, apparently as a combined stalking and predator-avoidance mechanism. Such primates never leap, and the tail is completely reduced; they are mainly nocturnal. Movements are accomplished slowly, a hind foot being advanced to immediately behind the forefoot and the hand then taking a new grasp. In this type of movement only one limb is moved at a time. Grasping abilities are at a maximum, and there is a tendency to reduce the size and length of the second digit on hand and foot so as to increase the spread of the grasp (Figure 14).

Figure 14 *Perodicticus potto,* slow-climbing. Sequence reads from left to right, above, then below. The animal rarely releases the grasp of more than one limb at a time. Movements are slow and deliberate. (After Alan Walker, 1967b.)

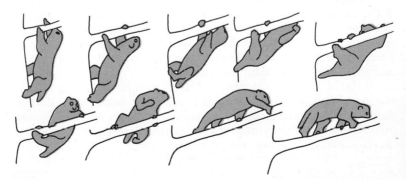

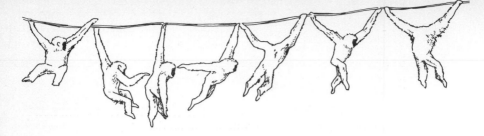

Figure 15 A gibbon (*Hylobates*) brachiating. In this mode of locomotion the arms alone provide the propulsive force. The body, suspended beneath them, is swung in a pendulous manner, with alternative transference of support of body weight from one arm to the other. (After Eimerl and DeVore, 1965.)

Brachiation

"Brachiation" is a much misunderstood and misused term. The history of the concept has been reviewed by Trevor (1963). A traditional dogma that grew up before the days of studies of wild primates was that all the apes were brachiators. These were thought to habitually swing through the forests like gibbons with the body hanging below fully extended limbs, following the sequence of movements shown in Figure 15. Coupled with this misconception went another, that the elongated forelimb of all hominoids, other than man, arose by habituation to this brachiating or arm-swinging locomotion. It was thus felt that one could consider any fossil form with elongate forelimbs an arm swinger.

As is discussed elsewhere in this text, there is growing evidence that elongate forelimbs need not always correlate with brachiating capacities. The giant extinct gelada from Olduvai Gorge, Tanzania (Bed IV), is gorilla-sized and throughout its skeletal and dental system shows profound alterations for ground dwelling (see Jolly, 1970), yet it has forelimbs longer than hindlimbs.

Another debate that came about from overemphasis on the importance of arm swinging among apes was one concerning whether or not man ever had brachiating ancestors. This is a controversy that has not really been settled, but if the preliminary findings of Oxnard (1967, 1968a) on the fragmentary scapula and clavicle of *Australopithecus* are confirmed when better specimens are found, this possibility would be strengthened. It may just be that *Australopithecus* had forelimbs longer than hindlimbs.

As stated already, casual observation of apes in the wild had suggested that the primates listed below were brachiators. Recent, more careful field observation has shown that arm swinging is used by these animals only during the approximate time percentages on the right.

Ape	Time percentage
Hylobates	about 80
Symphalangus	about 80
Pongo	10 to 50
Pan	about 5–10
Gorilla	none
Ateles	about 35

Napier (1963a) has defined brachiation as "arboreal locomotion in which the forelimbs alone fully extended over the head are used to suspend the body and propel it through space."

The most clear-cut structural evidences in the skeleton that indi-

Figure 16 *Tarsius* and *Indri* vertically clinging and leaping (left to right). In this form of locomotion the animal springs from an upright support, utilizing its hind legs for the propulsive stroke. The hindlimbs are rotated forward during free flight so that they may be utilized for grasping another vertical support at the termination of the leap. An orthograde posture is a typical correlate of this mode of progression. (After Napier and Walker, 1967, pp. 204–219.)

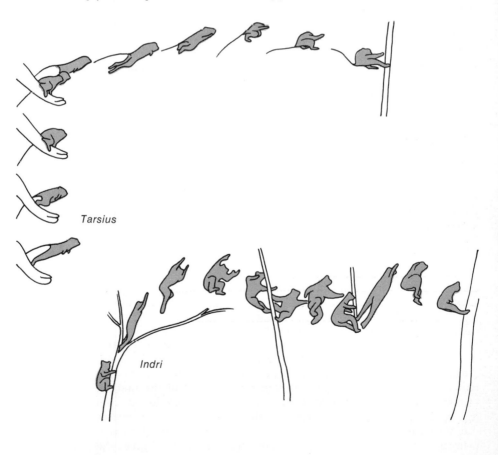

Tarsius

Indri

cate the presence of this type of locomotion are the following: (A) The bones of the hands are long, curved, and hooklike. For instance, the associated *Oreopithecus* skeleton from the Miocene of Tuscany, Italy, preserves several such curved phalanges. Correlated with finger elongation in some cases is thumb reduction. (b) The intermembral index (defined as the sum of the length of humerus and radius × 100, divided by the sum of femur and tibia length) is high. The forelimbs are elongate, with intermembral indexes at least over 100. Because the limbs (including the hand) are suspensory rather than supportive structures, the shafts of long bones (humerus, ulna, femur, tibia) usually are nearly straight. (c) The shoulder girdle is arranged in a more flexible manner, and together with this are associated characteristic features of the trunk.

Vertical clinging and leaping

The locomotor category "vertical clinging and leaping" has been understood for some years now to characterize some primates: galagos, sifakas, tarsiers, and such extinct forms as *Necrolemur* and *Tetonius* (see Simons, 1963a). Nevertheless, the extent to which this locomotor pattern occurs among primates and the possibility that it was in Eocene times a nearly universal pattern for prosimians have only recently been recognized, not without challenge, through the work of Napier and Walker (1967), who define VCL locomotion as

> An arboreal leaping mode of progression during which the two hindlimbs, used together, provide the propulsive forces in locomotion. The trunk is held in vertical position before and after each leap; vertical supports are preferred. On the ground this locomotor habit shows itself in bipedal hopping with the trunk held erect and the arms never, or rarely, involved in support. Tail movements mainly are up and down . . . .

VCL primates are generally of small to medium size, the largest living form being *Indri* (see Figure 16, page 59). There is evidence, discussed in Chapter 5, that the huge extinct lemur *Megaladapis* was a modified VCL primate.

Dental anatomy

The primates share with other therian mammals heterodont teeth, that is, teeth of different sorts, with different basic shapes and functions. There are, from front to back, the incisors, canines, premolars (the bicuspids or dentists), and molars. Teeth of the first three sorts are replaced once (except first premolars), the first set of "milk" or deciduous teeth serving the individual placental mammal during juvenile growth. As the individual matures, these teeth are replaced with a set of larger "permanent" teeth. The molars, which are carried throughout life, are actually part of the first set of teeth but are not replaced. If the tree shrews are excluded from the order, then a basic or primitive dental formula for primates can be defined as $\frac{2}{2}, \frac{1}{1}, \frac{4}{4}, \frac{3}{3}$. This number of teeth being carried primitively on each side of the midline, multiplying by 2 gives the

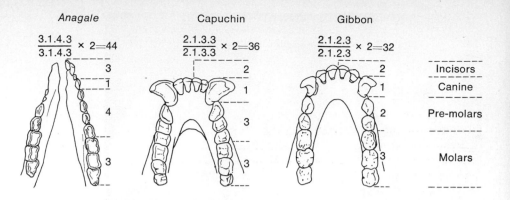

Figure 17 The dental heteromorphy and reduction of the dental formula in primates. *Anagale,* formerly thought to be a primate, has the full complement of placental teeth: three incisors, one canine, four premolars, and three molars in each jaw half. This is four more teeth than known in any undoubted primate. New World Anthropoidea, represented by the capuchin, show a dental reduction from three to two incisors and from four to three premolars. The dentition of the Old World Anthropoidea, represented by the gibbon, shows even further reduction, the premolars being reduced to two. (After Simons, 1964c. Copyright © 1964 by Scientific American, Inc. All rights reserved.)

complete number of teeth found in any primate—such as in *Adapis* a total of forty teeth (see Figure 17). In most of the major groups of the order there has been a trend toward some reduction in the total number of teeth, but such tooth loss has not been carried to the extremes among primates that can be found in other orders of mammals. Cases exist in which some or all of a given set of the four kinds of teeth have been lost, but in almost all species of the order thirty or more teeth are retained. Four general trends modifying the dentition are seen in primates:

1. Among many of the most ancient prosimians there is a tendency toward selective enlargement of the central incisors coupled with loss of the lateral incisor, canines, and front premolars and a trend toward the enlargement of the fourth premolar below. Such changes can be seen in carpolestids and among species of *Phenacolemur* and *Tetonius.*

2. In the case of most of the surviving prosimians, toothcombs have developed. The comb consists of the lower incisors and canines. These six teeth are narrow, tilted forward, and resemble the tines of a comb; they are the principal means of grooming. In correlation with possession of the comb below, the upper incisors are often small or vestigial and in some cases absent, and the upper canines interlock with canine-like lower P_2. Normally, placental lower canines ride in front of the upper canine when the jaws are shut. Among prosimians

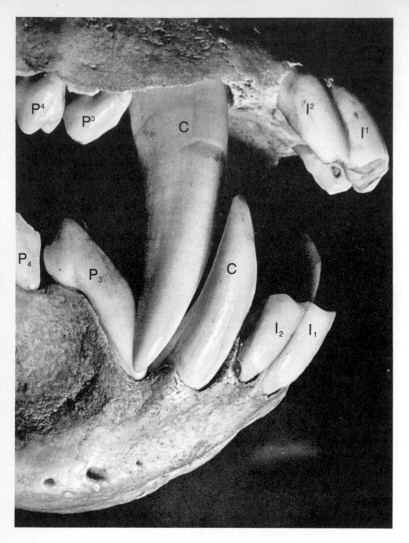

Figure 18 Anterior dentition of a baboon (*Papio*) showing functional interrelationships of canines and of upper canine with P_3, typical of Anthropoidea. P_3 serves as a hone for the back edge of the canine. (From Every, 1970.)

Figure 19 (opposite) Diagrams indicating the principal structures on the molars of higher primates. *A*: Upper molar. *B*: Lower molar. (After J. Hürzeler, 1954.)

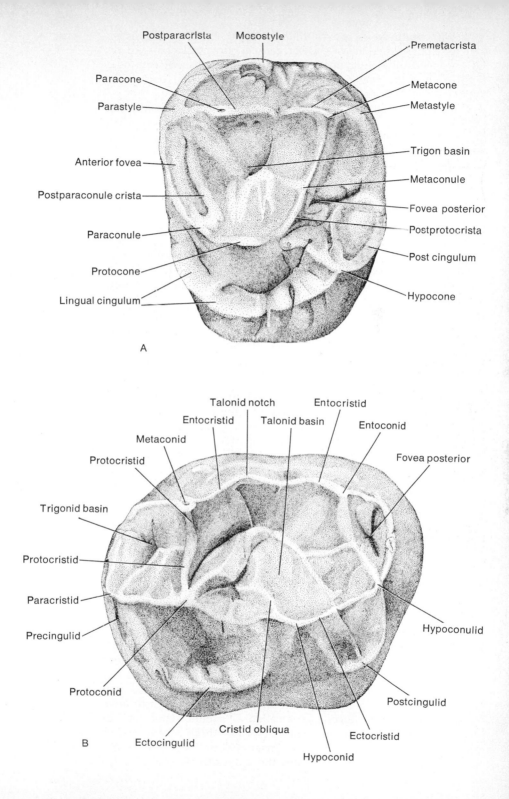

A

Postparacrista   Mesostyle   Premetacrista

Paracone

Parastyle

Metacone

Metastyle

Anterior fovea

Trigon basin

Postparaconule crista

Metaconule

Fovea posterior

Paraconule

Postprotocrista

Protocone

Post cingulum

Lingual cingulum

Hypocone

B

Talonid notch   Entocristid

Entocristid   Talonid basin

Entoconid

Metaconid

Fovea posterior

Protocristid

Trigonid basin

Protocristid

Paracristid

Precingulid

Hypoconulid

Protoconid

Postcingulid

Ectocingulid   Cristid obliqua   Ectocristid

Hypoconid

63

with toothcombs the caniniform premolar serves the same grasping function as a lower canine but interlocks with the upper canine on its posterior face. Toothcombs are seen today in all of the Malagasy lemurs and in the lorises (both living and fossil) but not among tarsiers.

3. Among the Higher Primates or Anthropoidea the front lower premolar, whether the P_2 (as in New World monkeys) or the P_3 (in the Old World catarrhines) is anterolaterally extended, bears comparatively thick enamel and typically serves as a hone that sharpens the posterior blade of the upper canine. In such animals, canines are usually comparatively large, and they seem to play an important role in shredding food and possibly equally in aggressive displays or group defense, the sharpened upper canine being almost as effective as a knife among baboons, for instance (see Figure 18, page 62).

4. A fourth tendency has been toward the general reduction of the height and the structural differentiation of the anterior teeth, coupled with the development of large cheek teeth with low or infolded cusps and thick enamel. In these primates the grinding efficiency of the cheek teeth has been emphasized and the grasping, juicing, and shredding activities of the front teeth have been de-emphasized. Trends in this direction are most marked among hominids, but also typify *Gigantopithecus*, geladas, and *Hadropithecus*.

A common convention when referring to particular teeth is to print the upper teeth as superscripts and the lower teeth as subscripts. Deciduous teeth are prefixed by lowercase "d," such as dP_4 or dI_1. Where tooth loss can be documented, it is with greatest frequency on either side of the canine. In consequence, it is usually assumed that the missing incisor of primates is the I_3^3 pair. In addition, many primates such as the catarrhines have lost front premolars. The dental formula of man, for instance, is I_1^1, I_2^2, C_1^1, P_3^3, P_4^4, M_1^1, M_2^2, M_3^3, or $\frac{2.1.2.3.}{2.1.2.3.} \times 2 = 32$. P_1^1 were already lost in most Paleocene and Eocene prosimians and in the catarrhines P_2^2 were lost as well, at some time before the Oligocene in hominoids and after that epoch in cercopithecoids.

Figure 19 (page 63) gives the names for the main cusps of primate upper and lower molars. The cusps on premolars may not necessarily be homologous with those on molars but are by general convention referred to by the same names as the cusps of the front half of the upper and lower molars. Primitively among mammals the upper molars carry three cusps. This is called the "trigon." Among primates of various lineages a heel or "talon" has more than once evolved, arising from the basal cingulum. This is the "hypocone," which is located posterior to the primitive internal cusp or "protocone." If a posterior internal cusp can be shown to arise by splitting of the protocone, it is called a "pseudohypocone." In lower teeth a heel also arises posteriorly. The three anterior lower molar cusps are spoken of as the "trigonid" and the heel is the "talonid." Among Higher Primates the anteriormost lower molar

cusp, the "paraconid," is reduced to a crest or is absent; the heel
of lower molars usually retains three cusps.

PROSIMII

General remarks

The living prosimian primates are commonly divided into five
or six extant groups, depending on whether or not the tree shrews
(or tupaias) are included in the order Primates. However, there
seems to be a growing feeling that they are best considered insectivores, but of a sort very divergent from other members of the living
Insectivora. They appear to differ from primates in having an
auditory bulla constituted from the entotympanic bone and not the
petrosal or petrosal plus the ectotympanic (see Figure 20). Tree
shrews do not have flat nails on any digits and retain three pairs
of lower incisors. Basic structures of the brain also differ. However,
even if they are not to be considered in this order, they remain
the most primate-like nonprimates, which comes out to be rather
like a distinction without a difference. Tupaias do indicate the
general grade of organization that one might speculate preceded
that of the lemurs.

Figure 20 Cross sections of the auditory bullae of *Tupaia* and various
primates, in order to show diagrammatically the bones that contribute
the component parts at various stages of complexity among primates.
(After E. Thenius, 1969.)

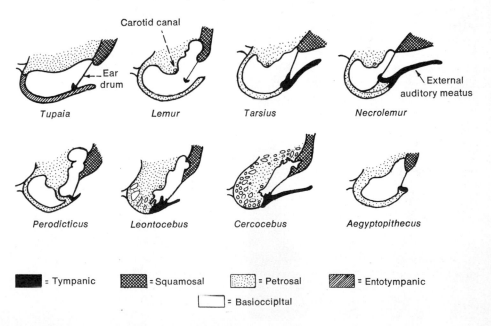

Figure 21 An example of the Malagasy prosimian family Lemuridae, a pair of *Lemur fulvus sanfordi*. This rare subspecies was named in the nineteenth century. Living populations were recently rediscovered. (Photo courtesy of Ian M. Tattersall.)

Figure 22 A present-day representative of the Malagasy prosimian family Indriidae, *Propithecus verreauxi*. (Photo courtesy of John Buettner-Janusch.)

The most primitive undoubted primates are the lemurs, which today are entirely restricted to the island of Madagascar. Living species are divided into three rather distinct families:

1. Lemuridae: Including small or fairly generalized arboreal quadrupeds of the genera *Microcebus, Cheirogaleus, Phaner, Hapalemur, Lemur* (see Figure 21) and *Lepilemur*, a leaping form.
2. Indriidae: Large, long-legged, and extremely agile leaping forms of the genera *Indri, Avahi,* and *Propithecus* (see Figure 22).
3. Daubentoniidae: Includes only the aberrant, nocturnal, rodent-like genus *Daubentonia*.

Outside Madagascar, prosimians are represented by two other families.

4. Lorisidae: Galagos (or bushbabies) and pottos of Africa (genera *Perodicticus, Arctocebus,* and *Galago*) and slow and slender lorises of the Far East (*Nycticebus* and *Loris*).
5. Tarsiidae: Includes only one living genus, *Tarsius*, which is distributed throughout many of the islands of the East Indies.

These living prosimians represent a wide range of adaptive types, which renders generalization about them difficult. Many of them constitute little-changed branches of the Eocene primate radiation, whereas apes, monkeys, and men represent more radically modified derivatives of the same radiation. Prosimians show marked dexterity in handling food objects; for instance, none of these animals ever needs to depend on a two-handed grasp of food objects such as is the typical posture for squirrels with nuts. Perhaps their most primitive retention is the greater dependence on the sense of smell in locating food. With much shorter life spans, there is also less time for transfer of learned behavior; nevertheless, the diurnal species have fairly complex social organization. Naturally, these primates have not remained totally unchanged throughout the Tertiary, and of course none of them represent actual ancestral stages of something else. Feeding habits and locomotor behavior are very diversified among prosimians, and consequently their skeletal proportions are also varied. For instance, in *Tarsius* the tibia and fibula are fused together, and the calcaneum and navicular are greatly elongated. The large orbits are critical to the visual acuity and dexterity in leaping that characterize this animal (see Figure 23).

The principal developments in prosimian evolution have been relative enlargement of the brain (bringing about an increase in the brain–body size ratio), refinements of locomotor function, and changes in the dental mechanics improving feeding and grooming. Prosimians today occupy two general habitats that relate to their competitive situation vis à vis other faunal elements. Those that have survived on the continents are usually nocturnal. This has presumably come about in order to decrease competition for food resources with monkeys and to avoid predators. In the case of the Asian lorises and African pottos there has been a further develop-

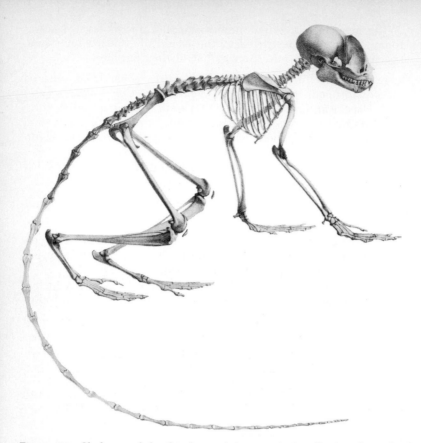

Figure 23 Skeleton of the Southeast Asian prosimian *Tarsius,* the only surviving genus of the infraorder Tarsiiformes. Scale × 0.5. (Reproduced from de Blainville, 1840.)

ment of cryptic, slow-moving behavior that seems to serve to obscure them from both predators and their insect and avian prey. In addition to nocturnal habits, the continental prosimians live normally either in small family groups or singly. The only exceptions to this are the crepuscular galagos of Africa. With the slow climbing habits of most lorises, limb proportions have changed. The hands and feet are comparatively large, and the index finger is reduced so as to increase the power grip. Because leaping is never attempted, the limbs are subequal in length and the tail is reduced (see Figure 24).

In Madagascar the lemurs have presumably had all the time since about the late Eocene, perhaps 40 million years, to diversify without much competition from other mammals. Under these conditions, diurnal prosimian species were abundant. Nevertheless, during the last 2,000 to 800 years there have been many extinctions of the larger or terrestrial and/or diurnal lemurs because of competition with and predation by man. Also, in the relative isolation of Madagascar the lemurs have developed more complex societies or

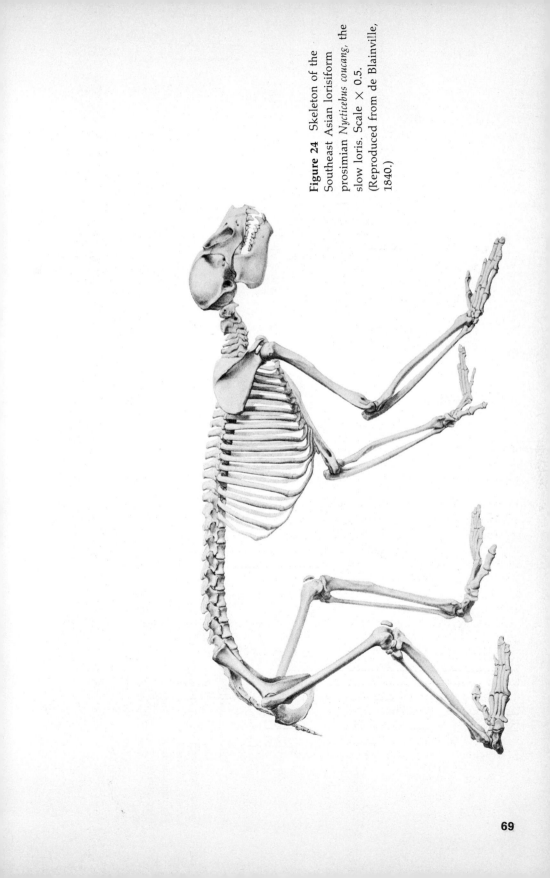

Figure 24 Skeleton of the Southeast Asian lorisiform prosimian *Nycticebus coucang*, the slow loris. Scale × 0.5. (Reproduced from de Blainville, 1840.)

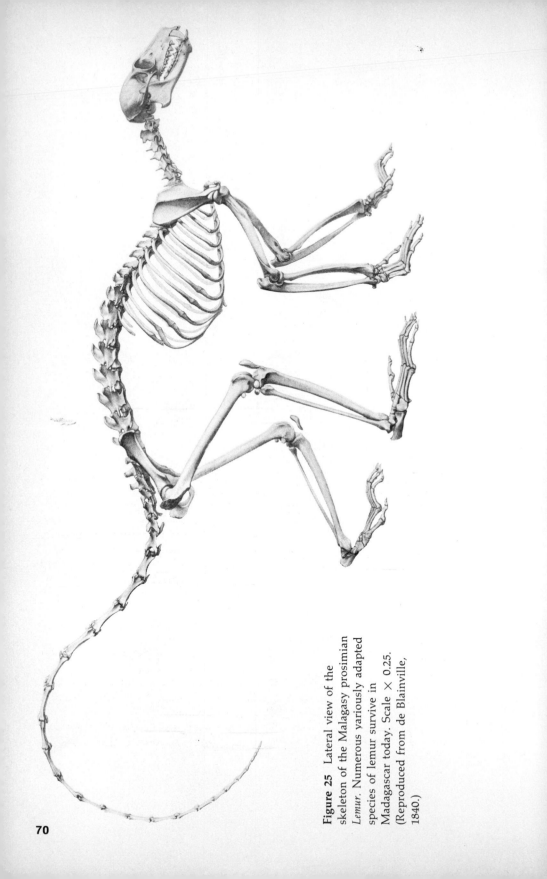

Figure 25 Lateral view of the skeleton of the Malagasy prosimian *Lemur*. Numerous variously adapted species of lemur survive in Madagascar today. Scale × 0.25. (Reproduced from de Blainville, 1840.)

social groupings than other prosimians. Such groups often include more than one adult male along with females and offspring living in year-round permanent societies. Such societies characterize species of *Lemur* and *Propithecus*. Elements apparently making for group cohesiveness or territorial delineation among prosimians but less clearly present, if ever, among higher primates are the scent-marking habits of lemurs and pottos and the urine washing of other lorises.

Little is known about the breeding cycle and associated habits of prosimians. Most species appear to have a polyestrus cycle. In *Loris* there seems to be only a biennial estrus. In *Lemur* the breeding season has been reported to be extraordinarily brief, perhaps restricted to only 1 day a year in females and 2 to 3 in males. Prosimian longevity records are also sparse, but presumably the durations of prenatal, juvenile, adult, and female reproductive periods of life are broadly comparable with those recently estimated for *Lemur* by Schultz (1968). Zoo longevity records for prosimian species, whose captive dietary and other maintenance is poorly understood, range from 7 to 27 years, with the captive maxima for many species around 10 to 12 years. It would appear probable that the average generation span for most prosimians might not be more than about 5 years. Unlike the indriids, species of *Lemur* are more generalized and run both on the ground and in branches on all fours, even though they are good at springing as well (see Figure 25).

The commonest locomotor behavior among prosimians is springing and vertical clinging and leaping. It is believed (Napier and Walker, 1967) that this is probably the basal locomotor pattern of the Eocene–Recent prosimians, although some would challenge this in favor of arboreal quadrupedalism. Vertical clinging and leaping locomotion is the adaptation indicated for such Eocene prosimians as *Necrolemur*, *Notharctus*, and *Smilodectes*; with other forms, locomotor interpretation is less clear. Such varied groups of prosimians as *Avahi*, *Galago*, *Indri*, *Lepilemur*, *Propithecus*, and *Tarsius* among modern forms all show this locomotor propensity as well. These animals are arboreal and when at rest cling in a vertical posture (see Figure 22, page 66); all employ a leaping type of progression in which the principal propulsion comes from the hindlimbs. As a consequence of this, great leaps of 15 to 30 feet can easily be accomplished. In addition, because of the strong and elongated hindlimbs, progression on the ground is often by bipedal hopping or a sort of bent-kneed walk, as in *Propithecus*.

It may well be that among primates, springing and vertical clinging and leaping as a locomotor category were both basal and preadaptive to arboreal quadrupedalism, brachiation, and bipedalism, the principal locomotor categories that have subsequently become common among the higher primates.

Development of visual acuity has been a principal trend among prosimian primates. In various lineages the orbits have come to be rotated forward so that fields of vision overlap.

It is possible that development of orbital frontality in some prosimians has been retarded by the retention of a long rostrum, correlating with a relatively strong olfactory sense in these animals. However, the selection pressures favoring binocular vision have produced an upward rotation of the orbits among the lemuroids, bringing about the required reduction in the angle between the visual axes without shortening the rostrum. This adaptation has taken place quite independently from that in Higher Primates, in which there was an early reduction of the rostrum, and appears to have occurred more than once among prosimians—once in the line that produced the middle and late Eocene European lemur-like *Adapis*, once in North American *Smilodectes*, and separately in the line that gave rise to such modern lorisiform lemurs as *Nycticebus* and *Perodicticus*.

In general, the degree of development of orbital frontality in prosimians is less than among Anthropoidea. For instance, the angle subtended by the axes of the orbits in lemurs ranges from about 60° to 70°, whereas that of monkeys, apes, and man is in the region of 30°. Nevertheless, the visual axis is always less divergent than that of the orbits, so that in the higher primates the optical axes are parallel. This is apparently less likely among prosimians. In addition, none of the prosimians other than *Tarsius* possess a retinal fovea, which in higher primates is the area of highest visual acuity. Because visual acuity is a necessary component of intense inspection of objects, it would appear that the prosimians, with their lesser abilities in visual focusing and stereoscopic sight, coupled with lesser manual dexterity, are only preadaptive toward the levels of object manipulation of the higher primates.

The intrinsic structure of the orbit also shows some variation (Figure 26), in particular in the degree to which the palatine bone takes part in the formation of the posterior wall. The condition in a primitive mammal is that the palatine does not take part in the formation of the posterior wall of the orbit. In lemurs the palatine has extended upward and forward between the frontal bone and the maxilla, meeting the lacrymal bone anteriorly to form a substantial element in this region. A similar condition is seen in *Tupaia* and has been used as a taxonomic indicator of affinity between tree shrews and the primates. It seems likely that this similarity reflects parallel development. In the lorises, tarsiers, and anthropoids the palatine bone is separated from the lacrymal by the introduction of an ethmoid element between the maxilla and frontal bone in this region. The orbitosphenoid element is expanded between the palatine and the frontal, and the alisphenoid truncates the palatine posteriorly in forming the lateral pterygoid lamina. In these animals the palatine therefore forms a much smaller portion of the inner wall.

The construction of the middle ear in primates has been used as an adjunct in classifying living and fossil forms. Primitively, mammals lack an ossified bulla protecting the ventral side of the middle ear region. Several groups of mammals have evolved bullae

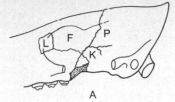

A

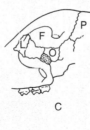

B

C

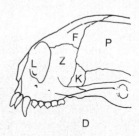

D

Figure 26 Diagram showing the bones that contribute to the formation of the orbital and temporal region of the skull in a primitive mammal and three primates. The palatine bone is indicated by stippling. *A* shows the primitive mammalian condition in which there is a broad contact between maxilla and frontal. *B* illustrates the condition typical of recent lemuriform primates where the orbital plate of the palatine reaches forward to the lacrimal. *C* shows the arrangement typical of lorises, *Tarsius,* and the catarrhines in which the ethmoid separates the frontal bone from the maxilla, the palatine from the lacrimal, and the frontal contact. *D* is the typical arrangement in a platyrrhine primate with zygoma and parietal contact. K—alisphenoid; F—frontal; L—lacrimal; O—orbitosphenoid; Z—zygomatic; P—parietal. (After Le Gros Clark, 1959.)

independently, but the Insectivora, a generally primitive group, normally lack the entotympanic bone (commonly defined as a bullar element ontogenetically derived from a center of ossification independent of the other bones in this region). In tree shrews (*Tupaia*) and elephant shrews (*Rhynchocyon*) entotympanic bones are present. In primates the condition appears to be otherwise, for in these the bulla consists of an extension from the ossification center of the petrosal bone. Inside the bulla, the tympanic bone, which is the ringlike support for the eardrum, is attached like a loop from the ventral part of the squamosal bone and hangs free within the bulla. This is the condition in all the nine genera of living Malagasy lemurs and is to be found also in the most lemur-like Eocene primates known, such as *Adapis* and *Notharctus.* Possession of a "free" intrabullar ring, then, is generally considered to be an ancestral condition from which more advanced bullar constructions arose, as seen in Figure 20, page 65. In lorises such as *Perodicticus* and

New World monkeys such as *Leontocebus*, the tympanic ring has fused with the lateral margin of the external opening of the bulla. A final development, seen in *Tarsius* and all the catarrhine primates, is that the ossified ring is produced outward to create a tubular tympanic bone and auditory meatus.

Changes in the details of arterial supply to the head have provided important information regarding the taxonomic affinities of some fossil primates. Variations of the internal carotid artery, which enters the skull in the region of the auditory bulla, and its subsequent branches are of particular importance. This is because among primates the vessels often have ossified coatings that are preserved in fossils.

Among insectivores and prosimians the internal carotid artery divides within the auditory bulla, giving rise to stapedial and promontory branches.

The tree shrew *Tupaia* has a greatly reduced promontory artery, and the stapedial artery is reduced in part. Primates in general show a great reduction in the stapedial artery. As in *Tupaia*, among lemurs the promontory artery is also much reduced. On the other hand, *Loris, Plesiadapis, Necrolemur,* and *Tarsius* have expanded promontory arteries, as do Anthropoidea. A further development in Antrhopoidea is the loss of the stapedial artery, although this is retained embryonically.

The brain

As a result of the limitations of the fossil record, the evolution of the primate brain is incompletely known. However, evidence may be gained from comparative studies of modern insectivores and primates, taken together with examination of such fossil endocasts as are available. But an obvious drawback of this approach is that the external configuration and relative size of the lobes of the brain (which is all that is ever available for the fossils) can only convey information of a general nature.

The mammalian brain is divided into three parts, the forebrain, midbrain, and hindbrain. The forebrain consists largely of olfactory bulbs, cerebral cortex, and thalamus. The olfactory bulbs, as the name suggests, are centers for the sense of smell. In prosimians these are relatively large compared with Anthropoidea, but relative to most other mammals they are small. The cerebral cortex receives sensory inputs of various types and emits impulses that help to initiate and control voluntary muscular movements. The cortex also contains association areas that serve to interrelate sensory and motor activities. The pyriform lobe of the cerebral cortex, phylogenetically the oldest part of the forebrain, receives impulses from the olfactory cortex. The remainder of the cortex lies above the pyriform lobe and is the so-called neopallium. The neopallium receives somatosensory, visual, and auditory stimuli. The thalamus includes a number of sensory ganglia that sort and relay stimuli between the brain stem and the cortex.

The dorsal part of the midbrain includes two pairs of hemispherical eminences, the anterior and posterior quadrigemina. The anterior pair is at the terminus of some of the optic tracts. They are thought to mediate ocular reflexes. Similarly, the posterior pair is associated with auditory reflex centers.

The cerebellum, the pons, and the medulla comprise the hindbrain. The cerebellum is dorsal to the medulla and pons and has a large central part divided into three parts by deep fissures. The middle division forms the main mass of the cerebellar hemispheres, traversed by a narrow elevation, the vermis, and the posterior part bulges laterally on each side to form the flocculus. Functions of the cerebellum include maintenance of equilibrium, muscle tone, and coordination. Both the pons and the medulla contain centers for autonomic function along with motor and sensory nuclei for most of the cranial nerves and a number of ascending and descending nerve fibers.

The external anatomy of the brain can tell us significant facts about fossil forms. First, the relative proportions of the lobes of the cerebral cortex lend themselves to broadly qualitative deductions concerning the comparative emphasis put on the senses relied on by particular primates. Second, the sulci, visible on endocranial casts, may in some limited way aid in delimiting the boundaries of different cortical areas.

The sulci seen on the exterior of the brain in lemurs do not delimit different functional areas of the brain. This suggests that the sulci of lemurs have tended to develop in conformity with the stresses imposed on the developing brain within the skull. The opposite appears to be the case in Higher Primates, in which many of the sulci that are visible delimit different functional cortical areas.

The endocranial cast of *Adapis*, a lemur-like early Eocene primate, indicates a smaller brain size to body size ratio than in modern lemurs. Other features of distinction in *Adapis* are relatively larger olfactory bulbs, limited expansion of the cerebral cortex in the occipital region, and larger temporal lobes. *Adapis* must have placed greater reliance on its sense of smell than the modern lemurs do. The endocast of *Archaeolemur*, a subfossil Malagasay lemur, shows sulci with transverse orientation, a feature that must have evolved in parallel with the evolution of similar sulci in Higher Primates.

The brain of *Tarsius* is most notable for its expanded visual cortex of the occipital lobe. However, the corpus callosum is much more primitive than might be expected in such a visually dominant form. Overall, the tarsioid brain is generalized. Superimposed on this is perhaps the most complex development of the visual centers of the brain to be seen in primates. The nonvisual areas of the neopallium, including the motor cortex, are poorly developed. The tarsioid brain appears to be of some antiquity, for the endocranial cast of *Necrolemur* is quite similar to the modern *Tarsius* and very distinct from *Adapis*; even compared with *Tarsius*, the occipital lobes of *Necrolemur* are quite large.

The postcranial skeleton

The locomotor adaptations of modern prosimians include three of the primate categories, vertical clinging and leaping, quadrupedalism, and slow climbing. In general, examination of the postcranial skeleton and muscular system, particularly with regard to the structures of the limbs, indicates an integrated functional complex suited for the needs of each animal. It appears profitable to compare briefly the functional adaptations of leaping and springing locomotion and quadrupedalism.

The axial skeleton is indicative of the mode of locomotion employed by an animal. The vertebrae of the thoracic and lumbar regions in quadrupeds form an arch between the pectoral and pelvic girdles, a bow from which is strung the abdominal musculature. When a quadrupedal animal leaps, it pushes off with the hind legs, straightens the axial bow, and reaches forward with its forelegs. At the conclusion of the spring, the hindlimbs are brought back under the body by the action of the abdominal musculature. Slow climbers such as the potto and slow loris (see Figures 14, page 57 and 24, page 69) have a more sinuous and deliberate locomotor movement. Broadly speaking, however, the adaptations of their axial skeleton show similarities to those of quadrupeds, with a considerable degree of mobility and a large number of vertebrae.

The other extreme in locomotion among the prosimians is to be seen in the VCL group, in which the trunk is held upright at almost all times and becomes a rod that is less flexible and has fewer vertebral elements. This is presumed to be part of a saltatory functional complex in which the femur, tibia, and foot are extended away from the body during the leap. A mobile structural column for the body would be disadvantageous in that it would dampen to some degree the spring of the leap.

Walker (1967b) has reviewed the functional complex related to vertical clinging and leaping. The first and most obvious adaptation of the appendicular skeleton is to be seen in limb proportions. In general, among VCL primates the radius is relatively longer than the humerus and the sum of the length of tibia and femur is always much greater than the sum of the length of radius and humerus. The lengthening of the hindlimbs is clearly related to increasing the moment arms, and speed of movement, in the locomotor power stroke. Intermembral indexes for various living and fossil prosimians are tabulated on page 138.

The forelimbs of the VCL group have a number of features in common that distinguish them from those of arboreal and terrestrial quadrupeds. In the shoulder girdle, the scapulae of the larger members of the group are expanded. This change is presumed to be related to an increase in rotational mobility in the shoulder joint, because this expansion increases the couple arm between certain shoulder muscles. The greater tuberosity at the proximal end of the humerus is the point of insertion of the supraspinatus muscle. This area is reduced in size in the VCL group. The relative expansion of this fossa among monkeys reflects the importance of the extension of the upper arm in quadrupedal locomotion.

In general, the forelimbs of vertical clingers and leapers do not undergo the same compressive forces as are normal for the quadrupedal forelimb. Function of the forelimbs in body support of vertical clingers and leapers is more suspensory in nature. For this reason, the features of the quadrupedal monkey forelimb related to resistance of compressive forces are not normally accentuated among most lemurs. Quadrupedal features are a deep trochlear notch, a long olecranon process, and a short styloid process. The features to be seen here in lemurs relate respectively to the prevention of forward dislocation at the elbow joint, to increased power in extension during locomotion and absorption of shock, and to spreading of compressive forces at the wrist joint. The VCL group shows the opposite trends, in the direction of improvement of the ability of the forearm to extend rapidly although not powerfully. This comes about by shortening of the olecranon process and increasing the ability of the forearm to absorb tensile stresses by lengthening the styloid process and preserving a shallow trochlear notch.

In the pelvic girdle and hindlimb, vertical clingers and leapers display a suite of features that relate to adaptations for power and speed in their saltatory locomotion. The pelvis has large areas for two powerful muscles that are extensors of the thigh. In addition, these muscles provide a portion of the springing and recovery powers of the lower leg, one being a lower leg flexor and the other a lower leg extensor. The expanded iliac blade apparently is related to the need for an area for adductor and extensor muscles of the thigh. This hypothesis is supported by the observed shortness of the trochanteric lever arm of the femur, an adaptation for rapid extension. These features relate respectively to the thigh extension capabilities of the gluteal muscles, and the greatly developed vasti (extensors of the tibia), the increased size of the pulley for the tibial extensors, and the habitual flexure of the lower leg at rest.

The tibia in the VCL group differs from that of arboreal quadrupeds in its more extreme lateral compression proximally. These lateral areas are the origin for the plantar flexors, actively involved in providing the power for leaping.

The hands and feet of this group are to be distinguished from those of arboreal quadrupeds in general for reasons related to their habitually vertical posture, excellent grasping ability, and, in the foot, the needs of powerful springing and leaping. Because habitual uprightness is the rule among vertical clingers and leapers, the lateral borders of the hands and feet have become areas of maximal stress, and therefore it is not surprising that this area has become expanded evolutionarily. However, among arboreal quadrupeds the major-weight bearing axis has shifted to the second and third digits, a pattern that is further developed among brachiators and digitigrade quadrupeds. Another feature distinguishing the VCL foot is the pronounced development of the peroneal tubercle of the first digit. This strengthens grasping power, for it provides the insertion for the peroneus longus, a powerful adductor of the big toe. This tubercle is poorly developed in arboreal quadrupedal monkeys. The elongation of the calcaneum and navicular among lemurs may relate to the need for great acceleration in the early phases of leaping.

Finally, the degree of elongation of the foot seems to correlate with the absolute size of an animal, because smaller animals need more power to accomplish long leaps (the average distance between branches remains the same whatever the size of the animal). Medium-sized forms such as *Notharctus, Lemur,* or *Lepilemur* have a fully extended big toe, but the navicular and calcaneum are not appreciably elongated as they are in smaller forms such as *Tarsius* and *Galago*. In slow-climbing prosimians such as *Loris* the bones of the big toe are even larger relatively and are curved to facilitate grasping. Heel elongation—shared by tarsiers and some lorisids— has apparently arisen in parallel in the two groups. Calcaneal elongation among microchoerines (*Nannopithex*) and omomyines (*Hemiacodon*) therefore does not provide reliable information as to which of the modern groups these early forms were closest, but it does tell us that leaping adaptations such as heel elongation go back to the beginning of the radiation of the primates of modern aspect in the Eocene. Nevertheless, several students doubt the widespread attribution of VCL capacities among primates for it seems that as far as modern forms are concerned many of the VCL characteristics are found only in *Tarsius* and the galagos. In turn, attribution of these capacities to extinct forms is largely an extrapolation from what is observed in recent animals and is not subject to certain confirmation.

Walker (1967a) has recently demonstrated another aspect of the behavior of prosimians that may be extrapolated to extinct forms. This regards their daily activity cycles. The living Malagasy lemurs constitute eleven diurnal and nine nocturnal species. Assuming that nocturnal forms have relatively larger eyes, he has compiled data regarding the relationship between orbital diameter and skull length. His assumption appears to be valid, for the lemurs that are most exclusively nocturnal are distinctly separable form the diurnal species. Between these extremes lie forms known to be crepuscular in habit.

ANTHROPOIDEA

General remarks

The Anthropoidea or Higher Primates represent the second main division or suborder of Primates. The term "Anthropoidea" was originated by Mivart and has been in general use since Simpson's (1945) classification of mammals was published. However, the common noun derived from it—"anthropoids"—is somewhat misleading because this is a term generally used for apes alone by English and French speakers. If used in a sense derived from the subordinal name, it of course refers to all monkeys, apes, and man.

The Higher Primates of the middle and late Cenozoic, like those of the present day, are separated by a considerable morphological gap from any Prosimii. However, there is little reason to doubt that they were derived from early members of Prosimii. The possibility exists that the three main divisions of Anthropoidea—ceboids, cercopithecoids, and hominoids—were polyphyletically, that is, separately, derived from Prosimii, but this has yet to be conclusively demonstrated from the fossil record. Nevertheless, earliest members of these three groups do not as closely resemble one another as would probably be the case had they all been derived from one small segment of Paleocene–Eocene prosimians. This raises the question as to whether or not the suborder Anthropoidea has any real meaning in terms of a shared common ancestor for the group.

However, taken together all known Anthropoidea share a series of features that can be considered as characterizing members of this suborder. General tendencies separating this section of the Primates from prosimians include possession of a relatively larger and more convoluted brain and a foreshortened rostrum with consequent reduction of olfactory lobes and sensory epithelium of olfaction. Mandibular rami and frontal bones are typically fused

Figure 27 A present-day South American monkey, the lion marmoset *Leontocebus*. Marmosets constitute one of the two living families of South American monkeys: Callithricidae. (Photo courtesy of Roy Winslow.)

at the midline suture in all adults. The orbits are relatively forward directed and are separated from the temporal fossa by a postorbital plate composed of extensions of the frontal, alisphenoid, jugal, and maxillary bones.

Anthropoidea are usually divided into two infraorders, the Catarrhini and Platyrrhini of Geoffroy Saint-Hillaire (1812), thus distinguishing all the Higher Primates of the Old World from the ceboid monkeys and marmosets of the Western Hemisphere, a distinction originally noted by Buffon in the eighteenth century. The two names refer to nostril placement in the two groups, but there are of course many other differences. Old World monkeys, apes, and man have the nostrils facing downward, hence the name "Catarrhini"—"curved or hook nosed." Middle and South American Anthropoidea have more widely separated laterally facing nostrils, so that Saint-Hillaire coined the name "Platyrrhini"—or "flat nosed"—for this group. Such evidence as we have from the fossil record indicates that both these infraorders have (since their origins) been restricted to the respective hemispheres in which they now occur.

The infraorder Platyrrhini contains but one superfamily, Ceboidea, in which a more-or-less expanded tympanic bulla is always present. This group is divided into the callithricids or marmosets (Figure 27, page 79) and the cebid monkeys, of which the most hominoid-like may be species of the spider monkey, genus *Ateles* (Figure 28). The tympanic ring is fused laterally around the auditory opening of the bulla but is not drawn out into an elongated external auditory meatus as in catarrhines; the postorbital plate is composed posteroexternally of the jugal, which reaches the temporal fossa, where it contacts the parietal; the orbitotemporal foramen is relatively large; and each upper and lower jaw holds three premolars, whereas among marmosets third molars are typically lost. Almost nothing anatomically informative is known about early ceboids, although a few Miocene and Pleistocene fossils exist that will be considered below. It is clear from shared similarities that all ceboids are the products of a single adaptive radiation.

Following Simpson (1945), almost all authorities divide the catarrhine infraorder into two superfamilies, Hominoidea (apes and man) and Cercopithecoidea (Old World monkeys), for which the terms "Anthropomorpha" and Cynomorpha," used by some European authors, are less acceptable equivalents. Catarrhini show little or no expansion of the auditory bulla, but as in tarsioids the tympanic bone is drawn out into an elongated external auditory meatus, part of the roof of which is made up by the squamosal bone. Among these primates the postorbital plate is composed of elements of the jugal, frontal, and alisphenoid bones, with the maxillaries contributing a small portion of the medial orbital floor. The alisphenoid does not contact the parietal, but in the region of the pterion at the front of the temporal fossa either frontal and temporal or alisphenoid and parietal may make sutural contact. The dental

Figure 28 A representative of the most diversified family of South American monkeys: Cebidae. Subadult female spider monkey *Ateles belzebuth*. (Photo by Ian M. Tattersall.)

formula is typically $\frac{2.1.2.3.}{1.1.2.3.} \times 2$, but if the Parapithecinae are to be included among Catarrhini they form a single exception in that the dental formula for this group is undoubtedly $\frac{1.1.3.3.}{1.1.3.3.} \times 2$.

Anatomically, cercopithecoids or Old World monkeys are all rather remarkably uniform in their shoulder and pelvic girdles, rib cage, limb proportions, etc. It is growing increasingly clear that this group represents a specialized adaptation somewhat off the main track of primate adaptation and that we should not expect to find—and in fact do not find—forms constituted like these monkeys among the earliest ancestors of apes. The Old World monkeys are therefore fairly stereotyped as arboreal quadrupeds that, in some cases in apparently fairly recent times (some baboons, *Macaca*, and *Erythrocebus*), have taken up a ground-living way of life, (see Figure 29).

The locomotor repertoire of the New World monkeys (ceboids or platyrrhines) is therefore more likely to reflect the basal range among the Anthropoidea. These primates retain more lemur-like

Figure 29 The Old World Higher Primates are divided into two superfamilies. The first of these, Cercopithecoidea, includes all of the Old World monkeys. The group is here represented by two subadult yellow baboons (*Papio cynocephalus*). (San Diego Zoo Photo.)

limbs, have great freedom at the shoulder joint, and in a few cases such as in species of *Ateles* and *Brachyteles* both brachiate and walk bipedally.

The Anthropoidea are well known for their complex behavior. Many if not most of the species commonly consort in multimale troops, but the gibbons and orangutans, most species of *Cerco-*

pithecus, and occasionally other members of Anthropoidea do move in single-male groups (that is, an adult male plus several adult females together with their recent offspring).

Group movements are usually coordinated by male vocalizations, which are warning calls, gathering calls, and flight calls indicative of the status of group interaction in often dense foliage where not all members of a troop can see each other. Individuals of a given species may also emit species-specific associative noises, which continuously inform others as to their whereabouts. As a consequence of these social tendencies, much more extensive communicative behavior is necessary. This is accomplished both by vocalizations and by gestures. Researchers have reported about thirty different vocalizations in the wild for such forms as the Japanese macaque and the chimpanzee. Probably, these sound categories have been too much divided in the two cases, but it is clear that the complexity of vocalization and gesture among Anthropoidea goes distinctly beyond that of the Lower Primates.

Equally, the reproductive cycle of the monkeys and apes is more elaborate than that of prosimians. In fact, Hill (1932) recognized the "pithecoid and anthropoid" stages of development of placental structure as more elaborate, in presumed correlation with progressive and more functionally efficient systems. Fairly widespread among the Higher Primates is occurrence of menstrual periods and/or periods of swelling of the female sexual skin that appear to correlate with the longer and more complex period of gestation in these animals.

The level of organization of the Higher Primates stands above that of the prosimians in numerous ways, but principally in the increasing complexity of the brain, manner of placentation, locomotion, social organization, and vocalization. Beyond generalizations such as these, it is difficult to summarize the adaptive level of a group of animals so diversified as to include the pygmy marmoset, the mountain gorilla, and man.

In the Old World, at least, there have clearly been independent trends toward the development of metabolic and dietary mechanisms that have allowed certain more advanced groups to range outside the forest and away from the tropical and warm-temperate zones. These are exemplified by the Japanese macaque and the Himalayan langurs, which are adapted to feeding in snow-covered terrain, and by the invasion of open-country habitat by the hominids, some macaques, and the savanna baboons of Africa.

None of the Anthropoidea retain the primitive vertical clinging and leaping locomotor pattern, but are characterized rather by broad locomotor diversity and by considerable plasticity in establishing variants of extremely divergent locomotor habits (of which the bipedalism of hominids and the quadrumanal or brachiating capacities of the orangutan and gibbons can be given as examples). The advanced abilities of the largest and longest-lived of the Higher Primates in play learning, manipulative behavior, and social integration clearly foreshadow their final elaboration during the evolu-

Figure 30 Superfamily Hominoidea includes the apes, near-man, and man. The African apes, here represented by a male pygmy chimpanzee (*Pan paniscus*), are man's closest living relatives. (San Diego Zoo Photo.)

tionary breakthrough that produced the early hominids and ultimately modern man.

The higher members of Anthropoidea are usually grouped as Cercopithecoidea (Old World monkeys) and Hominoidea (gibbons, siamangs, the great apes, and man). Of the latter group, the African great apes, such as the pygmy chimpanzee (Figure 30), are considered man's closest living relatives.

Cranial anatomy

Monkeys, apes, and man all share much enlarged brains relative to prosimians, and their cranial structures do not vary so greatly in relative shape and proportion as among the Prosimii. Among Anthropoidea the enlarged brain case overshadows the comparatively small face. Greater brain volume is accommodated by enlargement of the frontal and occipital areas. The frontal bone is expanded, and instead of retaining two separate halves as in prosimians it fuses at the midline in early stages of growth. Posteriorly, the cerebral fossa overlaps the cerebellar fossa within the cranial cavity.

Members of the two subfamilies of Old World monkeys can usually be distinguished by the fact that in the cercopithecines the squamosal bone normally extends forward beneath the parietal and touches the frontal, whereas among colobines and the South American monkeys the primitive mammalian condition is retained—that is, a part of the alisphenoid bone reaches up behind the orbits to touch the parietal (see Figure 26, page 73). There is a suggestion that postorbital closure among the South American monkeys may have been achieved independently of the development of this closure in the catarrhines, because in ceboids the jugal or zygomatic bone reaches back on the side of the skull to contact the parietal and therefore contributes to the upper part of the postorbital plate to the partial exclusion of the frontal, which makes up a larger portion of this plate in catarrhines.

Relative shortening of the snout among most Anthropoidea and Hominoidea in comparison with prosimians has been noted as an overall trend; however, no simple relationship can explain this phenomenon. In order to understand this retreat of the rostrum, one must consider not only the comparative reduction in the size of the olfactory apparatus but also allometric differences that are related to the size of the dental arcade and the muscles of mastication. In correlation with this reduction among Anthropoidea and Hominoidea, the premaxillae at the alveolar border are moderately developed, but unlike the condition in more primitive members of the order the ascending wings of these bones are much reduced in living Anthropoidea.

Generally, one can find a marked degree of flexure around the basicranial axis in skulls of Higher Primates. This has produced, broadly speaking, a relative decrease in the resistance moment arm of the tooth row, compared with the moment arms of the muscles of mastication turning about the temporomandibular joint. This change tends to enhance capabilities for more powerful chewing forces along the tooth row. In addition, tucking the mandible under the cranium in this fashion would also have contributed to the shortening of the horizontal ramus of the mandible compared with the ascending branch of the mandible, a feature that has also been accentuated by an increase in the height of the ascending ramus above the tooth row. Once again, such adaptations appear to be related to improvements in the mechanical advantage of the muscles of mastication about the temporomandibular joint. Fusion of the mandibular symphysis, characteristic of all Anthropoidea, also appears to contribute to the strength of the mandible when resisting increased stresses on the body of the mandible.

Postorbital closure, by development of bony plates from the frontal, jugal, and maxillary bones between the orbital and temporal fossae of the skull, has reached a degree among Anthropoidea not seen within the Prosimii. Many anthropoids also show a more robust zygomatic arch, stronger lateral ends of the brow ridges, and, among some of the larger species, a sagittal crest at the top of the skull. Changes in the degree of development and differences in the size and position of the brain relative to mandible and orbits have been influential in bringing this about.

The ear region provides a considerable contrast among various Anthropoidea. Ceboids differ from the other Higher Primates in showing a bulla inflated and filled by cancellous or spongy bone internally with the tympanic ring fused into its external margin. In cercopithecoids and hominoids the tympanic bone forms a tubular meatus running out to the external ear opening. *Aegyptopithecus,* the oldest catarrhine for which the skull is known, retains a primitive type of bullar construction, superficially similar to that of the New World forms in most respects but without the inflation characteristic of these animals.

The postcranial skeleton

The anthropoids have retained many of the skeletal characteristics typical of primitive mammals. Thus there is no excessive increase in the number of thoracic vertebrae, the number of digits is typically the primitive five, and there is no reduction in the number of finger bones, even though some of the digits may be reduced. Both bones are retained in the lower leg, although one of them may be shortened, and there is no development of extra limb segments by elongation of the middle foot bones, as is seen in the tarsiers. The clavicle is also present, even in four-footed terrestrial forms such as the baboons. Both bones of the forearm are present in all anthropoids and remain fully functional, permitting the hand to be rotated, although in monkeys the amount of rotation is less than in man, where the hand may be held palm up or palm down.

However, newly evolved ways of walking have resulted in some changes. In the apes there is a reduction in the number of vertebrae in the lower back and complete loss of the tail. The forelimbs and hands of the gibbons are modified for arm swinging, whereas in chimpanzees and gorillas the bones of the hand and wrist, together with special tendons, permit knuckle walking. In hominids the foot and pelvis have been entirely remodeled in the process of adapting to a bipedal gait.

The backbone

All primates retain the primitive seven neck vertebrae, but these may become elongated, as for instance in *Ateles*, to produce a greater flexibility of the neck. However, the back vertebrae are more variable, the total number of segments in this part of the column being between seventeen and twenty in the New World monkeys, more constant in the Old World monkeys at nineteen, and reduced in the hominoids to between fifteen and nineteen. The length of the vertebral column between the girdles is related to methods of walking, and the difference in lengths of the backbone noted above reflects more versatility in the way New World monkeys and Old World hominoids walk than in the Old World monkeys. In certain prosimians the pelvis has moved backward, resulting in an elongate backbone that can be thrown into sinuous curves as the animal progresses hand-over-hand along a branch. This type of flexibility is also of advantage in four-footed running, when the backbone acts as a bow stave strung by the muscles of the belly. The Old World monkeys are all essentially quadrupeds (both arboreal and terrestrial), as are certain of the New World monkeys. The long backbone is therefore retained. However, in forms that use their arms for climbing the forelimbs and the muscles of the shoulder become more important, and a long flexible backbone does not have the same advantage. Indeed, when the body is being raised or suspended by the arms alone, or when the animal is progressing on two legs—typical in many primates such as the gibbon, orangutan, and spider monkey—a long sinuous backbone may become an actual disadvantage.

With the loss of vertebrae in the backbone of the hominoids, there is a loss of flexibility in general, particularly in *Gorilla* where powerful neck muscles result as well in a stiffening of the region. The flexibility of the lower back is proportionally even more greatly reduced because the number of segments in this region is reduced, with respect to the number in the chest region, much more than in the monkeys. The number of lower back segments varies from five in *Homo* and *Hylobates* to four in *Pongo* and three to four in *Gorilla* and *Pan*. Especially in *Gorilla*, the great elongation of the hip bones reduces the flexibility of the lower back region even further. Most monkeys, especially the Old World monkeys, retain the primitive number of six or seven segments in this region, (see Schultz, 1961).

The vertebrae incorporated into the pelvis are more consistent in number in the various anthropoid genera, ranging from an average of 2.9 (*Callithrix*) to 5.7 (*Pan* and *Gorilla*). The hominoids in general have more pelvic vertebrae than the monkeys. This is probably associated with increasing body size and the adoption of upright posture. It does not seem to be related to the loss of tail vertebrae, because there are various monkeys with short tails that still retain the primitive two or three pelvic vertebrae. Man has a lower average of vertebral segments in the pelvis. This is at first sight anomalous in view of the bipedalism of this genus. However, it should be noted that the sacral vertebrae are greatly expanded to form "wings" that fit between the hip bones and provide as much support as would extra segments not so modified. Also by this means the birth canal is less constricted, an important factor in a genus in which the infants are large at birth and have the added disadvantage (from a giving-birth point of view) of proportionally large heads.

Tail vertebrae are present in all primates, but whereas in the New World monkeys the tail is typically long (and may become modified to function as a fifth limb), in certain Old World monkeys such as the macaques and baboons it is greatly reduced. In the hominoids no external tail is present except during prenatal development. The reduction of the tail in the Old World primates is probably associated with a greater tendency to use the forearms for climbing coupled with a disinclination for four-footed leaping (the long tail of the cercopithecines is used for steering and balance during long leaps between branches).

In all the Higher Primates there is an angle developed between the pelvic and lower back sections of the vertebral column. This is typically small in the monkeys, although (perhaps significantly) in *Theropithecus* it may be as high as 30°. In hominoids the angle reaches as much as 45°, being usually slightly higher in females. In man the angle has become much greater, so that the pelvic girdle is held closer to the quadrupedal position than would otherwise be possible. This angle is about 60° in human males and 65° in females. The acquisition of a high degree of sacral bend is an important feature in bipedal locomotion, for it aids in the distribution of the weight of the trunk.

A further feature of modern man associated with erect posture is the migration of the vertebral column into the rib cage so that it becomes truly axial within the body.

The pelvic girdle

The proportions of the limb girdles vary considerably among the anthropoids in ways that can be more-or-less directly related to the preferred means of locomotion. In the monkeys the pelvic girdle is typical of a quadrupedal form, being a long narrow bone that forms a high angle with the long axis of the backbone and juts above it. It serves as an area of attachment for various muscles at the thigh; also, because the gut does not depend on the upper part of the pelvis or the abdominal musculature for support (it hangs from folds of skin attached to the backbone), there is no tendency for the pelvis to form a broad plate, curved around the hips, as in man. The lower part of the pelvis is also a long narrow bone and also provides leverage for muscles that straighten out the thigh. This part is also roughened to provide a support for the callosities that are an obvious feature on the rump of monkeys and apes. The birth canal is relatively quite large, but, because the offspring reach an advanced stage of development before birth, parturition is a difficult process for monkeys. The apes have adopted semiupright gaits. Because in the upright posture the gut is no longer supported as in a quadruped, the abdominal muscles have taken over this function and necessitated a broadened pelvic plate as in man. Only the hylobatids and orangutans among the apes retain ischial callosities. The reorganization of the pelvis serves to close the birth canal, but the suppression of the tail vertebrae, combined with an increase in body size of the adult and a retention of the original size of the newborn (that is, a newborn proportionally small compared with the adult), does in fact make parturition easier for apes than for man or monkeys. In man, the only fully bipedal primate, the mechanical arrangement of the pelvis has changed considerably (see Figure 31). In particular, the "buttocks" muscle has a new function and is strongly developed. The broad pelvic bones serve as origins for the muscles that are essential in maintaining the upright posture.

In small monkeys the shaft of the thigh bone is straight and slender, but in the larger monkeys and the great apes it is stouter and bowed. In arm-swinging forms and man the shaft is straight, and in the latter greatly thickened. In apes the weight of the body passes mainly through the inside of the knee joint, producing a

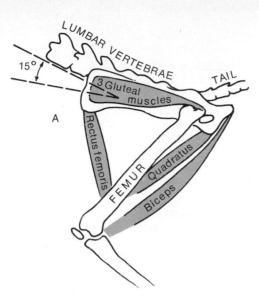

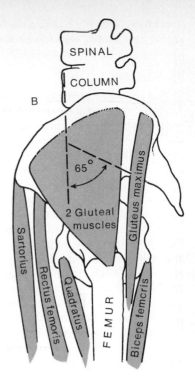

Figure 31 Diagrams comparing the arrangement of the hip musculature in a generalized quadrupedal primate (*A*) and in upright walking man (*B*).

typically bowlegged gait, whereas in man the weight passes through the outside. In women, in whom the pelvis is proportionally wide, the effect of transmitting the weight via the outside of the knee produces a "knock-kneed" effect, and walking is less efficient than in human males. In man, the need to rotate the foot is greatly reduced and the lower leg is supported mainly by only one bone, as it is to some extent in other terrestrial primates. However, in the arboreal forms rotation of the foot is essential, and both bones are well developed.

The feet of Higher Primates show considerable variation. In primitive mammals there was probably some degree of opposability between the big toe and the other digits. This capacity has been refined in the monkeys, especially those arboreal forms that need to grasp branches with their feet. In the four-handed climbers such as the orangutan the big toe spreads out, but in ground-living forms, particularly the mountain gorilla, the big toe has been reduced and the foot is more nearly like that of man. However, the similarity is superficial, because the bones of the foot differ considerably between men and gorillas. The antiquity of the bipedal mode of locomotion in the hominids has been dramatically illustrated by the discovery of an almost complete foot at Olduvai Gorge. This specimen, Olduvai Hominid 8, has been assigned to *Australopithecus habilis* and except for small size is in almost all functional respects like that of modern man.

The shoulder girdle

The shoulder girdle of primates consists of scapula, clavicle, and sternum. With differing adaptations these bones show certain responses that may be functionally related to walking. In quadrupeds the scapula acts as a strut, bearing the muscles that suspend the body on the forelimbs. Motion of the scapula is typically a rocking movement, backward and forward. Although the forelimb is not so restricted in its degree of flexibility as in, say, a deer or horse, the essential movements are fore and aft, resulting in an elongated shoulder joint. Associated with such quadrupedalism is the reduced clavicle. Among the quadrupedal monkeys the scapula lies at the side of the rib cage, which is typically deep and narrow (see Figure 32), whereas in man the rib cage is broad and the scapula lies flat on the back. In the primates that habitually hang the weight of the body on the forelimbs the scapula is modified considerably. The bone is more elongate in the craniocaudal direction, rather than laterally. Neck and back muscles act on the scapula to rotate it so that the lateral margin is elevated (in arm raising) or depressed (arm lowering). The well-developed back and chest muscles are able to swing the full weight of the body while powerful musculature, originating on the greatly expanded blade of the bone, stabilizes the shoulder joint during tensional stresses. The general

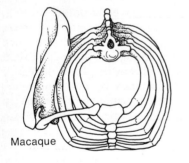

Macaque

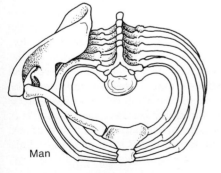

Man

Figure 32 Comparative view of thoracic region and right shoulder girdle of macaque and man, illustrating the ventral–dorsal flattening of the rib cage and the dorsal position of the scapula typical of Hominoidea. (After Schultz, 1957.)

mobility of the arm is reflected by the subcircular outline of the socket of its shoulder joint, particularly in the gibbon. To further facilitate the freedom of movement of the arms, the shoulders are pushed back by stout clavicles. This orientation of the clavicles in conjunction with the strongly developed neck muscles gives the nonhuman hominoids a typically short, thick-necked appearance and contrasts with man, in whom the neck musculature is less well developed (because of the better balance of the head on the vertebral column) and the shoulders are held much lower. In arm swingers the sternum fuses in adult life into a solid bone bracing a broad, shallow rib cage that must take far greater muscular stresses than is the case among quadrupeds.

The humerus of quadrupedal monkeys is backwardly directed at the shoulder end and lies in a plane perpendicular to the axis of the elbow joint. In arm swingers, brachiators, or leaping arboreal forms the degree of backward bending of the humerus is much less marked, and the head rotates medially to make an angle of about 30° with the axis of the elbow joint. The degree of rotation in *Apidium* from the Oligocene of the Fayum, Egypt, is somewhat intermediate between that of a quadrupedal and a brachiating form. The thickness of the shaft is related to the size of the animal, as with the femur.

The hands and feet

Among the arm-swinging primates the thumb is often much reduced. In most monkeys too it is usually somewhat reduced, although never lost (it is present in *Ateles* but not visible externally). The thumb of New World monkeys is generally less opposable than that of Old World monkeys because its base is near the base of the index finger. In all the monkeys the weight of the body is taken on the axis of the central finger when they are standing above a branch. This contrasts with the condition in the hominids, in which the weight passes through the webbing between the thumb and the index finger. Terrestrial baboons walk in a plantigrade fashion, with the palm of the hand on the ground. Spider monkeys also occasionally do this, usually if the surface over which they are walking is smooth. To compensate for the weight stresses on the hand, the forelimbs may be lengthened (as in *Gorilla* and *Pan*) to throw the weight back over the hindlimbs. Hyperextension of the fingers is prevented by shortening them. *Theropithecus* in particular has a finger-to-thumb ratio very close to that of man. In the apes the thumb is well developed and fairly opposable. *Hylobates* in particular has a well-developed thumb joint that permits the thumb to be tucked across the palm so as not to interfere with the hooklike grip of the fingers in swinging beneath branches. The knuckle walkers, *Pan* and *Gorilla*, show modifications of the hand and wrist to prevent hyperextension and have developed volar pads bearing dermatoglyphs on the upper surface of the second segment of the digits. Orangutans frequently walk quadrupedally on the ground, either on the flat of the palms with the fingers turned out

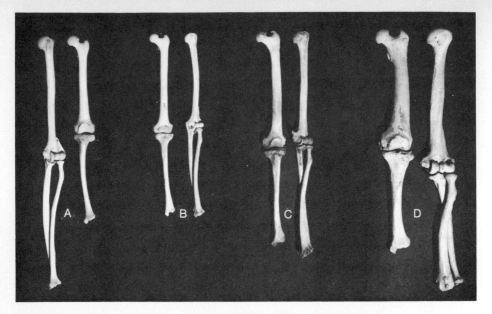

Figure 33 Comparative view of the forelimbs and hindlimbs of the great apes. *Pongo pygmaeus* (A) is a fully arboreal arm swinger. The three African apes (B: *Pan paniscus*. C: *Pan troglodytes*. D: *Gorilla gorilla*) are terrestrial knuckle walkers; changes in limb proportions with greater size seem related to changes in overall body weight. Scale × 0.1. (Photo courtesy of A. H. Coleman, Yale Peabody Museum.)

or on the sides of their bunched fists, but lack the particular specialization for knuckle walking seen in African apes. In man the hand is not normally used for locomotion and has developed as a precision grasping instrument with complete opposability of the thumb and fingers. However, during walking, the hands swing through the same sequence as they do in the symmetrical gaits of primate quadrupeds.

According to one of the most persistent dogmas of anthropology, forelimb elongation among primates has arisen as a result of the importance of suspensory locomotion or arm swinging to the present-day species (or their ancestors) that show elongation. Nevertheless, comparison of the size gradient of the African apes, indicated by their intermembral indexes, shows that the relatively longest forelimbs are found in the largest species (Figure 33). As is discussed later (pages 102 and 202), it may be due to the necessity of shifting posteriorly the weight of the heavier body in the large terrestrial quadrupeds or may relate to the propensity to feed while sitting seen in the gorilla and gelada.

The Extinct
Malagasy Lemurs

The subfossil lemurs of Madagascar are of no great antiquity. In fact, most may be less than 2,000 years old. The site of Amparihingidro in the northwest, which contains bones of *Archaeolemur*, *Megaladapis*, and *Lemur* (including extinct large species of subgenus *Pachylemur*), has been dated by the radiocarbon method at 2,840 B.P. $\pm$ 200. At Lake Itampolo on the southwest coast, subfossil lemurs have been dated at around 1,000 B.P. $\pm$ 100 years. Nevertheless, in spite of recent extinction they are of considerable interest to paleontologists and evolutionary biologists, for many of the extinct forms are quite unlike the surviving lemurs. Some show numerous interesting structural and functional parallels with monkeys, apes, and earliest hominids as well as with certain nonprimates. Thus, although extinct, most represent the extremes of the adaptive radiation of Lemuriformes. Study of the kinds of advances or structural adaptations they share with non-Madagascan primates helps to demonstrate the latent potential for diversity in adaption among the order Primates, as well as the evolutionary processes through which these changes came about.

The fossil lemurs have been recovered from faunas collected in swamp or lake deposits as well as from caves and are often associated with the bones of the giant flightless bird *Aepyornis*, possibly the "roc" of Arab legend, and a small species of *Hippopotamus*, both now also extinct.

Since the description in 1894 by the English scientist Forsyth-Major of a giant lemur skull from the west coast site of Ambolisatra, a rapidly growing series of these subfossil lemurs has been assembled. A great many monographs on these extinct animals have been produced, but most are relatively inaccessible to students, and few of these earlier authors undertook to analyze the adaptive and functional reasons for the many and varied differences these subfossil primates exhibit. Moreover, the often-expressed idea that many of them were aquatic or semiaquatic has been shown more than once to be naive. Recently, Walker (1967b) analyzed the locomotor capacities of these animals, but much remains to be learned about the differences in their dental mechanisms and the relation of these striking differences to their various ways of life.

The Malagasy subfossil lemurs are of two sorts: those resembling surviving forms of the genera *Lemur* and *Daubentonia*, and seven extinct genera, which according to Ian Tattersall (personal communication) should be divided into three families (Megaladapidae, Archaeolemuridae, and Indriidae, including Palaeopropithecinae).

Walker has recently summarized previous work on the way of life and locomotor adaptations of extinct Malagasy lemurs. His summary is as follows:

Lemur (Pachylemur) insignis—Carleton (1936): A bent-limbed arboreal quadruped leaping about in the tops of branches.

Archaeoindris fontoynonti—Piveteau (1957): Arboreal.

Palaeopropithecus—Standing (1908): Aquatic. Carleton (1936): Arboreal, locomotion as in *Bradypus* and *Choelopus*, the sloths. Sera (1938, 1950): Aquatic, climbing trees and plunging into lakes. Lamberton (1944): Arboreal, as *Pongo*. Hill (1953): Possibly arboreal and aquatic phases alternated with the seasons, a swamp existence being the equivalent of estivation. Piveteau (1957): Arboreal.

Archaeolemur—Carleton (1936): Arboreal. Lamberton (1937): Arboreal, had begun to experiment with brachiation but failed to reach the level attained in higher primates. Sera (1950): Aquatic.

Megaladapis—Lorenz von Liburnau (1905): Arboreal, but perhaps with more of the habits of the "cave bear." Standing (1908): Arboreal, locomotion as in *Pan* and *Gorilla*. Lamberton (1934): Ground living. Sera (1950): Aquatic. Hill (1953): "Presumably aquatic." Zapfe (1963): Arboreal.

Perhaps the oddest of these extinct lemurs are the species of genus *Megaladapis*. These were giants among the lemurs and in fact were probably the bulkiest prosimians that ever lived. Some skulls are said to be nearly 20 inches long (see Figure 34*D*). The skull is characterized by a large and long snout and a comparatively small brain case. The skull and teeth of *Megaladapis* are broadly reminiscent of certain selenodont herbivores such as the extinct North American oreodonts. The resemblance extends even to M_3 having a long heel, as in most artiodactyls, whereas in most Malagasy lemurs the M_3 heel tends to be reduced. The development of the sagittal and nuchal crests on the brain case, as well as the deepened mandible with its lengthened ascending ramus, suggests that powerful chewing was important to this animal. The enormous skulls viewed in isolation led to some misunderstandings about *Megaladapis*, for the size of these crania alone would make one think that the postcranial part of the largest species was as big as that of a cow or a gorilla. Actually, the head is disproportionately large, and the body skeleton is of no greater size than that of a half-grown bear cub or a Saint Bernard dog (see Figure 34*D*). Nevertheless, there are several huge primate femora of unexplained affinities from Madagascar. The eye sockets in *Megaladapis* are ringed by heavy ridges, the cheek bones flare, and the long downwardly flexed nasals suggest that there may have been an incipiently mobile upper lip. This is perhaps also related to the lack of upper incisors. At least, the general arrangement of the nasals is similar to that seen in the earliest tapiroids, whose later descendants had (and have) flexible snouts. Moreover, the anterior facial area shows strongly vascularized bone, which implies a thick tissue cover of the snout.

The skull base is also distinctive in that the auditory bullae are flattened—not bulbous—and generally unlike those of the living lemurs. In *Megaladapis* the tympanic bone is extended out of the bulla as an auditory tube resembling that seen in the Old World Anthropoidea. Ossified auditory canals have apparently arisen repeatedly and independently among primates, and three extinct Malagasy lemurs possessed this trait.

The mandible of *Megaladapis* confirms forest-browsing adaptations, vaguely similar to those of the extinct oreodont herbivores, deer, and tapirs as well as some extinct browsing rhinoceroses. Clearly, the two halves of the mandible at the symphysis were strongly fused together in the adults. This is a rare condition in most living prosimians but characterizes all Higher Primates. Crompton has recently suggested to me that this indicates a refinement over the condition in primitive placentals and definitely a change that could allow for more powerful or more horizontally directed stresses during chewing. The symphysis is long, and the angular region of the jaw is enlarged. The occlusal surfaces of the dentition curve

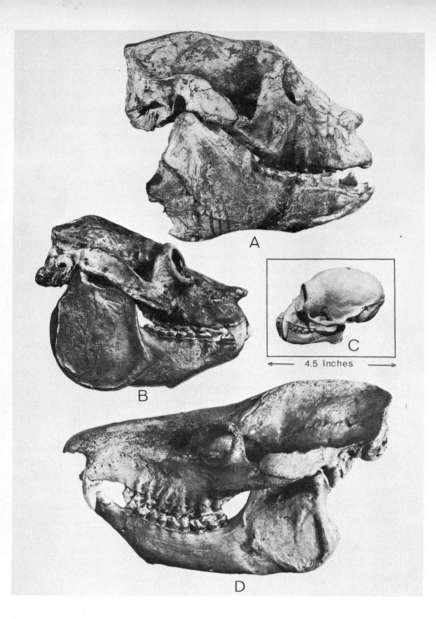

Figure 34 The large subfossil lemurs of Madagascar. *A: Archaeoindris fontoynonti. B: Palaeopropithecus maximus. D: Megaladapis edwardsi.* A gibbon skull (*C*) is provided for size comparison. All photos are to the same scale. (Courtesy of Ian M. Tattersall and A. H. Coleman, Yale Peabody Museum.)

upward to the front. The dental formula is $\frac{0.1.3.3}{2.1.3.3}$. The lower incisors retain the typical kind of lemur toothcomb, but although deciduous upper incisors erupted, they were not replaced by permanent teeth in the adults. The upper canines are comparatively large and more curved than is typical of other lemurs, and the cheek teeth increase markedly in size from front to back.

Some students have suggested that a dentition of this sort would be effective in feeding on tough substances such as branches, roots, or fibrous herbage, and one paleontologist even suggested that *Megaladapis* was an aquatic animal that fed on crayfish and mollusks. Apparently, several of the early workers were overly impressed with the occurrence of the subfossil lemurs in lake sites along with the bones of fish, crocodiles, *Hippopotamus,* and the like. We know now that, apart from the fossil primates that have been found in cave deposits, in fissure fills, or on living floors, practically all fossil primates ever found come from riverine/lacustrine deposits associated with aquatic vertebrates and that this sort of a death assemblage (thanatocoenose) seldom reflects a life assemblage (biocoenose). Standing (1908), thinking that limb bones of *Megaladapis* (which he took to be those of *Palaeopropithecus*) showed clear evidence of swimming adaptations, started the erroneous ideas about aquatic living. However, others have shown that the limb bones do not suggest aquatic adaptations but rather are suited to hopping and climbing. Recently, Walker has demonstrated that the best structural analogies to *Megaladapis* are to be seen in the Australian koala "bear." This animal is presumably derived from arboreal phalanger-like leaping forebears just as the Malagasy lemurs were, but the koalas have grown too large for swift movements or long-distance leaps—an evolutionary development that characterizes the orangutan as well. In the opinion of Walker (1967a), *Megaladapis* may have progressed by slower, shorter, and more careful leaps that still retained a basic vertical clinging and leaping quality. A koala-like locomotor habitus would have well suited this creature for arboreal browsing, and the very large, long hands and feet are a definite indication of arboreal living. The comparatively small eyesockets indicate that *Megaladapis* was diurnal. All crepuscular and nocturnal primates have much larger eyes, relative to skull length. A large animal, active during the day, would have fallen prey most readily to human hunters after the Malagasy people reached Madagascar. Such evidence as there is indicates that this was a relatively recent event, possibly about 2,000 years ago and most likely somewhere between 1,500 B.C. and A.D. 500. The Frenchman Flacourt, writing in the seventeenth century, reported that the natives near Fort Dauphin believed that a large animal with hands and face like a man, about the size of a calf, and known as "tra-tra-tra-tra" lived nearby. He wrote that "the natives of the region flee him as he does them." If this was *Megaladapis* we can only regret having so closely missed a chance to observe alive what must have been one of the most curious primates ever to have existed.

From deposits at Ampasambazimba, in the center of the island, has been recovered another very large extinct lemur with a skull comparable in size to that of *Megaladapis*. However, the whole appearance of the skull is quite different from the latter (see Figure 34*A*, page 96). *Archaeoindris* has a cranium more shortened from front to back. The cerebral region is also reduced in length, and a number of features mimic the Higher Primates. The auditory bulla is not inflated, and the tympanic ring is not free, but the mastoid process is large. Seen from the rear, the occipital is flat without the central ridge present in most lemurs, the zygomatic arches are short and heavy, and the rounded orbits are forwardly directed and more closely approximated than in any of the other subfossil lemurs. The mandible is large and much deeper than in any of the other giant lemurs with the possible exception of *Palaeopropithecus*. This, together with the deep face, gives the entire skull a vaguely monkey-like appearance. The frontals bulge out above the orbits, and as in *Palaeopropithecus* the distal ends of the nasals are swollen and turned slightly upward in a snub-nosed effect. In *Archaeoindris*, unlike *Palaeopropithecus*, the nasal aperture is raised considerably higher above the alveolar border at the incisors, and the distal ends of the nasals are spaced apart.

In addition to the great mandibular depth, the angular region is particularly expanded, with a large and well-defined area for insertion of the pterygoid muscles. Incisor function must not have included fur combing in this animal because these teeth are considerably less procumbent than in most other lemurs. The dental formula, $\frac{2.1.2.3.}{2.0.2.3.}$, is as in the other indriids (the lower canines and $P_1^1–P_2^2$ are missing). One difference of *Archaeoindris* from its living relatives is the presence of a large diastema between a vertically implanted upper canine and P^3. The form of the upper molars is intermediate between the three-cusped molars of the lemurids and the four-cusped molars of the living Indriidae. The addition of a fourth cusp (hypocone) to the basic trigon (three-cusped tooth) of primitive mammals and archaic primates has occurred many times within different primate lineages, but in the absence of a fossil record for the Malagasy lemurs it is difficult to say whether it was the lemurids that lost this cusp or the indriids that gained it.

As with the other giant, exotic, and extinct Malagasy lemurs, there have been several speculations about the way of life and manner of feeding of *Archaeoindris*, but none has been particularly satisfactory. The small and relatively vertically implanted incisors and the wear differential on the molars, which decreases to the rear, suggest that the front teeth may have played more of a role in cropping and cutting and the cheek teeth in grinding than is the case in most of the living lemurs, in which the front teeth are used to comb the fur.

Walker has concluded that the large lemur named *"Lemurido-therium"* by Standing (1910) is *Archaeoindris*. There are also two adult fibulae and several fragmentary bones from an immature specimen. These provide little evidence as to locomotion, but in Walker's opinion their similarity to the same bones of *Megaladapis* suggests a koala-like pattern.

PALAEOPROPITHECUS

Palaeopropithecus, a large fossil indriid, seems closest to *Archaeoindris* but differs from it in many significant regards. The whole cranium is much flatter, and the brain case, at least from the outside, is comparatively larger. Endocranial casts indicate that the brain did not have a very advanced structure. The orbits are directed upward and are encircled by a bony ridge as in *Megaladapis*, a structure vaguely resembling the orbital region in *Hippopotamus*—a phenomenon interpreted by Standing and others as a possible indication of an aquatic way of life (see Figure 34B, p. 96). Simons (1961a) has suggested alternatively that such orbital orientation may evolve in order to achieve greater orbital frontality and thus better stereoscopic vision in an animal that has a comparatively large snout. A similar orientation occurs in the Eocene *Adapis* and among the modern lorises. In the living species at least, the head is usually carried in a "hangdog" posture in which the snout is below the overlapping fields of vision. Consequently, upwardly directed orbital orientation is much more suggestive of a highly arboreal form, for which selection for stereoscopic vision and ability to judge the exact distance to the nearest branch becomes a major concern. Walker's studies on the postcranial skeleton of *Palaeopropithecus* were therefore highly relevant in this context, for he was able to show that this animal had comparatively elongate apelike forearms, possessed long fingers with curved finger bones (useful in climbing or hanging from branches), and in general showed many resemblances to another large, arboreal, hanging-feeding primate, the orangutan. Curiously, the pelvic bones are quite broad. Just as in the orangutan, the teeth of *Palaeopropithecus* are exceedingly crenulate or wrinkled. This might be a coincidence, but it could mean that *Palaeopropithecus* sought foodstuffs of similar consistency to those eaten by the orangutan.

In contrast to *Archaeoindris*, the frontal region is not swollen out but is depressed. Both genera share with *Megaladapis* an ossified external auditory meatus.

At the back at least, the mandibular rami of *Palaeopropithecus*, in the region of the angle, are relatively even more enlarged than in *Archaeoindris*. The fused symphysis extends at least as far back as the second molar.

The teeth are different from those of *Archaeoindris* in several ways:

the upper canines are quite elongate from front to back, increasing their effectiveness as shearing blades; the lateral upper incisors are less reduced; and there is a much larger diastema between C and P^3. There is no lingual cingulum on the molars, and the molar hypocones are larger. Below, the third molar is relatively smaller.

In conclusion, it would seem confirmed that *Palaeopropithecus* exhibits skeletal modifications that might have facilitated arm swinging and hanging feeding in a manner that would make it more analogous to the apes than is any other prosimian living or fossil. In fact, Walker (1967a) has concluded that in certain features of hand and foot *Palaeopropithecus* seems to have been more of a hanging feeder than any of the modern apes. The hindlimb had great mobility, which suggests a greater resemblance to the orangutan than to the arm-swinging gibbons. The hooklike curvature of fingers and toes seems almost slothlike. Preuschoft (1970) has recently maintained that the phalanges of *Palaeopropithecus* were constructed to endure tensile, not compactive, stresses.

ARCHAEOLEMUR

The third unusual subfamily of extinct Malagasy prosimians is that exemplified by *Archaeolemur* (Figure 35E). In fact, its resemblances to monkeys are so intriguing and extensive that the English scholar Forsyth-Major (1900) initially put forward the view that this animal and its allies represented a halfway house between the South American monkeys and the Old World Higher Primates. Actually, the similarities constitute parallel and independent developments that appear to have been evoked by occupancy of similar environmental zones. Nevertheless, there can hardly be a more striking approximation of form independently arrived at than that seen in the molars of *Archaeolemur* and those of certain Old World monkeys such as *Papio*. In *Archaeolemur* the facial component of the cranium is comparatively much foreshortened, and the incisors show much less procumbency than in most other lemurs: in both regards the animal resembles the monkeys. The incisors (above) are separated by a gap from short, small—rather premolariform—canines that appear to have become incorporated into a kind of four-tooth cutting edge that also involves the three premolars. These teeth are closely packed together, and each crown slopes from inside and outside to a central anteroposteriorly oriented ridge or blade.

Species of *Archaeolemur* are not giants among their relatives, but some skulls reach a length of 5 inches—greater than that of any living lemur. The endocranial volume is large, about 130 cm^3, and brain casts show numerous radially arranged frontal convolutions, a large frontal sinus, and sizable olfactory bulbs. The eyes were directed forward, and the nasals were relatively short, but not as short as in *Hadropithecus* (see Figure 35D and E).

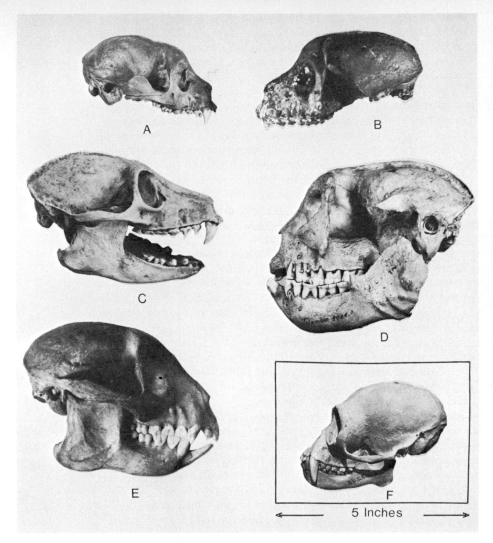

Figure 35   Medium-sized and small extinct Malagasy lemurs. *A: Mesopropithecus globiceps. B: M. pithecoides. C: Lemur (Pachylemur) insignis. D: Hadropithecus stenognathus. E: Archaeolemur majori.* A gibbon skull (*F*) is provided for size comparison. All photos are to the same scale. (Courtesy of Ian M. Tattersall and A. H. Coleman, Yale Peabody Museum.)

The dental formula is $\frac{2.1.3.3.}{2.0.3.3.}$. In addition to the monkey-like bilophodont molars, the milk dentition appears to have been retained for a relatively long time, which might suggest that the juvenile period was longer than typical for most of the lemurs. The incisors are relatively large for a prosimian and occlude functionally—the toothcomb adaptation has been lost. The upper canines are short, the premolars form a cutting crest, and the molars are bilophodont, decreasing in size to the rear. The lower incisors are separated by a gap from P_2, and the uppers are similarly separated from the canine. Unlike the reduced upper canine, which in part opposes it, P_2 is much the largest tooth in this animal. It has been said to be caniniform, but, because the longitudinal crest at the P_2 crown begins the sectorial blade carried back across the two teeth that follow, it clearly functioned with the other premolars as a sort of cutting blade. Fossils of *Archaeolemur* have been recovered from wide areas and presently different environments of the island. It apparently could inhabit open country and was quadrupedal. The forelimb was longer than the hindlimb (intermembral index 120), quite the reverse of the living lemurs, which have long hindlimbs. The dentition of this animal, like that of *Hadropithecus*, seems well suited to feeding on grasses, grass corms, or grains. Among Higher Primates, highly terrestrial graminivorous species have arisen only very rarely. The most extreme development in this direction now living is the Ethiopian gelada baboon, *Theropithecus gelada*. Moreover, the only Old World monkey to exhibit an intermembral index over 100 was an extinct Pleistocene East African species of *Theropithecus* ($=$ *Simopithecus*). In addition, if one considers the intermembral index of African apes in the increasing size sequence pygmy chimpanzee, chimpanzee, lowland gorilla, and mountain gorilla, the mean intermembral index for the four appear to rise in an evenly graded series from little more than 100 to nearly 120. These two facts would suggest that forest hanging feeding and arm swinging are not the only reasons why the forelimb of a primate may become elongate. There exist only these few examples of highly terrestrially oriented primates, but it may be that if such do not become bipeds some advantage is given by long forelimbs that shift the center of gravity backward. This would be useful for animals standing on three legs and feeding with the other, and equally advantageous for animals that often sit while feeding, as do *Gorilla* and *Theropithecus*, because long arms increase the area an individual can canvass for food before moving on. As Walker (1967a) has suggested, if *Archaeolemur* species (and *Hadropithecus* as well) were diurnal, open-country feeders, they would have been prey for the first Malgache settlers, and indeed archaeolemurine skulls. showing the blows of weapons have been found in sites that also bear evidence of human activity. According to Lamberton, the folklore of Southwest Madagascar collected before such fossil lemurs were found mentions ancient animals of this sort.

HADROPITHECUS

Hadropithecus resembles *Archaeolemur* in many ways. It was of similar size, was even shorter faced than the latter, and had a similarly advanced brain with many convolutions in the frontal lobes, comparable with the most advanced lorises and South American monkeys (see Figure 35D, page 101). Both *Hadropithecus* and *Archaeolemur* have rounded brain cases with heavy cheek bones, and the postorbital bar is enlarged so as to close off (to a greater extent than in other Malagasy lemurs) the orbital and temporal fossae. This, together with their frontally directed orbits, constitutes an interesting parallel with the visual achievements of anthropoids. Even so, *Hadropithecus* differed somewhat from *Archaeolemur* in both its locomotor and dental mechanisms. The forelimbs were not longer than the hindlimbs. The incisors are even more vertically implanted than in *Archaeolemur*, and the cheek teeth show thickened, infolded enamel—coupled with reduced pulp cavities. The cheek teeth are basically bilophodont, and the thick enamel infoldings seem analogous to gelada baboon cheek teeth or to those of some rodents. There is usually heavy, flat wear on the cheek teeth, implying powerful grinding activities. Chewing must have had a considerable horizontal component. In addition, the overall grinding surface is increased by molarization of P_4.

Jaws of *Hadropithecus* show other analogies to the Higher Primates; the symphyseal cross section closely resembles that of modern African apes as well as that of *Australopithecus*. There is a quite deep genioglossal fossa between superior and inferior tori. This latter structure is often called the "simian shelf" and is clearly an unusual feature for a lemur. The two halves of the mandible fuse together in the midline, and the anterior symphyseal border, together with the incisors it bears, is oriented more toward the vertical than in other lemurs. The jaw is thick, and in the region of the angle there are several well-expressed, obliquely arranged crests that must represent the attachment areas of extremely powerful chewing muscles. In correlation with all this, *Hadropithecus* shows a forward shifting of the temporal fossa such that the anterior origin of the temporal muscle would have lain above M^1—not above or behind M^3 as in all the other subfossil lemurs. All these combined features would tend to sling the grinding tooth-surfaces beneath more vertically oriented muscle masses. They constitute an intriguing functional convergence toward Higher Primates (such as *Australopithecus* and *Theropithecus*), which show powerful grinding adaptations. In all three of these primates the zygomatic arches are comparatively very large and the anterior insertion of the zygoma lies far forward—in *Hadropithecus* above the P^4.

Clearly, this animal had a dental mechanism evolved to triturate either large tough objects or perhaps, as does the gelada, many small objects gleaned on the ground.

OTHER SUBFOSSIL MALAGASY PRIMATES

Finally, a few subfossil forms that are very closely related to extant lemurs should be mentioned. *Mesopropithecus globiceps* and *M. pithecoides* (Figure 35A and B) are cranially very similar to *Propithecus*, as their names suggest, although Walker has proposed that they had abandoned vertical clinging and leaping for an arboreal quadrupedal mode of locomotion. The genus *Prohapalemur* does not appear to represent anything more than a rather robust variant of *Hapalemur*, and *Daubentonia robusta* seems not to differ from the living aye-aye in known parts (no skulls have been recovered) in any way but size. Two species of large lemurs resembling *Lemur variegatus* have been named and separated from *Lemur*, in the strict sense, at the subgeneric level: *Lemur (Pachylemur) insignis* and *L. (Pachylemur) jullyi*, although according to Tattersall (personal communication) they are conspecific, the name *L. (P.) insignis* having priority (see Figure 35C, page 101). Walker has studied their postcrania and concluded that they were heavier, slower animals than their living congeners: in fact, quadrupedal animals without much facility in leaping.

The Archaic Prosimians

Although most texts discussing primate origins touch on the question of their basal transition from or origin within Insectivora in the broadest sense, there appears to be almost no actual fossil material that convincingly documents any aspect of this transition.

The lengthy discussion on primate origins has its roots in hypothetical considerations. From what is known of the evolution of tetrapods in general, and of Cretaceous and subsequent placentals in particular, it has been considered plausible that the forerunners of primates, as we know them, were small terrestrial animals. Because so few groups of placentals have ever become skillful arborealists, it seems most unlikely that the basal forebears of the primates could have included in the earliest periods of placental history many, or even any, arboreally adapted stocks. Nevertheless, the fossil evidence to date provides no information regarding locomotor adaptations of relevant groups of Mesozoic mammals.

In consequence, paleontologists have traditionally turned to the practice of attempting to associate the most archaic insectivores of

TABLE 2 THE BROAD INTERRELATIONSHIPS OF MESOZOIC PLACENTALS

Cretaceous				Tertiary
Neocomian	Albian	Cenomanian	Maestrichtian	Paleocene

All genera below are of North American occurrence

Neocomian	Albian	Cenomanian	Maestrichtian	Paleocene
				leptictid ——→
			Gypsonictops ↗	line
		Zalambdalestes Mongolia		*Purgatorium* and *Protungulatum*
		Kennalestes Mongolia		
Peramus ——→	*Pappotherium*	↗		
pantothere	first true	↘		
pretherian	therian	*Deltatherium*		
	Trinity Sands, Texas	Mongolia ↘		palaeoryctid ——→
Britain			*Cimolestes*	line
			↘	
			Procerberus	

Paleocene column (right):
?rodents?, ungulates, primates, erinaceids, condylarths, creodonts, miacids, insectivores, tupaias, taeniodonts

Note that arrows are not meant to indicate direct lines of descent.

Cretaceous and early Paleocene age with basal primates on grounds of similarities either in dental anatomy or in basicranial, particularly auditory, structures.

Interpretation of the functional meaning of the tooth structures and the wear facets to be seen on teeth of archaic insectivores and earliest primates in the period between 90 million and 60 million years ago is now in a state of flux. Such studies as have been undertaken are summarized in McKenna (1963a, 1966) and Szalay (1968). Table 2 is an attempt to associate some of the known Mesozoic mammals with apparently related forms judged on the basis of tooth morphology.

The oldest primates for which we know anything of the skeleton exhibit clear evidences of arboreal adaptations in their limb bone construction. The dentitions of many archaic prosimians, with their forward jutting and enlarged front teeth, may possibly have been adapted for husking seeds and fruits. The low-cusped cheek teeth suggest herbivorous habits. In the tropical forest, fruit, seed-, and leaf-eating activities usually occur away from the ground.

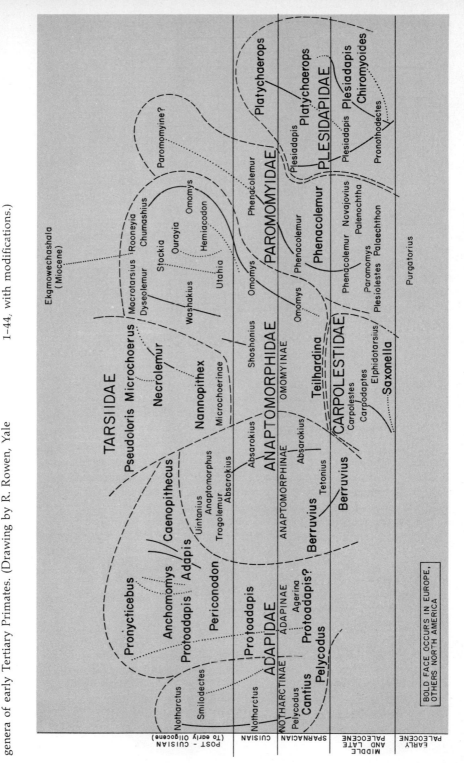

Figure 36 Diagram showing the principal groups and the known genera of early Tertiary Primates. (Drawing by R. Rowen, Yale Peabody Museum, after Russell, Louis, and Savage, 1967, pp. 1–44, with modifications.)

The basal radiation of the primates into the trees put a premium on visual acuity and locomotor agility, for which since then there has been strong selection. The ultimate resultant of arboreal survival is intense selection for greater intelligence as well.

Another factor that may have contributed in a round about way to improved quality of perceptions relates to the bearing of young and to primate longevity. In the arboreal environment the establishment of a wide-ranging social group with no fixed base requires that the mother carry her infant wherever she goes. For tree-living mammals the principal alternative to this is the mated pair who feed multiple juveniles in a nest all at one time, as squirrels do. Among arboreal primates without permanent nests, only one offspring can be managed. This necessitates that the mother live for a long time in order to maintain a constant population size in the face of loss due to infant mortality. The same dynamics are operative among long-lived birds such as cranes. Long life conveys another primary advantage: there is time enough to learn and to convey complex things. It is in this that the Higher Primates excel.

In some cases the interrelationships of the early Tertiary families and subfamilies of primates are poorly known. The temporal range and contained members of these groups as they are presently understood are indicated in Figure 36 (page 107).

A recently described genus, *Purgatorius* (see Figure 37), coined by Van Valen and Sloan (1965), is possibly the oldest known primate. *Purgatorius ceratops*, a species based on a single tooth, is of the same age as the dinosaur *Triceratops*. A later species of Paleocene age is based on some fifty isolated teeth from a single quarry. These teeth are surprisingly similar to those of *Protungulatum*, a condylarth contemporary with them. Both do show specific

Figure 37 *Stereoview.* A M¹ or M² of *Purgatorius,* the oldest known primate, from Cretaceous and Paleocene deposits in Eastern Montana. Scale × 17.0 approximately. (Photo courtesy of A. W. Crompton.) To take full advantage of stereoview illustrations (Figures 37, 50, 51, 66, 75, 87, 89, and 93), you may obtain stereoglasses from most camera shops or scientific supply houses.

structural similarity to undoubted primate molars, but in the present state of knowledge (isolated teeth) this could be a functional convergence and not an indication of phyletic relations. The *Purgatorius–Protungulatum* molars form a coherent type quite distinct from other contemporary mammals. To the extent that these animals are correctly associated with primate ancestry they suggest that this order arose from *Gypsonictops*-like Cretaceous mammals (see Figure 36, page 107).

Later, Van Valen (1965) grouped several genera together (one, "*Mckennatherium,*" was a previously described insectivore) and proposed the subfamily Purgatoriinae. Choice of *Purgatorius* as the type for the group was awkward, for it was the least well-known animal concerned. In the system followed here, *Purgatorius* is considered as of uncertain placement among the paromomyid prosimians.

PLESIADAPIDAE

The family Plesiadapidae was originally named in 1879, but the first member to be described was *Platychaerops* (Charlesworth, 1854). The type of this genus—a nearly complete palate with five upper teeth in place—was found in early Eocene deposits near Herne Bay, Kent, and is now in the Yorkshire Museum. Sir Richard Owen discussed this specimen in 1865. He believed that it was an ungulate and proposed a new genus, *Miolophus*, for it, ignoring Charlesworth's name. No one realized the primate nature of *Platychoerops* until Teilhard de Chardin (1921), who, in fact, wished to refer it to another genus, *Plesiadapis*.

Meanwhile, the French naturalist Lemoine began to collect from the Paleocene site at Cernay les Reims in Northern France, which produced the first named species of genus *Plesiadapis*. Much later, finds of this animal in North America were recovered and named *Nothodectes*, but later the synonymy with the European genus was recognized. In 1916, Stehlin named another variety *Chiromyoides campanicus*. Matthew (1914), Stehlin (1916), and Teilhard de Chardin (1921), as well as Abel (1931), all associated *Plesiadapis* and allied forms with the apatemyid insectivores, then considered primates. This was done principally because all these groups have the low flat molar crowns with low trigonids and low rounded cusps characteristic of primitive primates.

Development in plesiadapids of anterior enlarged, procumbent, gliriform incisors, and a tendency toward reduction and loss of teeth between these and the third or fourth premolars, caused most early workers to consider the whole heterogenous group as related to the living Malagasy prosimian *Daubentonia*, the aye-aye (then often known by a junior synonym, *Chiromys*). Jepsen (1934) showed that apatemyids and plesiadapids are not closely related, and Simpson (1935a) stressed that the similarities between plesiadapids and

Daubentonia arose in parallel. Postcranially, the aye-aye is much like other lemurs. That these animals are not phyletically allied has been sustained as more has become known of the cranium and skeleton of *Plesiadapis*.

The best skeletal remains of this creature are those of *Plesiadapis gidleyi* from the late Paleocene Tiffany beds of Colorado and *Plesiadapis tricuspidens* from the Cernay region of France. A skeleton described by Weigelt (1933) as of this group, and named by him *Megacheiromyoides*, turned out to belong to the rodent genus *Ailuravus*. D. E. Russell (1967) demonstrated that "*Menatotherium*" Piton (1940) is really a specimen of *Plesiadapis*.

The evolutionary history of Plesiadapidae is relatively uncomplicated. The middle Paleocene *Pronothodectes* serves as a good basal form from which later species evolved. The group apparently died out without descendants, surviving last in the early Eocene species of *Platychaerops*.

Plesiadapis

As mentioned, the best-preserved remains of any Paleocene primate belong to species of the genus *Plesiadapis*, species that are also the most widespread, and perhaps the most abundant in fossil sites, of any early member of the order Primates. The upper central incisors are distinctive, with three projecting cusps that make the tooth look like a tiny glove. It has been conjectured that such teeth, for which there are no close modern parallels, would be effective in seed and fruit husking.

The genus was first named by Gervais (1877) on the basis of finds made near the village of Cernay les Reims in Northern France.

Figure 38 Skull of *Plesiadapis*, seen from above. This specimen is the most complete Paleocene primate skull ever found. It was discovered in Northern France. (Photo courtesy of Donald E. Russell.)

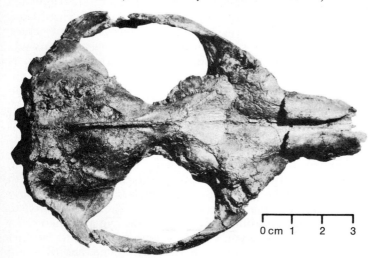

0 cm 1   2   3

More recently, excavations carried out by D. E. Russell, of the Paris Museum of Natural History, at the nearby site of Mont de Berru have brought to light a skull and much of the postcranial skeleton of this animal. The other principal finds of skeletal remains of a smaller species of *Plesiadapis* are from the Mason Pocket site in older Paleocene deposits of Colorado. The skull recovered at Mont de Berru in France apparently shows that at a Paleocene grade of primate evolution the orbits were not yet encircled by a bony rim or postorbital bar. This structure in more advanced primates serves as a lateral buttress protecting the eye. In addition, the facial component of the skull is enormous compared with the brain case (see Figure 38). Russell (1964) has provided a thorough discussion of the cranial characteristics of the French species of *Plesiadapis*, the oldest primate genus for which the skull has been well described. In overall appearance the skull of *Plesiadapis* resembles those of archaic mammals generally and is not nearly so advanced as such Eocene primate skulls as those of *Adapis* or *Notharctus*.

The skeletal remains indicate that *Plesiadapis* may have had a mode of locomotion resembling that of the modern gray squirrel. However, it was more heavily built, and one may doubt that so heavy an animal could have been efficiently arboreal. In Figure 39 a composite skeletal reconstruction of *Plesiadapis* is shown. The sacrum is from the Colorado find, and remaining parts were recovered at Cernay. The forelimb was adapted to extreme flexion, as are those of modern vertical clinging and leaping prosimians. It may well be that the locomotor pattern of *Plesiadapis* represented a stage preadaptive to the springing or vertical clinging and leaping apparently characteristic of many Eocene prosimians.

Le Gros Clark (1959) has compared *Plesiadapis* favorably with

Figure 39 Skeletal reconstruction of *Plesiadapis* based on cranial and postcranial remains from near Cernay, France, and from Colorado. Shaded parts are preserved. Scale × 0.25. (From Tattersall, 1970.)

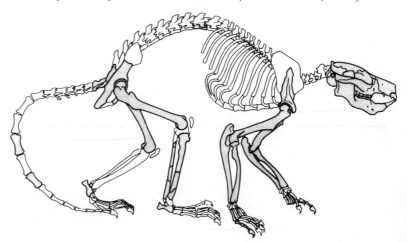

the tree shrews. Certainly, both groups represent very generalized mammals. Perhaps, like some kinds of tupaias, *Plesiadapis* species were semiterrestrial. However, large claws, compressed from side to side, associated with other bones of the skeleton at Mont de Berru suggest an adaptation for scrambling up the bark of large trees. Whatever its ecological niche, *Plesiadapis* established a broad range throughout Holarctica toward the end of Paleocene times. Along with the Paleocene–Eocene genus *Phenacolemur* and the early Eocene species of *Pelycodus*, *Plesiadapis* shares with *Homo* the distinction of being one of only four genera of primates that, so far as we know at present, ever ranged into both New and Old Worlds.

D. E. Russell (1964) has reviewed the new French cranial material and discusses the relationships of the French members of this genus to those of North America. He follows Gidley (1923), Simpson (1937a), and others in supporting the view that *Pronothodectes* from the North American Torrejonian age deposits in New Mexico could be near the basal ancestry of the family. From an origin somewhere in or near this genus, Russell (1964) visualized two subgeneric groups of *Plesiadapis*. From each subgeneric group arose one highly divergent stock. These are regarded by most scholars as of valid generic distinction: the two branches are represented by the species *Chiromyoides campanicus* from the late Paleocene of France and *Platychaerops* species of the early Eocene, *P. richardsonii* and *P. daubrei*. Later, Russell (1967) published his identification, as a specimen of *Plesiadapis*, of the previously poorly understood skeleton of "*Menatotherium*" described by Piton in 1940. This had been recovered from Paleocene coal deposits of Southern France. The type specimen of "*Menatotherium*," recording, as it does, the outlines if not the precise details of a plesiadapid skeleton, is important in showing intermembral proportions within one individual of an early primate species.

Most accounts of Paleocene primates give the impression that they were all extremely small mammals, but remains of some of the younger species of *Plesiadapis*, such as *P. tricuspidens* from Northern France and *P. cookei* from Northern Wyoming, prove that at the close of the Paleocene these creatures were at least cat size if not larger. *Platychaerops* species may have attained an even greater size, exceeding the proportions of any of the present-day tropical squirrels, which they may have adaptively resembled.

Pronothodectes (See Figure 40C)

Pronothodectes, the oldest genus of the Plesiadapidae, was named by Gidley in 1923 on the basis of finds made in the middle Paleocene deposits in Sweetgrass County, Montana. The dental formula is probably $\frac{2.1. \text{ or } 0.4.3.}{1.1. \text{ or } 0.4.3.} \times 2 = ?\ 38$. The cheek teeth have low rounded cusps, and the anterior lower incisor has a relatively slender caliber and is more procumbent than in some later plesiadapids. During the course of evolution of the genus *Plesiadapis*, there was gradual reduction in tooth number from the relatively high number

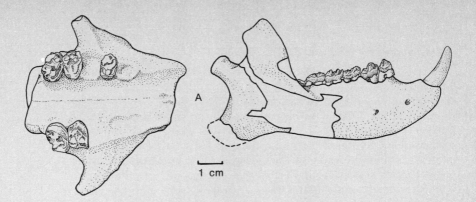

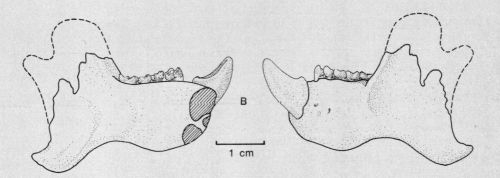

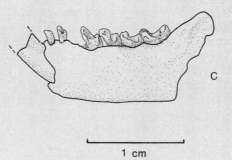

Figure 40 Three kinds of plesiadapid. *A: Platychaerops*, the largest and latest-surviving member of the group. Fossils of this genus occur in the early Eocene of England and France. *B: Chiromyoides* from the late Paleocene of France. It shows the greatest convergence known with the living aye-aye. *C: Pronothodectes*, the oldest known plesiadapid from the middle Paleocene of Montana. (Drawing by R. Rowen, Yale Peabody Museum.)

of *Pronothodectes* to what may have been about thirty teeth or less in *Platychaerops* and *Chiromyoides*.

Chiromyoides (See Figure 40*B*, page 113)

Chiromyoides was named by Stehlin in 1916 from a find made at Cernay, France. The dental formula is apparently $\frac{1.?2.?3.?3}{1.\,0.\,2.\,3}$. Although this genus was placed in synonymy with *Plesiadapis* by Teilhard de Chardin in 1922, it is clearly one of the most distinctive of Paleocene primate genera. The mandible was well figured and fully discussed by Stehlin (1916), and more recently Russell (1964) has presented more information, including data on some of the upper teeth. Russell suggested that *Plesiadapis walbeckensis* from the apparent Torrejonian equivalent fauna recovered from a fissure near Walbeck, Germany, may have been ancestral to *Chiromyoides*. The lower incisors are extremely large and shorter, stubbier, and thicker than is the case for other plesiadapids. This is also true of the upper three-lobed incisor of this species figured by Russell (1964). The mandible is extremely deep and the angular area is large, with a deeply excavated area for the insertion of the pterygoid muscle. The enormous root of the incisor extends posteriorly as far as M_2. There is a very short diastema between this tooth and P_3. In the molar trigonid, the paraconid of M_1 is situated inside and next to the metaconid. Going from M_1 to M_3, these two cusps tend to be more and more confluent. Heels lack the hypoconulid except on M_3, which is large and in which the entoconid is confluent with a flat hypoconulid lobe. As in some *Plesiadapis*, the cusps of lower molars are higher on the outside. Although somewhat smaller than the modern aye-aye, the parallelistic resemblance to the present-day Malagasy form is most remarkable. This was clearly the most short-faced of the Paleocene primates, and an adaptation to some form of powerful chewing seems clear-cut. The comparatively huge incisor is much less procumbent than in other plesiadapids. The upper molars are more squared off in outline than in *Plesiadapis*. This is a consequence of the fact that they are comparatively long anteroposteriorly. Unlike *Plesiadapis* and *Platychaerops*, *Chiromyoides* apparently did not survive into the Eocene. Russell (1964) also suggested that *P. walbeckensis*, a possible ancestor for *Chiromyoides*, might in turn have been derived from an early species of *Pronothodectes*.

Platychaerops (See Figure 40*C*, page 113)

By far the earliest-named genus of its group (Charlesworth, 1854), the type palate of *Platychaerops* belongs to the museum at York, England. *Platychaerops* differs from *Plesiadapis* in having only two cusps on upper central incisors instead of three. P^4 lacks the paraconule, and external cusps are subcrescentic with a well-developed mesostyle. P^3 is partially and P^4 is wholly molariform. Lemoine (1878) named teeth he had found in France *Plesiadapis daubrei*. Teilhard de Chardin (1921) pointed out that the French material did not differ significantly from the British type, but nevertheless he continued the use of *P. daubrei*. Teilhard de Chardin (1927) described a second species, *Platychaerops orsmaelensis*.

This genus shows a tendency toward selenodonty in the lower teeth, with heels becoming short and very broad. M_3 is extremely long and complex in structure, with the third lobe divided into two lobules with much variation. Species of this genus were probably the latest surviving plesiadapids. The palate is about the same size as that of the common lemur (*Lemur macaco*), so *Platychaerops richardsonii* was probably about the size of a lemur or a housecat.

Figure 41 Three unusual primates from the early Tertiary. *A: Saxonella* from late Paleocene deposits in Northern Germany. This animal is probably related to *Plesiadapis*. *B: Carpodaptes* from the late Paleocene of Western North America, representing the family Carpolestidae. *C: Picrodus*, an aberrant middle Paleocene form thought to be allied to the other early primates. (Drawing by R. Rowen, Yale Peabody Museum, after illustrations supplied by F. S. Szalay.)

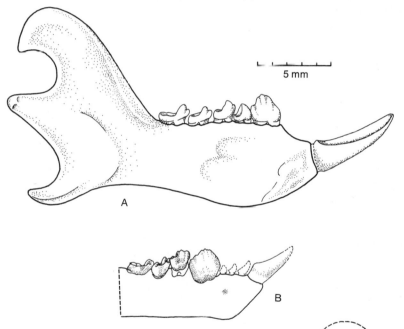

5 mm

A

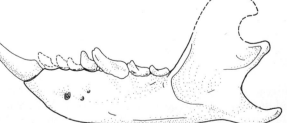

B

C

Saxonella (See Figure 41A, page 115)

The single species of the genus *Saxonella* is *S. crepaturae* (Russell, 1964) which is based on materials from fissure fills near Walbeck, Germany. There are about twenty-five specimens, mostly isolated teeth and one good mandible with incisor, P_3, and M_1. A second mandible preserves an incisor and M_1; the dental formula is $\overline{1.0.2.3.}$. P_3 is large and bladelike, and P_4 is small, rounded, and not molarized. In M_3 there is a large trigonid that is broad transversely and short anteroposteriorly.

Russell (1964) is of the opinion that *Saxonella* represents a new subfamily of carpolestids, the Saxonellinae. The name is derived from Saxony, the region in Germany where the specimens were found. More recently, I have come to the conclusion, in agreement with Szalay (1968), that *Saxonella* probably should be associated with plesiadapids and not carpolestids.

CARPOLESTIDAE

The family Carpolestidae was proposed by Simpson in 1935 to include three unusual middle Paleocene–early Eocene genera *Elphidotarsius, Carpodaptes, and Carpolestes.* A survey of most specimens of the three genera seems to support the original suggestion that they demonstrate a structural sequence in time; that is, they represent a single phylogeny, succeeding each other in the order given above.

The unusual features of the dentition led to an early belief that these primates fed on small fruits and seeds, hence the name *Carpolestes*, from the Greek meaning "fruit stealer." These primates may well have been arboreal. The size of the jaws and teeth suggests that the smaller species were no larger than a small mouse.

The family is known only from jaws and teeth and a few skull fragments; no postcranial material can be definitely assigned. All representatives are characterized by an enlarged, bladelike P_4 with from four to nine cusps and a talonid that varies from a separate, distict heel in *Elphidotarsius* to a nearly indistinguishable cusp merging with the main blade in *Carpolestes*. The lower jaw also holds a single, enlarged, semiprocumbent incisor. There are three teeth between this and P_4. Whether the first of these represents P_1 or C is debatable, but Simpson (1935b) suggested that, analogous to other early primates, it is the canine (much reduced). On this basis, the lower dental formula of all three genera is $\overline{1.1.2.3.}$. The upper dentition is not completely known; however, there were two reduced teeth anterior to the two enlarged premolars (P^{3-4}). In *Elphidotarsius* the premolars are not yet larger than the molars, but in both *Carpodaptes* and *Carpolestes* they become much larger than the molars and develop three longitudinal cusp rows. Molars in both the upper and lower jaws are similar to those of many other early primates.

Carpolestids share with certain multituberculates, with an extinct group of New World marsupials, and with some living Australian marsupials enlarged, slicing lower fourth premolars. This has been termed by Simpson (1937a,b) the "plagiaulacoid" type of dentition. Basically, the polycuspidate uppers appear to hold fast a food item while it is sliced by the bladelike lower tooth. The living marsupials with this dental arrangement are said to be herbivorous and to feed principally on grasses, seeds, and roots.

Carpolestids are confined predominantly to Paleocene beds in Wyoming and Montana, although representatives have been found as far south as Tiffany, Colorado, and as far north as Swan Hills, Alberta; there are a few specimens recorded from the Graybull beds (early Eocene) of Wyoming. A European form, *Saxonella*, was originally assigned to a new subfamily of the Carpolestidae by Russell (1964) but is here placed in the Plesiadapidae, which it more closely resembles in the anatomy of cheek teeth and in having polycuspidate upper incisors.

Similarities among the earlier carpolestids and some other Paleocene primates (especially *Pronothodectes*) have led to the suggestion that plesiadapids and carpolestids shared a common ancestor sometime prior to the middle Paleocene.

The total number of carpolestid specimens is probably over 150. The majority of specimens and the most complete specimens are in the collections of Princeton University made by G. L. Jepsen, from the Bighorn Basin, Wyoming.

Elphidotarsius

Elphidotarsius, described by Gidley in 1923, is the earliest-occurring genus (Torrejonian) of the Carpolestidae. The type species, *E. florencae*, which is the only described species of the genus, is based on a mandible from the middle Paleocene Gidley Quarry in Southern Montana. This left jaw, with P_4–M_3, displays the enlarged, bladelike P_4 characteristic of the family. P_4 is larger than M_1 and has four cuspules and a distinct and lower talonid heel. M_1 differs from that of the other two carpolestid genera in that the three cusps of the trigonid are separate and distinct, not forming a supplementary blade to that of P_4, and the paraconid is noticeably internal to the protoconid. The trigonid is also much higher than the talonid heel of P_4.

Unpublished *Elphidotarsius* specimens from the Bighorn Basin, Wyoming (Rock Bench), reveal interesting although predictable details of the upper and lower dentition and dental formula. The genus demonstrates many features that would be expected in a form ancestral to *Carpodaptes*—among them, less specialized P_4 and P^{3-4} and less reduced, double-rooted P_3. No skull or postcranial material is known.

Elphidotarsius was the smallest carpolestid. P_4 is relatively much smaller, and in actual size may be less than half as long as in *Carpolestes*. The jaw is much shallower than in *Carpolestes*.

Carpodaptes (See Figure 41B, page 115)

The genus *Carpodaptes*, named by Matthew and Granger in 1921, is a late Paleocene Tiffanian form with a far wider geographic range than that known for its presumed ancestor, *Elphidotarsius*. The type species, *C. aulacodon*, is a left mandible with P_2–M_3 from the Mason Pocket at Tiffany, Southwest Colorado. Subsequent discoveries of the genus have been made in the Hoback and Bighorn Basins in Wyoming, at the Scarritt Quarry in Sweetgrass County, Montana, and near Circle in Eastern Montana.

Specimens of both the upper and lower dentitions exist. The anterior upper teeth are as yet unknown, but there are two much reduced teeth anterior to the enlarged P^{3-4}. The three molars are all smaller than either P^3 or P^4 and are typical of most primate genera of this and early Eocene age. P^3 and P^4 are both considerably more hypertrophied than in *Elphidotarsius* and are characterized by three longitudinal cusp rows, superficially similar to those in some multituberculates. The lower jaw has a single, enlarged, semi-procumbent incisor; a reduced, single-rooted canine (or P_1); much reduced P_{2-3}; enlarged bladelike P_4 with five or six cusps and a distinct talonid heel (though not so low or distant as in *Elphidotarsius*); and three molars. In this genus, the paraconid and protoconid of M_1 begin to form an accessory blade adjoining that in P_4, although this transition is not quite so pronounced as in *Carpolestes*.

There are three described species of the genus; the most complete specimens are the type of *C. hobackensis* Dorr (1952), which includes the entire lower dentition (the three teeth anterior to P_4 are broken but are preserved as impressions in the matrix), and left maxillary of *C. hazelae* at the American Museum with C–M^3.

Simpson (1937a,b) noted the possibility that *Elphidotarsius*–*Carpodaptes*–*Carpolestes* represent a direct evolutionary sequence but commented that the age difference between the last two seemed insufficient to accomplish the structural changes necessary. Specimens from the Bighorn Basin support his early view, for in this one area exist beds of decreasing age with *Elphidotarsius*, *Carpodaptes*, and *Carpolestes*, respectively. Several specimens showing intermediacy have been recovered.

Carpolestes

Carpolestes, named by Simpson in 1928, contains the most progressive carpolestids. There are four described species, found at several localities in Wyoming, Montana, and Alberta. This is the best known genus of the family. The material includes several nearly complete mandibles and maxillae. A partial skull is known, but its description has not been published.

The most significant differences between this genus and *Carpodaptes* are the relatively even larger and slightly more complex P^{3-4} and the larger P_4, which usually has eight or nine cusps and a nearly indistinguishable talonid heel merging with the blade. P_4 is often several times larger than M_1. The trigonid of M_1 forms a blade that functions with that of P_4. The upper jaw contains two in-cisiform teeth that are probably incisors. Isolated upper incisors have been found that could be of carpolestids. These are similar in conformation to plesiadapid incisors, although much smaller. Members of this genus vary considerably in size; the smallest species is *Carpolestes cygneus* of L. S. Russell (1967). This find from North Central Alberta is also the northernmost occurrence of a carpolestid.

Carpolestes is the only genus of its family to extend into deposits as late as the early Eocene or Graybullian age. Especially in these latest finds the P^3 is extended to the front and side and resembles to a considerable extent a multituberculate tooth.

PAROMOMYIDAE

The original concept of the family Paromomyidae goes back to its usage as a subfamily of Anaptomorphidae by Simpson (1940) to include the genera *Paromomys, Palaechthon, Plesiolestes,* and *Palenochtha.* At that time he clearly did not have *Phenacolemur* under consid-eration as allied with these forms. The subfamily was defined as characterized by possession of two large lower anterior teeth; moderately developed P_4; molar paraconids internal, distinct, or close to metaconids; trigonids short and subquadrate; M_3 with elongated heel, typically with more than one cusp except in *Pal-enochtha*; P^3 with long axis anteroposterior; P^4 low, with long axis transverse to the tooth row and with large internal cusp; and upper molars with simple hypocones and a posterointernal cingulum basin.

Almost everyone who has listed the relationships of the five genera discussed above has come to quite different conclusions as to their interrelationships and how they should be ranked taxo-nomically. The history of these rankings is complex, but a review of it here seems useful, if only to reveal the rambling practices that tend to obtain when the true interrelationships of a supposed group of mammals have not been carefully worked out.

Simpson in 1955 published a monographic study of *Phenacolemur,* a late Paleocene and early Eocene primate genus that he had for-merly considered to be of uncertain relationships. For this genus he established a new family, "Phenacolemuridae," but in it he included *Paromomys,* which he remarked was nearer to *Phenacolemur* than "any other genus known to me." He observed further that it was in general more primitive than *Phenacolemur* and, whether or not a direct ancestor, was clearly structurally close to what one would expect for an ancestral stage of *Phenacolemur.* For the reasons he then outlined, few if any would consider placing these two genera in different families. However, McKenna (1960) pointed out that if a group containing *Paromomys* were to be elevated from subfamily to family rank, the name "Paromomyidae" should take precedence in accordance with the international rules of nomenclature. *Phenacolemur* can be shown to be more different from *Paromomys* on grounds of dental anatomy and dental formula than can the other forms included in this group and consequently should probably be in a separate subfamily. For instance, both *Plesiolestes* and *Paromomys* have two large anterior lower teeth, not one, and possess more premolars than does *Phenacolemur*. If *Purgatorius* should prove to be a valid base for a primitive subfamily of the Paromomyidae, then the division of the remaining paromomyines into two tribes proposed by Szalay (1968) would seem acceptable.

Paromomys

Gidley provided the original description of *Paramomys*, which is one of the earliest members of the order for which we have knowledge of the dental mechanism. Recent studies suggest that the dental formula is $\frac{2.1.3.3.}{2.1.3.3.}$. *Paromomys* shows molar resemblance to *Pelycodus* and *Notharctus*. Trigonids are high for primates, upper molars entirely lack a lingual cingulum, and, as is typical of earliest primates, hypocones show little development. Gidley (1923) described two species of *Paromomys* from the same quarry. He also managed to find there two other species of a related genus, *Palaechthon* (*P. alticuspis* and "*P.*" *minor*). Later, Simpson proposed the latter species as the type of a new genus, *Palenochtha*, which is an anagram of the former generic name assigned it.

Simpson (1955) tentatively assigned *Paromomys* to the same family as *Phenacolemur* and considered that—without its being the actual ancestor—it represented a good structural approximation to what could have given rise to *Phenacolemur.*

Palaechthon (See Figure 42*A*)

Palaechthon was described by Gidley in 1923 with a type species *P. alticuspis*, which comes from middle Paleocene, Torrejonian deposits in the Gidley and Silberling Quarries, Crazy Mountain Field, Montana. The lower dental formula is $\overline{2.1.3.3.}$ according to Szalay (1968). There are two large incisors below followed by the canines, resembling *Paromomys*. *Palaechthon* has a distinct paraconid and metaconid on P_4, with higher molar trigonids than in related genera and M_3 heel comparatively smaller and narrow.

A few upper cheek teeth are known. They are broad from inside to out. On M^{1-3} both conules are well developed and an external cingulum is present. There is expansion of cuspules in the parastylar and metastylar areas and molars have much more flaring antero- and posterolateral corners than do those of *Pronothodectes* or *Paromomys*. In these features and in its slightly smaller size *Palaechthon* is more like *Purgatorius* than are *Pronothodectes* and *Paramomys*. However, like *Pronothodectes* it possesses a metacone on P^4. The internal part of M^{1-3} is not as bilobed as in *Paromomys* and the hypocone is less well developed.

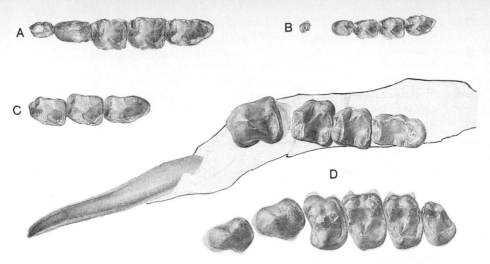

Figure 42 Various genera of paromomyid prosimians. *A*: Left P_3 through M_3 of *Palaechthon*. *B*: *Palenochtha* P_2; P_4 through M_3. *C*: *Paromomys* left M_1 through M_3. *D*: Upper and lower dentitions of *Phenacolemur pagei*. Scale $\times$ 4.5. (From G. G. Simpson, 1955.)

Palenochtha (See Figure 42*B*)

The type species of *Palenochtha* was originally described as belonging to *Palaechthon*. The lower dental formula is probably $\frac{}{2.1.2.3.}$; the anterior lower dentition is shorter than in *Paromomys* or *Palaechthon*; probably P_2 is absent; P_4 is comparatively higher than in *Palaechthon*, with no metaconid; and the paraconid is vestigial.

Phenacolemur (See Figure 42*D*)

Phenacolemur occurs at many localities of late Paleocene (Tiffanian) age and early Eocene (Wasatchian) age of the Rocky Mountain region. It has recently been identified as occurring in France by Russell, Louis, and Savage (1967). These authors described two species of Sparnacian age from Mutigny and Avenay, France.

Matthew (1914), when naming the genus, considered it an apatemyid—a family that some have supposed to be insectivores. European writers such as Schlosser (1923) and Abel (1931) lumped *Phenacolemur* and the apatemyids among the plesiadapids and considered the whole group as ancestral or related to the Madagascan aye-aye (*Daubentonia* or "*Cheiromys*"). There were only four first-hand studies on *Phenacolemur* before 1960. Simpson (1955) considered that Tiffanian–Wasatchian *Phenacolemur* could have been derived from something like *Paromomys* of the Torrejonian but implied that it was equally as divergent as the omomyines or microchoerines, the plesiadapids, and the adapids and thus deserved separate family status.

The earliest (Tiffanian) *Phenacolemur* is *P. frugivorus* Matthew and

Granger (1921) from the Tiffany and Melville Formations of Colorado and Montana. This species was originally described under the generic name *Ignacius*. It is the smallest known species of the genus (mean length of M_1 1.9 mm); and consists of six or seven specimens. *P. pagei* is of the same age *P. frugivorus*, but a valid species, and is known from nearly twenty lower jaws. This largest single sample of the genus gives no indication of sexual dimorphism. *Phenacolemur* fossils at Princeton and Yale suggest that from Sand Coulee through lower Graybull, upper Graybull, and Lysite deposits the mean size of this animal decreases.

The two French species of *Phenacolemur* are known only from composite dentitions assembled from isolated teeth. In the smaller of these, the P_4 seems relatively less large than in the American forms. In both French species the M_3 third lobe is somewhat more bulbous than in most North American individuals.

Simpson (1955) described a skull of *Phenacolemur* showing the following features:

1. Anterior root of zygoma inserts above M^{1-2}.
2. Zygoma has a broad, sloping, anterior face below a relatively large infraorbital foramen.
3. Skull broad and low, postpalatal length shorter than palatal.
4. Low median sagittal crest.

(These features all suggest that the calvarium was broad, short, low, and relatively small.)

5. Palate unusually broad and only gently concave.
6. Rim of the choanae at about the posterior end of the molar series.
7. Fragments of external auditory meatus, as well as ossified auditory bulla, present.
8. Sharply defined, almost styliform, postglenoid process anterior to meatus.

Guthrie (1964, in manuscript) resurrected Matthew's *Phenacolemur citatus* from the upper Graybull, which Simpson (1955) had considered only a subspecies of early Graybull *Phenacolemur praecox*. The late Graybull population is distinctly smaller than that of the earlier levels. *Phenacolemur* specimens average slightly larger than several new Lysite jaws discussed by Guthrie. He confirms Simpson's findings that this lineage was decreasing in size with time. Surprisingly, Robinson (1968) has recently reported the survival of this genus in the form of a new species, *Phenacolemur mcgrewi*, into late Eocene (Uintan age) times in the Badwater area of Wyoming. Interestingly, the new form, which could be 15 million years younger than oldest members of the genus, is small and shows no divergent or "specialized" features.

Originally, Simpson (1937a) and more recently Szalay (1968) touched on the view that the Picrodontidae, small Paleocene and earliest Eocene mammals, might be assigned to the order Primates. The construction of the anterior molars and posterior premolars of these unique mammals is greatly removed morphologically from anything seen elsewhere among Primates. The first-described member of the group, *Zanycteris*, was suggested as having affinites with bats. Having transferred the Picrodontidae to the Primates, Szalay remarks on the extraordinary degree of convergence toward the dentition of some Chiroptera that *Picrodus* exhibits (see Figure 41C, page 115). *Picrodus* has procumbent and elongated lower front teeth, set in a fairly shallow horizontal ramus, and enlarged, flat, and specialized premolars. If these animals are to be considered primates, then their highly divergent molars and premolars suggest that a very wide range of dental adaptations had already been achieved among Primates by the middle Paleocene, when *Picrodus* first occurs, more than 60 million years ago. Although no significant cranial or post-cranial parts of these animals survive, their dental anatomy suggests that they may have been adapted for arboreal frugivorous diets. Szalay remarks: "Thus postulating feeding on fruit pulp, seeds of fruits, or nectar for the tiny paromomyid derived Paleocene picrodontids is warranted both on the basis of their size as well as the convergent similarity of their cheek-teeth to nectar and fruit pulp feeding bats." A lateral view of the mandible with teeth of a species of genus *Picrodus* is shown in Figure 41C (page 115).

7 The First Primates of Modern Aspect

ADAPIDAE

Adapidae is a prosimian family from the Eocene Epoch that shows striking postcranial resemblance to modern lemurs. The concept of the group is based on species of the European middle and late Eocene *Adapis*. Knowledge of the latter comes principally from copious remains of skulls and limb bones recovered in the Quercy phosphatic deposits of South-Central France. Opinions have varied as to whether or not to include the North American genera *Pelycodus*, *Notharctus*, and *Smilodectes* in this family, as a separate subfamily Notharctinae. Gazin (1958) recently advocated placement of the notharctines in a separate family, following the views of Stehlin (1912). However, Gregory (1920) argued that both the European and North American groups could conveniently be placed in the same family, an opinion followed here. In any case it is likely that too many early Tertiary primate families have been proposed. When these animals become better known skeletally, there will probably be further coalescence of some of these groups. Both subfamilies are well known from much cranial and postcranial material, which makes it possible to draw up extensive lists of the minor differences between *Adapis* on the one hand and *Notharctus* on the other. Nevertheless, Gregory's discussion, which is one of the better analyses of how broadly mammalian families ought to be drawn, succeeds in showing that within Viverridae, Mustelidae, and Procyonidae, for instance, much greater spread of dental and cranial anatomy exists. The principal features that adapines and notharctines share are discussed in great detail by Gregory (1920). They constitute a group of anatomical features unique among early prosimians. These include

1. Fused mandibular symphyses (except in *Pelycodus*).
2. Retention of four sets of premolars.
3. Recurved canines and vertically placed incisors.
4. Large pterygoid plate of the alisphenoid.
5. Lacrymal within the orbit.
6. Free tympanic within the bulla (internal carotid enters posteroexternal angle of bulla).
7. Trend toward two lateral cusps on the P^4.

As presently constituted, the adapines are all of European occurrence, and the notharctines, with one possible exception (*Cantius*), are North American. The genus *Protoadapis*, considered to stand close to the notharctines by Stehlin (1912), Teilhard de Chardin (1921), and Simpson (1940), was transferred to the Adapinae by Simons (1962b). McKenna (1966), following earlier workers, recognized the following genera in the two groups, to which, however, he gave family status:

Adapinae
  Adapis
  Protoadapis
  Pronycticebus
  Anchomomys
  Caenopithecus
  Gesneropithex (now considered an adapisoriscid insectivore)
  Lantianius
Notharctinae
  Pelycodus
  Notharctus
  Smilodectes

He also considered *Cantius* a synonym of *Pelycodus*, but direct comparative proof of this synonymy has yet to be undertaken. Furthermore, *Pelycodus* has a single-rooted P_1 and a double-rooted P_2. In *Cantius* there are only two alveoli between the canine and the P_3 instead of the three sockets expected for *Pelycodus*. In addition, the anterior teeth of *Cantius* are packed together rather than being spaced out with diastemata between canine and P_1, between P_1 and P_2, and separating P_2 and P_3 as well. In conjunction with this, the set of the long axis of the symphysis in *Cantius* is more vertical than in *Pelycodus*. Nevertheless, the two genera are closely similar, as was indicated by Russell, Louis, and Savage (1967), who, however, did not carry out a synonymy. Szalay (personal communication) believes that *Gesneropithex* is an insectivore but that *Lantianius* may be an adapid. *Pronycticebus* and *Anchomomys* are retained by Simons (1962) in the Adapinae, but they also show resemblances with the Miocene lorisids of Kenya.

Adapis (See Figures 43B and 44A)

Adapis was the first genus of fossil primate to be described—in 1821 by Cuvier. However, its true affinities were long misunderstood. Cuvier considered it to be a pachyderm, although by coining the name "ad-apis" he perhaps intended to suggest artiodactyl affinities, because it means "toward (the sacred bull) *Apis*."

Figure 43 Skull of *Pronycticebus* (A) compared with that of *Adapis* (B). Both were recovered from middle to late Eocene deposits, the Quercy phosphorites of South-Central France. Scale (A) × 1.25 and (B) × 0.8 approximately. (A: Simons. B: Photo courtesy of E. Genet-Varcin, 1969.)

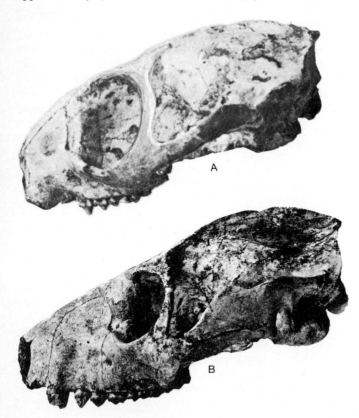

Figure 44 The mandible of *Adapis magnus* (*A*) compared with that of *Protoadapis* (*B*). Scale × 0.75 approximately. (Drawing by R. Rowen, Yale Peabody Museum, after Gregory, 1920, and Russell *et al.*, 1967.)

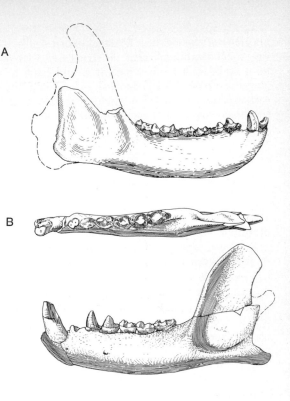

A

B

The original finds came from "Plaster of Paris" quarry sites in the middle Eocene gypsum deposits of Montmartre. In 1859, Gervais concluded that a mandible of *Adapis*, which he mistakenly named "*Aphelotherium*," was an anoplotherid artiodactyl. Fourteen years later, Delfortrie described a skull of one of the smaller species now recognized as belonging to this genus and took it to be a new primate genus, "*Palaeolemur*." Gervais (1873) and Filhol (1873) reassigned materials of "*Palaeolemur*" and "*Aphelotherium*" to *Adapis*. Most nineteenth century students believed that *Adapis* was a transitional form between artiodactyls and primates.

There is a clear-cut size difference between the two commonest species of *Adapis*, *A. parisiensis* and *A. magnus*, and typically the latter, larger form has heavier cranial cresting and more massive zygomatic arches as well as other size-related features. Fossils of both of these species proved to be abundant in the middle Eocene Quercy phosphatic deposits of South-Central France, and many skulls and postcranial bones are now scattered throughout the museums of Europe. These have served as the basis for numerous, mainly descriptive, studies. In 1901, Forsyth-Major suggested that the extent of similarity between *Adapis parisiensis* and the Malagasy lemurs was so great that "it may be fairly taken to be in their ancestral line." He had also noted that the construction of the middle ear (with free, contained tympanic ring) was the same in both groups. It is now clear that *Adapis* itself could not be a direct ancestor of the modern Malagasy forms. It has a number of "crossing specializations," that is, structures that are either specialized or unique to it from which it would have to revert to produce a supposed descendant. Because in evolving lineages structures once lost are not regained as such, reversals of this sort are unlikely. In *Adapis* some of these specializations are

1. The lacrymals are not extended onto the face, as in modern forms and in "primitive" primates generally.
2. In *Adapis* the mandibular symphysis fused before adulthood, but in extant lemurs it usually remains open.
3. Fourth upper and lower premolars of *Adapis* are molariform, unlike those of modern lemurs.

Stehlin's review (1912), followed by the comparisons and contrasts made by Gregory (1920), covered very thoroughly the craniology of *Adapis*. An excellently preserved skull of *Adapis* at the British Museum allowed for the preparation of a good endocranial cast, described by Le Gros Clark (1945). The olfactory bulbs of *Adapis* were relatively large. Compared with the overall size of the cranium and the facial part of the skull, the brain was small relative to that of Malagasy lemurs. The floccular lobes of the cerebellum were proportionately larger than in *Notharctus*, with a broader cerebrum. The frontal lobes were small and narrow, and the cerebral hemispheres were smooth. There is considerable variation in the development of the sagittal and nuchal crests, and juvenile skulls show both that these developed with age and that they were largest in males. Stehlin also concluded from variations in the absolute size of the canines that *Adapis* was sexually dimorphic. Gazin (1958) supported the view that *Adapis* and *Notharctus* should be placed in different families. His argument is not without merit, but it rests principally on the idea that "the marked overall resemblances which can be brought about by similar adaptations are the key in this case. The resemblances are due not to relationship but to parallel adaptation."

Protoadapis (See Figure 44B, page 127)

Protoadapis was initially recognized from two lower jaws found in Normandy in deposits of early Eocene age. Although limited in extent, these Eocene deposits have traditionally been used to enrich the soils of the vineyards of the champagne country. The first specimens of the type species of *Protoadapis* were found scattered in vineyards, and so for many years, without knowledge of exact sites, little additional material came to light from the sands of Epernay and related localities in France. Initially, the French naturalist Lemoine (1878) named two species of this genus, but the type of the second species is either a synonym of the other or is too worn to serve as a type. This leaves as valid Lemoine's species *Protoadapis curvicuspidens*. Much later, in 1933, Weigelt named a "new" genus and species "*Europolemur*" *klatti*, the type of which consisted of a crushed skull with a complete upper dentition from middle Eocene brown coal deposits near Halle an der Saalle in East Germany. Simons (1962b) pointed out that this species really constitutes a middle Eocene member of the genus *Protoadapis*. In addition to these two species there is a late Eocene or perhaps even early Oligocene species from the Quercy Phosphorites of South-Central France that was named *Protoadapis angustidens* by Filhol. The three species may conceivably represent a single lineage, as they clearly succeed each other in time, but although the samples of material of each species are quite small it seems probable that *Protoadapis klatti* was not as large as the other two species. If other proportions corresponded with jaw size, species of *Protoadapis* might have been slightly smaller than a house cat, perhaps about the size of the living gentle lemurs. As such, it was probably one of the larger primates of the Eocene, about comparable with *Notharctus* and *Smilodectes* in size or with the smaller species of *Adapis*.

Unlike *Adapis*, P_1^1 are lost, so that the dental formula is probably $\frac{2.1.3.3.}{2.1.3.3.}$, a resemblance to North American notharctines.

Pronycticebus

The genus and species *Pronycticebus gaudryi* was based on a sole type skull and mandible found in 1893 and described by Grandidier in 1904 as having possible affinities with the modern lorises. It is reported to be of Bartonian (late Eocene) age from Mermerlein-le-Quercy in South-Central France. Although both Stehlin and Gregory early considered it to have possible tarsioid relationships—perhaps because the skull is fairly short and the brain case rounded—it is much larger than any of the early Tertiary primates that have been conjectured as relatives of the tarsier, the skull being about as large as that of *Adapis parisiensis* or *Pelycodus* (See Figure 43A). Like *Adapis*, the frontal area is flattened and centrally depressed and the slightly developed sagittal crest has a domed-out look when viewed from the side similar to that of *Adapis parisiensis*. As in *Adapis*, there is a marked postorbital constriction. In resemblance also to *Adapis* the cheek bones flare out widely but the orbits are relatively much larger and were probably more frontally directed. Walker (1967a) has shown that the nocturnal Madagascan lemurs can be separated from the diurnal by plotting the ratio of orbital diameter to skull length. My estimated skull length and orbital diameter for *Pronycticebus* put it definitely on the nocturnal side of the plot. Orbital width is less reliably estimated in the Kenya Miocene lorisid skull of *Progalago* described by Le Gros Clark (1956), but it also appears to be on the nocturnal side of the line. Nearly all the literature on this single skull emphasizes that there is no postorbital bar—an unusually primitive condition even for an Eocene primate. On examination of the specimen, it was apparent to me that the zygomatic arch, preserved on the left side only, was covered by a layer of plaster. When this was removed, the very distinct base of a broken-off postorbital bar projected upward, and careful examination of the region of frontal attachment of the bar dorsally showed a clearly recognizable area of cancellous bone where the bar had been broken away. However, because of the size and location of these attachments, the bar must have been more delicate and considerably more flaring than in *Adapis,* another resemblance to the Lorisidae. In view of the fact that this skull does show both an area of frontal attachment and a zygomatic base for the postorbital bar, and in the complete absence of any evidence that any other primates of this general grade do not possess postorbital bars, no real basis remains for thinking that the bar was not complete as restored in Figure 43 (page 126). Unlike *Tarsius,* the bullae are less inflated relatively, the position of the carotid foramen is different, and the tympanic bone lies at the external opening of the middle ear, where it appears to be fused with the bulla wall in its posterior third. This constitutes an approximation toward the lorisid condition and a difference from *Adapis,* where the ring is free within the bulla. Retention of *Pronycticebus* in the same family with *Adapis* seems warranted as long as the notharctines are also included, but the cranial differences between the two European forms are extensive and about equal to those separating *Notharctus* and *Adapis,* both of which have free, intrabullar tympanics. Nevertheless, the dental resemblances among *Pronycticebus, Caenopithecus, Anchomomys,* and *Adapis* are stronger, particularly in the lower molars, where the trigonids are open widely and a reduced paraconid lobe reaches only to about, or a little beyond, the midline of the long axis of the tooth. This resemblance and their common geographic distribution appear to justify their retention for the present in one subfamily. A single tooth from Spain was recently made the type of a new genus of Eocene primate, *Agerina.* A recent unpublished study by Szalay indicates that *Agerina* is an adapid related to *Pronycticebus.*

The breadth of the palate of *Pronycticebus* and its resemblance to that of *Nycticebus* were noted by Hill (1953). It seems to me that even though the premaxillae with incisor roots have been broken away in the skull of *Pronycticebus,* the canines are set so far apart as to suggest that, like *Progalago, Pronycticebus* may have had reduced, widely spaced upper incisors and procumbent teeth below.

Anchomomys (See Figure 45)

Anchomomys is a relatively small adapine described by Stehlin in 1916 that ranges from early Lutetian to the beginning of the Ludian provincial age in Europe. The proposed species, which number four, do not differ greatly among themselves except in size. In naming the animal, Stehlin implied a relationship to *Omomys,* which was then considered a tarsioid. In consequence, Abel and others took it to be a tarsier relative. After Le Gros Clark (1934a) had shown that the skull of *Pronycticebus* is not constructed like that of *Tarsius,* but conforms more closely in its anatomy to lemurs, lorises, and *Adapis,* Simpson (1940) transferred both these genera to the Adapidae. *Anchomomys* is close in dental structure to *Pronycticebus* and probably should be classified in the same subfamily with it. Both

Figure 45 Palate of *Anchomomys* from the Eocene phosphorites of Quercy, France. (Photo courtesy of F. S. Szalay.)

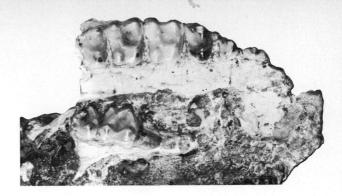

```
|||||||||||||||||||||||||||||||||||||||||||||||||
0 cm                    1                    2
```

Stehlin and Teilhard de Chardin (1916) described *Anchomomys* in detail. No definitely associated postcranials are known for it, and most of the specimens consist only of mandibular and maxillary fragments. The type of one species, *Anchomomys latidens*, from the Quercy Phosphorites preserves part of a crushed cranium from which little can be determined without further cleaning. In 1962, I was of the opinion that *Anchomomys*, like *Pronycticebus*, resembled significantly the Miocene lorisid *Progalago* and this still seems probable (see Simons, 1962b). This resemblance could not have been noticed before, for all the original papers on *Anchomomys* were published decades before the discovery of the East African fossil lorises. After studying the Kenyan primates, Simpson (1967) tentatively agreed to the possibility of a relationship between European Eocene forms and those of the Miocene of East Africa, but felt that "the Miocene lorisids do not really help to close the gap [between Eocene and modern prosimians] because in the known parts they are little if any more primitive than some, at least, of the recent species." Had lorisids been an ancient African stock such as phiomyid rodents, elephant shrews, or tenrecs, one might have expected to find some evidence of them in the Egyptian Fayum deposits, where all the above groups occur, but in spite of the abundance there of other small mammals, including other primates, no evidence of this group has turned up. Unlike the lemurs and tarsiers, the Lorisidae are today distributed both in Eurasia and in Africa. These lines of evidence suggest that lorisids may well have entered Africa from the north, perhaps in early Miocene times.

Caenopithecus (See Figure 46, page 132)

The genus and species *Caenopithecus lemuroides* was named by the Swiss paleontologist Rütimeyer in 1862 on the basis of a type maxilla from the Eocene fissure fills of Egerkingen, near Soleure, Switzerland. Later, Rütimeyer and Stehlin (1916) referred additional materials of this animal, all from Egerkingen, to the species. Rüti-

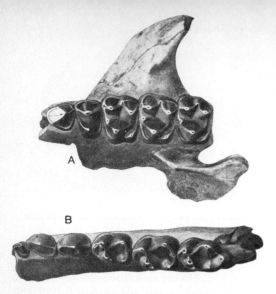

Figure 46 Upper (*A*) and lower (*B*) dentition of *Caenopithecus*, an Eocene primate from Europe. (From H. G. Stehlin, 1916.)

meyer (1862) was far ahead of his time in initially claiming full primate status for this species. This was at a time when other paleontologists considered such forms as *Adapis* and *Notharctus* somehow intermediate between primates and ungulates, or entirely ungulate in character. For instance, Leidy thought *Notharctus* might be a procyonid carnivore or later suggested that it might be close to the odd-toed pachyderms. In the fall of 1872 both Marsh and Cope apparently first realized that some of the North American early Tertiary mammals were primates. Marsh's publication was but four days earlier than Cope's, on October 8. In it he discussed three genera he had proposed (which we now know are synonyms of *Notharctus*) as indicating "the discovery of fossil quadrumana in the Eocene of Wyoming." Marsh reported that his primate synonyms of *Notharctus* had lemur-like postcranial anatomy. On October 12, Cope described the species *Anaptomorphus aemulus* and contrasted its teeth to those of *Simia* (now *Pongo*) and *Homo*. The first publications by European authors other than Rütimeyer (1862) in which tarsier and lemur affinities were urged for Eocene forms are dated 1873 and 1874, after initial recognition of early Tertiary primates by Marsh and Cope.

Stehlin (1916) thought, incorrectly, that *Caenopithecus* was a tarsioid or specifically related to *Tarsius.* This may have been because one of the mandibles of this primate shows only one lower incisor alveolus, as in *Tarsius.* The anterior alveolar border of this particular find is broken away at such a low level that the break could have cut below small central incisor sockets, were these like those typical of most other primates. Some nineteenth century paleontologists thought that *Caenopithecus* was a synonym of *Adapis*, but it is not. Unlike *Adapis*, *Caenopithecus* has distinctly developed upper molar mesostyles and a much more vertically oriented symphyseal axis. Placement with the adapines is compatible with its European occurrence. There is also a broad similarity between them in molar size and common presence of open lower molar trigonids with centrally placed paraconids, as well as in overall structure.

Stehlin referred a talus from Egerkingen to this species. This bone is of smaller size and greater relative length than in *Adapis*, particularly the neck and the fibular facet, the latter feature also being rather less distinct.

Both maxillae and mandibles of *Caenopithecus* suggest that the face was short relative to the condition seen in *Adapis*. This is a possible resemblance to *Pronycticebus*, which is of similar size. In correlation with the short face, the anterior part of the cheek bone projects laterally at a sharper angle to the snout than in *Adapis* and is deeper in the vertical dimension. The lower jaw is also shortened, the horizontal ramus is ventrally convex, and as in *Adapis* symphyseal fusion occurred early in life. The masseteric fossa is particularly well defined, but the markings of the mylohyoid insertion are fainter than in *Adapis*. *Caenopithecus* thus appears to have had a shortened, deepened snout, undoubtedly related to changes in its manner of feeding away from that of *Adapis*; the canines are large, long, and vertically implanted, and there may have been incisor reduction. Russell, Louis, and Savage (1967) concluded that placement in Adapidae is warranted but considered that development of upper molar mesostyles is aberrant. The age of *Caenopithecus* is late middle Eocene (lower and middle Lutetian provincial ages).

Northarctinae was first proposed as a family by Trouessart (1879), a usage followed by Stehlin (1912) and Gazin (1958). The group was dropped to subfamilial rank by Gregory (1920) and Hill (1953). The most striking dental distinctions from adapines are that the hypocone of the upper molars, which was still differentiating in *Pelycodus*, appears to have arisen as a posterior budding of a lobe off the protocone, above the basal cingulum, whereas in most primates and in other mammals generally hypocones arise as an enlargement of one of the cuspules on the posterointernal cingulum. This is an occurrence of the "pseudohypocone" much discussed by European authors, although the evidence for the two kinds of derivation seems to me to be overrated, particularly as long as we do not really know what governs the formation of cusps and cuspules genetically. Clearly, selection was favoring the development of two internal upper molar cusps in the various lineages of the Adapidae, as a modification or "improvement" of the mechanical function of the cheek teeth. Just how this was accomplished would be expected to differ in detail once there was no more genetic exchange between separate lines. What is more significant to detect in the evolution of a group such as a taxonomic family or order are the general trends, not the small differences of detail that must exist in order for the group to justify a separate group name.

Hill (1953) reported the skull of notharctines as being "proportionately longer and narrower than in Adapinae," whereas in contrast to this Gazin (1958) remarked that "in a comparison with *Adapis*, one is immediately impressed by the relatively much shorter and broader skull of *Notharctus,* and particularly of *Smilodectes."* The complete oppositon of these statements is in part due to the fact that Gazin had studied much more extensive notharctine cranial material than had Hill, but it is still a good example of the sort of informational handicap awaiting overly accepting readers of this subject. It would still seem to be a good idea, whenever possible before generalizing, to resort to the study of original fossils.

The nasals are longer and more slender in notharctines and do not widen at the nasal aperture as in *Adapis.* The frontals are broadly expanded, particularly in *Smilodectes,* and take up a relatively larger area of the top of the skull. Whereas the frontals of *Adapis* are centrally depressed, those of *Smilodectes* are inflated, *Notharctus* being intermediate in this regard. The sagittal crest is relatively small and the orbits are large in comparison with *Adapis.* The cheek bones are smaller and flare less widely in notharctines. In *Notharctus* and *Smilodectes* a slightly greater portion of the lacrymal lies anterior to the orbital margin than in *Adapis,* but in all three this portion of the bone is unusually restricted for a prosimian. With regard to the teeth of notharctines, the paraconids are more distinct and more in line with the metaconid in *Pelycodus* than in the early adapines, but in some late species of *Notharctus* they are almost completely reduced. Particularly in *Notharctus* the upper molars are anteroposteriorly long and squared in outline. Laterally distinct mesostyles are typically present, as they are in *Caenopithecus* among the adapines. In notharctines the premolars tend toward greater transverse breadth, and the canines are more rounded in cross section. Incisor crowns are relatively smaller and narrower than in *Adapis.* Most Adapidae show a tendency toward early fusion of the mandibular symphysis. Such fusion definitely changes the mechanics of chewing from the situation in primitive mammals generally, where the two halves of the mandible remain separate. Moreover, it would appear that the notharctines may have had freer masticatory excursion, for the mandibular condyles are rounder in members of this subfamily. Notharctines are restricted to the early and middle Eocene of North America, except for *Pelycodus* in France.

Pelycodus

Cope, who published the original description of *Pelycodus* in 1875, originally associated foot bones of a nonprimate with it, and in consequence its affinities were long misunderstood. It was not until 1887 that Schlosser pointed out that the postcranials could not be associated. In 1902, Osborn reported its relationship to middle Eocene *Notharctus.* It soon became apparent that *Pelycodus* gave rise to *Notharctus.* All species of the transition of the older genus to the younger could be elaborately analyzed, for scores of successively younger samples have been collected. More materials indicating this transition appear to exist than for any other short phyletic series known among primates (see Figure 47).

No very complete skulls of *Pelycodus* are known, but there are numerous associated postcranial bones, none, however, represent-

Figure 47   Jaws of *Pelycodus* from the early Eocene of the Bighorn Basin of Wyoming, showing variation to be found among different individuals and species. Scale × 1.5. (From W. K. Gregory, 1920.)

ing very complete individuals. The face was apparently longer and less deep than in *Notharctus*. The lower jaw is long and shallow, and the incisors were probably more procumbent, with a relatively longer, unfused symphysis. The upper molars are more triangular than in its descendants, and the mesostyle and hypocone or pseudohypocone are only incipiently developed. The postcranials, so far as they have been studied, resemble those of *Notharctus*.

Until recently, its distribution was thought to be restricted to the Wasatchian Eocene of North America, but at least some of the isolated teeth from France reported by Russell, Louis, and Savage (1967) under the name of *Cantius* appear to be referable to the North American genus; the British type specimen of the latter genus may not be as close.

According to a recent study by Guthrie (1964, in manuscript), *Pelycodus* can be separated from *Notharctus* by the fact that it shows only rudimentary development of the upper molar hypocones and mesostyles. Moreover, the mandibular symphysis remains open in *Pelycodus*. The genus apparently has two lineages running simultaneously throughout Lysite and Lostcabinian times (the latter two thirds of the Wasatchian), but before that there appears to have been only a single phylum. Guthrie reports that in both lineages the most robust individuals show *Notharctus*-like tendencies, whereas in smaller individual animals development of these structures (mesostyles, hypocones) is less fully expressed. A few of the latest Lysite finds are so far along toward *Notharctus* that they should clearly be referred to the younger genus. Nevertheless, he concludes that earlier authors and curators have treated the entire Lysite sample as being *Pelycodus* because the great majority of such primates from that substage are referable to it. Similarly, the younger Lostcabinian finds have all been placed in *Notharctus* by convention.

As a result of such arbitrary identifications of fossils, by horizon and not anatomy, Guthrie believes that misconceptions have arisen. For instance, he considers that Gazin's (1952) species *Notharctus limosus* results from these poor provisional identifications in the American Museum's specimen labels. Gazin remarked that the chief characteristic of "*Notharctus*" or *Pelycodus limosus* is that "the lower molars average noticeably smaller in size than those in the American Museum specimens of *Notharctus nuniensus* from the Lost Cabin beds." But, according to Guthrie, Gazin's figures for Lostcabinian *Notharctus* are skewed upward in size because they do not include the smaller half of the series, which are there incorrectly labeled as *Pelycodus*. The whole question of the transition from *Pelycodus* to *Notharctus* clearly deserves detailed study. The samples are large because both were common mammals. In fact, the appearance of *Pelycodus* is one of the faunal changes that is used to identify the beginning of the Eocene in North America.

Notharctus

Notharctus was the second New World fossil primate to be described, by Leidy in 1870. The first had been his—*Omomys carteri*, named in 1869. At first, neither was recognized as being assignable to Primates, and, in fact, Leidy made the same mistake Cuvier and other European paleontologists had with *Adapis*, for he suggested that *Notharctus* was a carnivore and in 1872 reported further that it might be an odd-toed pachyderm, but one of carnivorous feeding habits. Meanwhile, Marsh (1872) described his trio of synonyms for *Notharctus*—"*Limnotherium*," "*Thinolestes*," and "*Telmatolestes*"—and by the fall of 1872 had received from Wyoming sufficient material of limb bones to recognize the antomical similarities of these fossils to those of the lemurs. Cope (1872b, 1973) described another synonym of *Notharctus*—"*Tomitherium*"—and by this time both he and

Figure 48 *Notharctus* skull (left) compared to that of *Smilodectes* (cast, right). Species of both genera are closely related, and both are found in the middle Eocene beds of the Bridger Basin of Wyoming. These two related animals are said to differ in that the frontal region of the skull is relatively expanded in *Smilodectes*. Postcranial skeletons in the two are virtually indistinguishable. More is known of the skeletal anatomy of each than for any other Tertiary primates. Scale × 0.75. (Photo courtesy of A. H. Coleman, Yale Peabody Museum.)

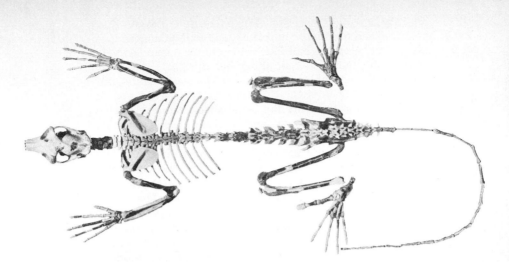

Figure 49 Skeleton of *Notharctus* from the Bridger Basin middle Eocene. Dark-colored bones represent one individual. Light-colored bones are restored. Scale × 0.2, approximately. (From W. K. Gregory, 1920.)

Leidy had recognized some primate resemblances in various members of this suite of "genera," which, however, had to wait until 1899 before their synonymy with *Notharctus* was pointed out by Matthew. Shortly after that, Osborn produced a revision of the American Eocene Primates (1902) in which he accorded this animal full primate status, but still confused the hyopsodont condylarths with primates.

In certain fine-grained sandstones of the Bridger Basin, Wyoming, mammalian fossils are often found as complete or nearly complete skulls and skeletons (see Figure 48). This is a type of occurrence of fossils all too uncommon in the North American early Tertiary. Yet because of it several relatively complete skulls with associated skeletons of *Notharctus* as well as of the closely related genus *Smilodectes* have been found. These finds make species of these two genera the best anatomically understood early Cenozoic primates (see Figure 49). Several extended studies of these materials exist, but the best notharctine postcranial skeleton ever found was recovered recently by Gazin and is yet to be described. In fact, there is so much information on the postcranial skeleton of *Notharctus* in the published literature that a complete review of its anatomy will not be attempted here. The most comprehensive discussions of the whole animal are by Gregory (1920) and Hill (1953), and Gazin (1958) has contributed much new information on the craniology and dental antomy of the notharctines.

Gregory (1920) concluded that the skeleton of *Notharctus* shows reasonably advanced specializations for grasping, leaping, and perching. He remarked: "Hallux strongly divergent, with very large process for attachment of peroneus longus muscle. Finger tips, ungual phalanges and nails more or less expanded. Phalanges elongate, heads of metapodials ball-like. The animals leap actively among the branches but do not sit altogether upright." His study definitely showed the resemblance to modern Malagasy lemurs, but he was probably wrong in suggesting that *Notharctus* did not sit upright. In the skeleton there are the usual seven cervical, twelve thoracic eight lumbar, three sacral, and at least nineteen caudal vertebrae. The lumbar vertebrae have centra that are distinctly elongated from front to back and flattened from top to bottom. The tail vertebrae have (ventrally) chevron bones, and the very long tail presumably performed the same balancing function that it does in the modern vertical clinging and leaping primates. The bones of the pectoral girdle resemble closely those of lemurs, whereas the humerus is relatively short and curved with a comparatively small head. The thumb may have been less divergent than in the present-day prosimians. The femur is a little stouter than modern forms of the same length but is very long relative to the humerus, contributing to a very low intermembral index. No member of Anthropoidea has such a low index as does *Notharctus,* and of those indexes collated by Napier and Napier (1967) and listed below only clinging and leaping forms are close to *Notharctus.* The four living kinds of lorisine primates, some of which at least may well descend from Miocene vertical clingers, have abandoned this type of locomotion, and their intermembral indexes are very different from those of more active primates listed below. Their intermembral indexes are all between 90 and 92.

	Intermembral index (mean)	No. specimens
Notharctus	60–61	2
Avahi	56	4
Euoticus	63	5
Galago	62	10
Hapalemur	65	1
Indri	64	13
Lepilemur	64	6
Propithecus	64	10

Smilodectes

Smilodectes gracilis was distinguished from *Notharctus* by Wortman (1903) because he midunderstood the anterior dental formula. Later, Troxell (1926) and Robinson (1957) both came to the conclusion that the dentition could not be distinguished from that of *Notharctus.* Gazin (1958) reported on some excellent skulls of this species collected from the Bridger Basin by groups working under him. These were associated with much of the postcranial skeleton as well (see Figure 48, page 136). These skulls show a series of distinctions from *Notharctus,* which were reviewed by Gazin. He also determined that the rounded brain case with expanded frontals at Yale also collected from the Bridger Basin and named *Aphanolemur gibbosus* by Granger and Gregory (1917) is a synonym of *Smilodectes.*

In contrast with *Notharctus*, the frontals of *Smilodectes* are broader, are domed upward or inflated, and, seen from the side, give this region of the skull a convex outline; posteriorly, the sagittal and lambdoid crests are less well expressed, and the orbits appear to be more widely spaced apart and are perhaps a little more directed upward than in *Notharctus*—a similarity to *Adapis*. Behind the post-orbital bar, the cheek bones are distinctly deeper and more robust than in *Notharctus*. On the base of the skull the pits between the pterygoid wings are larger, and the bullae of the middle ear are much larger and project farther downward with less space between them.

Dental distinctions are in general slight, but their occurrence is consistent with the cranial features that separate species of the two genera. Typically, the size of the upper teeth relative to overall skull size is smaller in *Smilodectes*. M^3 in *Smilodectes* appears to be somewhat larger relatively with more rectangular outline, probably resulting from a tendency for the hypocone to be comparatively larger. Although Robinson (1957) did not accept a generic distinction, because he published before detailed knowledge of the skulls of *Smilodectes* was available, he did point out that a centrally placed crest on the lower third molars was disposed differently in the two types of primates. Gazin examined collections of *Pelycodus* from the end of the early Eocene (Lostcabinian substage) for individuals that might foreshadow *Smilodectes*, but with little success. According to Robinson, *Smilodectes* survived longer than *Notharctus*, at least in the Bridger Basin deposits.

A composite skeletal mount of *Smilodectes* is on exhibit at the Smithsonian Institution, Washington. This is probably the most completely known pre-Pleistocene primate. As is the case with *Notharctus*, the resemblance of the bones of this animal to those of Malagasy lemurs is remarkable considering their separation in space and time. The limb bones of *Smilodectes* are comparatively heavier, thicker, and more robust than those of *Lemur* or *Propithecus*, the hindlimb was much longer than the forelimb, and both thumb and big toe were fully opposable.

Gazin (1958) pointed out that there is hardly any difference between *Notharctus* and *Smilodectes* in the postcranial skeleton.

ANAPTOMORPHIDAE

The family Anaptomorphidae was first referred to by Cope in 1883, but he gave no description or discussion of it. Later, Wortman (1903, 1904) treated it as a family that included omomyines and *Necrolemur*, as did Simpson (1940), who also placed in it the Microchoerinae (= Necrolemurinae), the Paromomyinae, and, what only he considered a subfamily, Pseudolorisinae. *Microchoerus* and its allies have been generally given subfamilial rank under Anaptomorphidae or within Tarsiidae (see Simons, 1961a), and *Pseudoloris* has been transferred to Anaptomorphidae. Paromomyidae was raised in rank by Simons (1963a) and is here considered to include Phenacolemuridae (Simpson, 1955). Gazin removed the omomyines to a separate family and took the view that the central or typical group remaining in the Anaptomorphidae was that of *Anaptomorphus, Tetonius, Absarokius,* and *Uintanius,* with *Trogolemur, Anemorhysis,* and *Uintalacus* being more divergent. Other forms that have been placed here are *Uintasorex* and its probable junior synonym *Niptomomys* from the early Eocene. Species of the last two genera have usually been considered peripheral or doubtfully referred anaptomorphines. Szalay (1968) has cogently demonstrated that these two are better associated with microsyopids, which he currently considers to be insectivores.

Russell, Louis, and Savage (1967) suggested that the supposed new kind of omomyine *Chlororhysis knightensis,* named by Gazin from a single lower jaw fragment from early Eocene deposits, is better placed among the anaptomorphines. Cheek teeth are not known, but the higher protoconid cusps and the size disparity between P_3 and P_4 are anaptomorphine features. Homomorphic incisor roots appear to be the chief distinction of the species. Both Szalay and I now believe that the type of this species belongs in *Tetonius.*

With these removals and one addition, the anaptomorphines are here dealt with as a much smaller and somewhat more cohesive group. Uncertainties about the number of anterior teeth remain in some species, but it now appears that most if not all anaptomorphines have one or the other of the following dental formulas: $\frac{2.1.3.3.}{2.1.3.3.}$ or $\frac{2.1.2.3.}{2.1.2.3.}$. Consequently, they are not nearly so divergent from omomyines in tooth number as was formerly thought. During the course of preparing this book, it has become apparent to me that two distinct families are not warranted. Such distinctions as there are depend mainly on characteristic and reasonably consistent differences in arragements of cusps and relative parts of teeth. However, if the two known relevant skulls, those of the anaptomorphine *Tetonius* and the omomyine *Rooneyia,* can be taken as reasonably typical of the groups that they represent, at least subfamilial separation seems justified. These two skulls are about as different from each other as either is from *Tarsius.* Both are more like *Tarsius* than they are like the so-called lemuroids.

The dental distinctions of this group, relative to omomyines, are that *Tetonius* and its allies have more inflated or swollen cheek-tooth cusps and upper trigonid basins and lower heels that are less expanded, being generally shorter and narrower. In consequence, the molar cusps are usually less marginally situated on the crowns of the teeth. The manner of posterior de-emphasis of the paraconid typically differs in the two subfamilies. In anaptomorphines like *Tetonius* the M_1 trigonid usually flares widely, the M_2 paraconid and metaconid are approximated, and in M_3 may be coalescent; in omomyines paraconid de-emphasis posteriorly appears to be due to its being more and more shifted toward the midline and decreasing in size from M_1 to M_3. In upper molars anaptomorphids often show the *Nannopithex*-fold seen in the European Eocene tarsiids but not normally in omomyines. Anaptomorphine lower premolars have one high cusp on the trigonid, with little if any development of paraconid and metaconid. In most species P_4^4 are much larger than adjacent teeth, but an awkward exception to this is *Anaptomorphus*, the type of the group. Where there is direct knowledge of lower incisors, the central are usually larger relative to the lateral, whereas in omomyines the relation is the same (larger central pairs) but the size disparity is much less. Both groups reverse the lower incisor proportions of Anthropoidea, where the laterals are larger.

Anaptomorphus

The type species of the genus *Anaptomorphus, A. aemulus* (Figure 50), was named by Cope in 1872. It consisted of a single left mandible with P_4 through M_2 preserved and with the sockets of the other teeth, indicating a dental formula of $\frac{}{2.1.2.3.}$, if one assumes that P_3 is two-rooted. The jaw was found in the lower Bridger beds (middle Eocene) near Ham's Fork, Wyoming. As far as Gazin (1958) could determine, no further material of this species has ever been found—a rather awkward situation for the type of a family and subfamily group. This is because so little of the animal is preserved that one cannot be certain to what extent it really possessed the characteristics of the family to which its name is attached. In fact, much of the concept of this family is based not on *Anaptomorphus* but on *Tetonius,* which is known from scores of specimens. This is particularly true because the skull of *"Anaptomorphus"* (now *Tetonius*) *homunculus* found in Wasatchian deposits of the Bighorn Basin of Wyoming in 1881 by Wortman became almost the sole basis for discussion of the tarsioid affinities of this family (see Cope,

Figure 50 *Stereoview.* Mandibles of *Omomys* (left) and *Anaptomorphus* (right). These represent the type species for the subfamilies Anaptomorphinae and Omomyinae. They are here compared in stereoview in order to show their similarity. Scale × 3.1 approximately. (Photo courtesy of A. H. Coleman, Yale Peabody Museum.)

1881, and Wortman, 1903). This cranium was later made the type of genus *Tetonius* by Matthew (1914).

Wortman also referred some lower jaws in the Marsh collection to Marsh's genus *Euryacodon*, whereas Gazin took the view that these were *Anaptomorphus* but of a species smaller than *A. aemulus*; these he named (1958) *Anaptomorphus wortmani*. Unlike most other anaptomorphids, sensu stricto, the P_4 of *Anaptomorphus* is not particularly enlarged, but as in other members of the group the protoconid is high and the other two trigonid cusps are hardly expressed. The lower molar heels are short and shallow, and the trigonid cusps are inflated and low with comparatively centrally placed cusps. Heels of the premolars are relatively very short. Roots of the anterior teeth suggest that the incisors may have been homomorphic in size and shape and that front teeth were relatively erect, unlike their procumbency in contemporary *Omomys*, which has a mandible about the same size. In probable correlation with more vertical front teeth, the jaw is a little deeper anteriorly. Throughout the dentition the enamel is smooth.

Tetonius

Tetonius is the best-known anaptomorphid primate. There are the one, nearly complete 1881 skull, the type of *Tetonius homunculus* (Figure 51), several isolated maxillae, and many lower jaws totaling over a hundred finds. These fossils come principally from the Bighorn Basin, Wyoming, and from the Four Mile Creek area of Moffat County, Colorado. All were recovered from deposits of early Eocene age. Since 1881, nearly a hundred expeditions to the Bighorn

Figure 51 *Stereoview.* Skull of *Tetonius homunculus* found by Dr. Jacob Wortman in the Bighorn Basin of Wyoming in 1881. It was located in beds of early Eocene age and remains the best-preserved skull of an anaptomorphine yet found. Scale × 3.0. (Photo courtesy of L. Radinsky.)

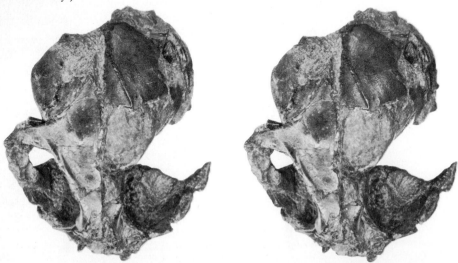

Basin have failed to turn up another skull of *Tetonius*. This skull is the oldest primate skull of modern aspect known, being the only known Wasatchian primate skull apart from cranial fragments of *Pelycodus*. Cope initially recognized it as a prosimian and considered its nearest ally among living forms to be *Tarsius*, noting that they shared several features unusual for prosimians. Wortman (1903, 1904) first listed a series of these features of resemblance, which can be tabulated as follows:

1. The entocarotid canal crosses the auditory bulla and opens far forward on the medial side of the bulla.
2. The malar does not unite with the lachrymal.
3. The lacrymal is relatively large and extends out on the face.
4. The external opening of the tear duct is outside the orbit.
5. The auditory bullae are inflated and are overlapped by the external wings of the pterygoids.
6. Overall tooth structure resembles that of *Tarsius*.
7. There is no tooth comb and the face is bent down on the basicranial axis as in *Tarsius*.
8. Both are similar in showing small size, coupled with orital enlargement.

Radinsky (1967) has recently reported on the anatomy of the natural endocranial cast preserved in this skull. The olfactory bulbs were larger than those of modern prosimians of about the same size such as *Microcebus* or *Tarsius*, but compared with primitive mammals generally were diminutive. In summary, he remarks: "The endocast of *Tetonius* indicates that as far back as 55 million years ago, at the very beginning of the primate radiation that gave rise to lemuroids and tarsioids, a remarkably modern type of brain had already evolved. At a time when ungulates had brains no more advanced, as far as external morphology shows, than that of a modern opossum . . . *Tetonius* had developed the enlarged temporal and occipital lobes and reduced olfactory bulbs that characterize all known primate brains . . . . The occurrence of enlarged occipital and temporal cortical areas in such old tarsioid and lemuroid prosimians as *Tetonius* and *Smilodectes* suggests that expansion of those regions, which are involved in optic and auditory function respectively, may have been one of the critical adaptations responsible for the Early Eocene radiation of the Primates."

At least some individuals of *Tetonius* have lost all but two pairs of premolars. There clearly was more than one species of the genus existing in North America in early Eocene times. The group is currently being revised by Szalay. The dental formula of *Tetonius homunculus* is typically $\frac{2.1.2.3.}{2.1.(2. \text{ or } 3).3.}$. The anterior incisor pairs are enlarged and spatulate, flanked by smaller lateral incisors. As in microchoerines and omomyines, C_1^1 are relatively small; in this, all three groups differ from all living non-hominid primates except the tarsier.

Tetonius (Figure 51) and, by extension from it, other anaptomorphines show significant resemblance to *Tarsius*. They therefore can rightly be called tarsioid. For instance, the cranial and dental

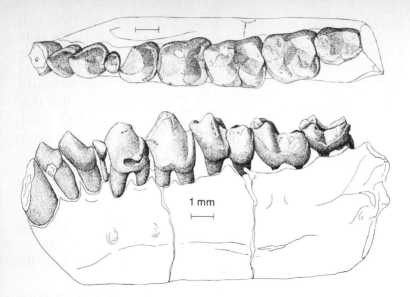

Figure 52 Mandibular dentition with remarkably well-preserved teeth ascribed to *?Tetonoides* but probably of *Tetonius*. It was recovered in the early Eocene Willwood formation, Bighorn Basin, Wyoming. (From Peter Robinson, 1967.)

anatomy of *Tetonius* is far more like that of *Tarsius* than is that of similarly adapted small members of Lorisiformes such as *Galago*, and therefore these resemblances are less easy to write off as parallelism.

Tetonoides

Gazin described *Tetonoides pearcei* as a new taxon in 1962, based on fossils collected on the east and west flanks of the Rock Springs uplift of Southwestern Wyoming. The type was found in what are thought to be earliest Eocene deposits (Graybullian substage of the Wasatch). Gazin's principal basis for generic distinction of *Tetonoides* from *Tetonius* was the slightly smaller size of this form and its possession of P_2. Nevertheless, study of the materials of *Tetonius*, sensu lato, in various collections suggests that there was progressive loss of P_2^2 in one subgroup, and in another, which evidently led to *Absarokius*, this never happened. It may become necessary to transfer the type species of *Tetonoides* to *Tetonius*, according to Szalay. An excellent mandible of this primate (Figure 52) was recently described by Robinson (1967). This specimen is important in confirming the anaptomorph lower dental formula. Butler (1963) has shown that normally tooth reduction in mammals takes place first in teeth adjacent to the canine. In this interpretation, the dental formula of this specimen can only be $\overline{2.1.3.3.}$.

Absarokius

The genus *Absarokius* was named for a species that had earlier

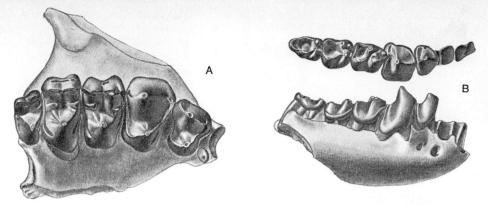

Figure 53 Upper and lower dentition of *Absarokius*. Specimens recovered from late early Eocene deposits in Wyoming. Scale (A) × 5.25 and (B) × 4.0. (From C. Lewis Gazin, 1962.)

been called *Anaptomorphus abbotti* by Matthew from the Lysite middle Wasatchian beds of the Bighorn Basin and for a much rarer species, *Absarokius noctivagus*, from the Lostcabinian late Wasatchian. The dental formula is probably $\frac{2.1.3.3.}{2.1.3.3.}$, judging from the specimens at Yale (see Figure 53). This is the second most abundant anaptomorphine after *Tetonius*; probably more than seventy-five specimens are known. It has usually been assumed that *Absarokius* was derived from a species of *Tetonius* in which there was no tendency toward loss of anterior teeth. In addition to a slightly larger overall size of comparable parts than *Tetonius*, *Absarokius* has relatively much larger P_4^4 and smaller M_3^3.

Guthrie (1967), who studied a large sample of *Absarokius abbotti* from the Wind River Basin of Wyoming, found little variation in cusp detail but did find one specimen that had complete lingual cingula on the upper molars not present in other individuals, a phenomenon that admirers of genus *Proconsul* should note. Some individuals have considerable crenulation in the talonid heels, and this tendency seems yet more pronounced in a middle Eocene species, *Absarokius witteri*, described by Morris (1954).

Absarokius noctivagus from the Lostcabinian stages is seemingly intermediate between the other two species.

Uintalacus, Uintanius, and Trogolemur

The types of the three genera *Uintalacus*, *Uintanius*, and *Trogolemur* (see Figure 54) appear to be anaptomorphids but have little in common other than that they are all known from very limited published samples—*Uintalacus* (one), *Trogolemur* (two), and *Uintanius* (three or four). I cannot see that *Huerfanius* (Robinson, 1966) is generically distinct from *Uintanius*.

Uintalacus comes from the late Wasatch deposits (Lostcabinian stage) northeast of Powder Springs, Uintah County, Utah. It differs from *Tetonius* and *Anemorhysis* in relatively minor features and may not be separate from the former genus, according to Szalay.

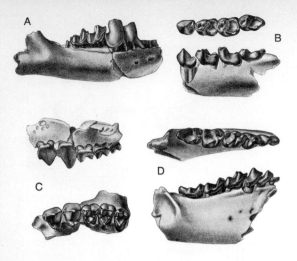

Figure 54 Comparison of the Eocene anaptomorphine prosimians *Uintanius* (A: Right lower jaw fragment. C: Lateral and occlusal views of left maxilla.), *Uintalacus* (B: Left jaw fragment, external and crown views.), and *Trogolemur* (D: Right jaw fragments with premolars and molars, external and crown views.). Scale (A, C) × 2.6 and (B, D) × 3.2 approximately. (From C. Lewis Gazin, 1958.)

Trogolemur comes from middle Eocene deposits in the Bridger Basin. *Trogolemur* is smaller than, and is different from, all other anaptomorphines in that the enlarged incisor root reaches all the way back under the molars. P_4 is not enlarged.

Anemorhysis and *Chlorohysis*

Gazin (1958) named the type of *Anemorhysis*. It is a mandibular fragment from the late Wasatchian Knight Formation of Southwestern Wyoming. He further referred a species Matthew described in 1914 as of *Tetonius* to this genus as *Anemorhysis muscula*. *Anemorhysis* seems to me to be closer to *Tetonius* than is *Tetonoides*, and therefore could not stand as a separate genus.

Chlororhysis knightensis comes from the same formation as the foregoing species. Only one half of a lower jaw with four teeth in it is known. The species was originally described as an omomyine, but is an anaptomorphine. The lower dental formula is probably $\frac{}{2.1.3.3.}$. The sole mandibular fragment may well prove to be assignable to *Tetonius*. Szalay (personal communication) has recently come independently to the same conclusion that both of these genera belong in *Tetonius*.

Gazin (1958) raised Omomyinae to family rank; this group of primates was first defined somewhat differently by Trouessart (1879) as a subfamily. Family status for these primates was accepted by McKenna (1967) but not by Russell, Louis, and Savage (1967). The group is rather vaguely characterized and is perhaps not as differentiated from the North American Anaptomorphidae as was implied by the former use of separate families for the two groups. Anaptomorphinae and Omomyinae are here ranked as subfamiles under Anaptomorphidae. The dental characteristics of the anaptomorphines could have arisen rather rapidly from an omomyine-like base, but we do not yet have enough dental evidence on this possibility. Moveover, both subfamilies are much more poorly known from cranial and postcranial material than are the Adapidae. Therefore, we are unable to show whether or not they differed in skeletal construction as much as they did dentally. The dental adaptations of the anaptomorphines (enlarged central incisors, variable loss of I_2 and P_2, and enlarged fourth premolars) suggest different feeding adaptations than omomyines (with enlarged talonid basins, tendencies toward wrinkling of tooth enamel, and development of additional cuspules on the cheek teeth). In all but one of the omomynes where information as to the number of teeth is available, the dental formula is a uniform $\frac{2.1.3.3.}{2.1.3.3.}$. Although the first pair of upper and lower incisors is usually larger than the second pair, there is no tendency toward development of procumbent, rodent-like front incisors, and incisor enamel is restricted to the crown. In those species where canines are known, both upper and lower are relatively small. Premolars in the lower series tend to have well-formed trigonid cusps and distinctly developed heels. There is no trend toward enlargement of P_4. In lower molars the trigonid cusps are conical, and there is a tendency for the relative size of the paraconid to decrease posteriorly in the molar series. The molar heels, or talonid basins, are large and particularly expanded transversely on the lower second molars, frequently giving this particular tooth a rounded outline. This is reminiscent of the general condition in second lower molars of primitive Anthropoidea. Compared with many other primates, the third lobes of M_3 heels are relatively unexpanded in most species. Primitively, as in *Omomys*, the upper molars show three principal cusps and the protocone is large. Internal molar shelves or cingula are typically well expressed and show a tendency toward development of an anterior cingular cusp, the pericone, a structure infrequently seen among living primate species other than some South American monkeys. The little known Paleocene primate *Navajovius* has conventionally been placed in this group by Simpson (1940) and Gazin (1958), but Szalay's studies suggest that it is certainly not very close to the Eocene omomyines.

Traditionally, most of the omomyines have been classified as tarsier-like or "tarsioids" (for instance, see Abel, 1931 or Hill, 1953). Both Simpson (1940, 1955) and I (Simons, 1963a) have criticized the practice of placing almost all of the small early Tertiary primates in relation to the modern Southeast Asian form. Where the skeleton is partly known, as in *Hemiacodon*, omomyines show no definite resemblance to *Tarsius*.

Omomyines have a holarctic distribution; that is, they appear to be restricted to the Northern Hemisphere. Their early presence in Europe stands confirmed by the very close resemblance among *Teilhardina* of the Belgian early Eocene, North American *Omomys* and *Loveina*, and other less completely known Eocene primates such as *Periconodon* from Switzerland and *Lushius* from China—all these show indistinct metaconules, well-developed protocones, and distinct periconid cusps. In consequence, they are more reasonably placed with this group than elsewhere. To me they seem at least as morphologically close, if not closer, to *Omomys* than is the North American omomyine *Shoshonius*.

Omomys (See Figure 55)

Omomys was the first-discovered member of the subfamily. *Omomys carteri* was described by Leidy in 1869. Leidy was initially confused by incorrectly associated fragments of a skull cap, probably referable to the condylarth *Hyopsodus*. From the size of the temporal fossae in this fragment, he took the animal to have possible relationships with carnivores. Moreover, he did consider the type jaw fragment most similar to that of *Tupaia* but otherwise compared the dentition generally to that of various insectivores.

The type specimen of *Omomys carteri*, along with numerous subsequent finds of this species, came from the middle Eocene deposits of the Bridger Basin. Several specimens show the lower dental formula to be $\frac{2.1.3.3.}{}$. The lower incisors are rather more procumbent than in other omomyines, and the lower jaw horizontal rami are very shallow. Wortman (1903, 1904) placed two additional species, *Omomys pucillus* (which proved to be a large individual of *Omomys carteri*) and *Omomys ameghini* (actually a specimen of *Uintanius*), in the genus.

Two further early Eocene species, *Omomys minutus* and *Omomys vespertinus*, were later established. Simpson (1940) considered that the latter of these two should probably be transferred to his then-new genus *Loveina*, but neither Gazin (1958) or Russell, Louis, and Savage (1967) accept this possibility.

Retention of the Wasatch species of the genus is seemingly correct, and this makes *Omomys* an unusually long-ranging form.

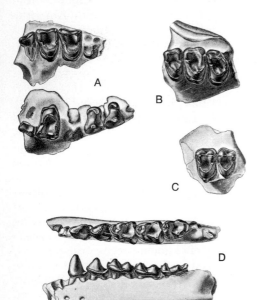

Figure 55 Various maxillary fragments (*A, B,* and *C*) and a left mandibular ramus (*D*) of *Omomys* from the Bridger Basin (middle Eocene) deposits of Wyoming. Note that the protocone of M² has a pericone cusp on its internal face. Scale × 2.35. (From C. Lewis Gazin, 1958.)

A further extension is possible, because *Chumashus*, named by Stock in 1933 on the basis of a half-dozen jaw fragments from the late Eocene of California, is apparently very close to *Omomys*.

Loveina

The type of *Loveina zephyri* was recovered from Wind River Basin, Lost Cabin Beds, by D. E. Love. It is of early Eocene age and was described by Simpson in 1940.

Loveina is distinguished from its contemporary *Omomys vespertinus* by its smaller size and more wrinkled crown enamel. In *Loveina* the anterior symphyseal region is deep, and the long axes of the incisor alveoli indicate that these teeth were probably much less procumbent than in *Omomys*. Published literature makes no reference to specimens apart from the type jaw. F. S. Szalay now believes that the type specimen of *Loveina* should be referred to *Omomys*.

Hemiacodon (See Figure 56)

The sole species of the genus *Hemiacodon, H. gracilis*, was described by Marsh in 1872. It occurs in middle Eocene deposits of the Bridger Basin of Wyoming. This is a medium-sized Eocene prosimian, smaller than most Adapidae but larger than several other omomyids. It probably had about the same order of body size as Eocene *Necrolemur* or modern *Tarsius*. Many lower jaws and maxillae are known. None of these, to my knowledge, preserves the anterior upper teeth, but the Smithsonian collections do include a partial facial fragment. This specimen shows that the orbits were large with a slightly everted dorsal rim, resembling *Necrolemur*. The frontals are broad and flat, except for a slight central doming. The orbits seem to be relatively larger and closer together than in *Notharctus*. Two other species of the genus were named by Marsh—*Hemiacodon nanus* and *Hemiacodon pucillus*. The types of both of these are referable to *Omomys carteri* whereas the *Hemiacodon pygmaeus* of Wortman actually is an individual of *Washakius*.

Gazin (1958) and other authors, such as Simpson (1940), considered this genus definitely related to the smaller and partly earlier species of *Omomys* on the basis that extensive dental resemblance between the two justifies reference to one subfamily. In contrast with *Omomys*, the teeth of *Hemiacodon* show a characteristic enamel wrinkling or crinkling, cusps are somewhat more acute or better defined, and there is a clear-cut tendency to develop accessory cuspules on the cheek teeth. Molar protocones sometimes show an angularly placed posterior crest running down toward the basal cingulum but distinct from it. This is the so-called *Nannopithex*-fold, also seen in *Notharctus*, some anaptomorphines, and typically in the European microchoerines. Larger hypocones on M^1 and M^2 give these teeth a more rectangular outline than in *Omomys*. In *Hemiacodon*, M^3 is smaller than M^2 but not as reduced relatively as in *Omomys*. In 1905, Granger found on Henry's Fork in the Bridger Basin partial skeletal remains that Simpson (1940) tentatively considered to belong to *Hemiacodon*. His identification of these bones as *Hemiacodon* is con-

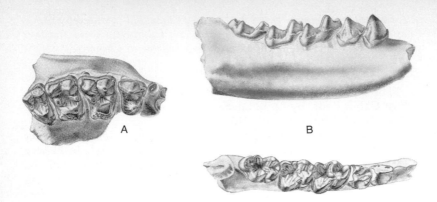

Figure 56 Maxilla of *Hemiacodon* (*A*) and mandible of *Hemiacodon* (*B*) from the middle Eocene Bridger beds of Wyoming. This genus and *Omomys* are the commonest omomyine prosimians. Scale × 2.6. (From C. Lewis Gazin, 1958.)

firmed by calcanea and tali of the same kind associated with partial dentitions of *Hemiacodon* in the Marsh collection at Yale. These skeletal remains provide more information about the postcranial skeleton than we have for any other omomyine. As has already been discussed, a confusion as to whether Eocene primates more closely resembled tarsiers or lemurs has long figured in the literature on early primates. *Hemiacodon* was usually considered a "tarsioid" prosimian, so that Simpson's (1940) resolution of its postcranial anatomy was much needed. In brief, he found that *Hemiacodon* was not particularly like *Tarsius* but rather resembled lemurs or lorises or was like early Tertiary mammals generally. Even so, this could always have been due to a relatively recent acquisition of the postcranial characteristics of *Tarsius* in its own lineage. Granger's find consisted of parts of the hindlimb of one individual, some associated vertebrae, and limb elements of a second individual. The vertebrae were uninformative apart from their definite prosimian affinities and the fact that several had strong keels or median ridges on the centra. The foot of *Hemiacodon* was somewhat elongate, a springing adaptation, but its structure is as much like that of galagos as of tarsiers. In consequence, the postcranium of this species provides little evidence as to the relationships of the omomyines. This is not the sort of foot that one might expect to find in an immediate ancestor of the quadrupedal cercopithecoid monkeys.

Washakius

Washakius insignis, named by Leidy in 1873, comes from the Bridger beds (middle Eocene) of Wyoming. Gazin (1958) concluded that the type of the species, *Yumanius woodringi,* described by Stock in 1938, should be referred to *Washakius.* The dental formula is

Figure 57 *Washakius.* This Eocene primate from the Bridger beds of Wyoming is distinguished from most contemporary forms by the presence of a metastylid on the metaconids of the lower molars. *A:* Left maxilla. *B:* External and crown view of mandible. Scale × 4.0. (From C. Lewis Gazin, 1958.)

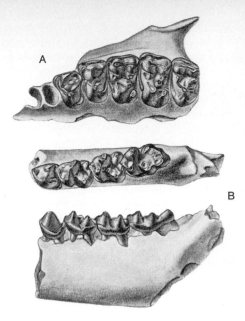

$\frac{2.?1.3.3.}{2.\ 1.3.3.}$. This species is like most other omomyines in having tooth enamel that is wrinkled or rugose and in exhibiting a tendency toward development of accessory cuspules. The most distinctive dental feature is the presence of an extra small cusp (the metastylid) on the back of the metaconid. This cuspule is also found in the omomyids *Dyseolemur* and *Shoshonius,* which are apparently closely related to *Washakius.* Such a cusp is common in ungulates but is almost never seen among primates (see Figure 57).

Anatomy, other than dental, is poorly known in *Washakius,* but one of the most complete maxillae preserves part of the ventral rim of the orbit. In this particular specimen the cheek bone (malar or jugal) ends short of the lachrymal, as in *Tarsius* and unlike the general condition among lemurs.

Dyseolemur pacificus, recovered from a Uintan equivalent in Ventura County, California, and named by Stock in 1934, is a little younger than *Washakius* but differs from it in relatively minor features.

Roots indicate that the incisors of *Washakius* were comparatively vertically implanted and were subequal in size. This, together with the wrinkled, crowded, and polycuspidate teeth, also seen in *Dyseolemur,* suggests that this particular subgroup may have been trending toward more hervivorous feeding. Gazin thought them to be near the source of the Ceboidea.

Shoshonius

The type maxilla of *Shoshonius cooperi* was found by C. Forster-Cooper, later Director of the British Museum of Natural History, and was named by Granger (1910). Four years later, Matthew described several lower jaws, one of which was associated with a single upper molar. None of these preserved anterior teeth. The type came from the Lost Cabin beds of the Wind River Basin of Wyoming and is therefore of latest early Eocene age. All who have studied them consider *Shoshonius* closely related to *Washakius* of middle Eocene age. *Shoshonius* is usually said to be distinguished from *Washakius* in the upper dentition by the presence of mesostyles between the lateral molar cusps. In both genera, crown enamel is markedly wrinkled. Mesostyles are flexures of the ridges between paracone and metacone that have repeatedly arisen among groups of mammals whose ancestors lacked them. Thus the development of mesostyles, rare among early primates other than *Notharctus, Smilodectes,* and *Caenopithecus,* would be an advance over the general primitive condition, and any subsequent loss would be a reversion. It is for this reason that one can reject the idea that middle Eocene *Washakius,* which is said not to have mesostyles, could be directly derived from *Shoshonius.* This is also true for late Eocene *Dyseolemur,* which lacks mesostyles. Nevertheless, differences in the three are restricted mostly to features of the M_3 heel, a notoriously variable area (intraspecifically). Moreover, Gazin (1958) even reports that *Washakius* sometimes does show mesostyles. Species of these three genera form a close-knit group.

In the lower dentitions they share the possession of a metastylid behind the metaconid, a feature rare in other primates, but they differ in that *Shoshonius* has a M_3 heel with a single hypoconulid cusp, asymmetrically placed. In *Washakius* there is a third lobe of M_3 with two or three separate cusps, and in *Dyseolemur* the heel is monocuspid and somewhat more symmetrical.

Macrotarsius

Macrotarsius montanus was described by Clark in 1941 and is based on a sole right jaw ramus with premolars and molars preserved and the roots or sockets of the anterior teeth. This is one of only two primate species known to survive into the Oligocene in North America. The dental formula, $\overline{2.1.3.3.}$, is that typical of omomyids, in which the central lower incisors are larger than the lateral (this proportion is reversed in Anthropoidea) and the lower canines are relatively small and premolariform, although larger than adjacent teeth. This species is the largest of the omomyids. The entire tooth row from front to back was about 1 inch long.

The one known specimen was found at Pipestone Springs, Jefferson County, Montana, in Chadronian (lower Oligocene) deposits.

Clark (1941) considered this genus more like *Hemiacodon* than any other, but clearly distinct from it. This species is divergent in the nearly vertical alignment of canines and incisors, the comparatively small M_2, and the long but narrow M_3 hypoconulid.

Robinson (1968) has described another species of the genus from late Eocene localities in the Badwater Creek area of Wyoming. He considers that *Macrotarsius* evolved from *Hemiacodon, Ourayia,* or the same general stock, and has commented on the striking dental resemblance to South American monkeys such as *Alouatta.*

Teilhardina (See Figure 58)

Teilhard de Chardin (1926), in reviewing the early Eocene Sparnacian faunas of Oursmael, Belgium, first described *Teilhardina,* but called it *Omomys belgicus.* The species is known from many lower jaws, at least one upper jaw, and several isolated teeth. Teilhard figured a calcaneum and talus from Oursmael as possibly belonging to *Teilhardina belgica.* The calcaneum does resemble that of *Hemiacodon,* but the talus does not and may not belong to this species. In 1940, Simpson recognized its generic distinction and named it *Teilhardina.* In 1958, I realized that Simpson and Teilhard de Chardin had both confused an insectivore ramus with the remaining material of *Teilhardina* and thus both derived the wrong dental formula. The insectivore jaw shows three incisor alveoli and alveoli for three premolars only, whereas *Teilhardina* shows two incisor alveoli and has four premolars.

Since 1940 many additional mandibles have been found but have not been fully described. These have been dealt with to some extent by Quinet (1966). Unfortunately, Teilhard de Chardin created in 1927 a valid senior objective synonym to *Teilhardina* at the end of his article, where in passing he suggested that *Omomys belgicus* could be placed in a new genus *Protomomys.* A request for suppression of this unused name, which otherwise would have to supplant *Teilhardina,* has been submitted to the Commission on Nomenclature. Most authors have pointed out the close similarities to North American *Omomys,* but there is one dental difference, in that P_1 is definitely present in some individuals, whereas this tooth never occurs in the North American Anaptomorphidae. My observations did not confirm the conclusion of Quinet (1966) that there are three incisors, a condition as yet unproven for any early Tertiary primate. The P_1, when present, is situated lateral to the long axis of

Figure 58 Unassociated upper-tooth series of *Teilhardina* from the early Eocene of Belgium. The teeth of *Teilhardina* closely resemble those of North American anaptomorphids, but the Belgian species seems to have retained four sets of premolars above and below, unlike the American forms. Scale × 15.0 approximately. (Drawing by E. L. Simons.)

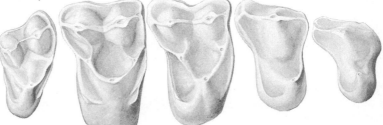

the remaining teeth, a situation also exhibited by the smallest anterior tooth of microchoerines.

Russell, Louis, and Savage (1967) described a second larger species, *T. gallica*, from the Avenay Quarry of French Sparnacian age. These authors suggest a resemblance between *Teilhardina* and an upper dentition figured by Seton (1940), which Gazin (1958) thought might belong to *Loveina* (the type is a mandible). They also suggest that a mandible figured by McKenna (1960) and considered by him to be cf. *Anemorhysis minutus* shows resemblance to *Teilhardina*. They further conclude that McKenna's jaw is not an *Anemorhysis*, but an omomyine.

Szalay (personal communication) has recently suggested that *Teilhardina* is not an omomyine but an anaptomorphine closely related to *Tetonius* from the North American Wasatchian. This seems quite improbable in view of the marked differences the two exhibit in incisor size and dental formula; P_4^4 are not enlarged as in *Tetonius* and morphology in premolar–molar crowns of *Teilhardina* is clearly closer to omomyines. Finally, the idea stressed by Hürzeler (1948) that *Teilhardina* is in or near ancestry of the microchoerines seems unlikely, as does the even more colorful deduction of Quinet (1966) that this species was ancestral to all the Old World Anthropoidea.

Utahia and Stockia

Utahia kayi (Figure 59) was described in 1958 by Gazin. The locality of the type is in the lower Bridger beds, 2 miles southeast of Powder Springs, Uintah County, Utah. In Gazin's view this form is intermediate between *Hemiacodon* and *Washakius* but possibly closer to the former. It is known from three fragmentary jaws and one doubtfully referred upper molar.

Because *Utahia* is apparently older than *Hemiacodon* of the upper Bridger beds, Gazin suggested that it might be its ancestor but thought that this possibly was weighed against by the relatively

Figure 59 Comparison of *Utahia* (A) and *Stockia* (B). These two genera from the North American Eocene of California appear to be related to *Washakius* and *Hemiacodon*. Scale $\times$ 4.0. (From C. Lewis Gazin, 1958.)

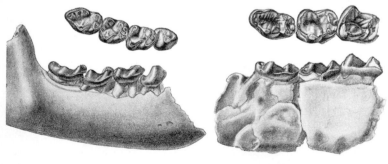

A   B

short M_{2-3} trigonids of *Utahia*, those of *Hemiacodon* being longer—a supposedly more generalized condition.

Stockia powayensis Gazin (1958) comes from a late Eocene site near San Diego Mission, California. The name is based on two lower jaw fragments and one lower molar, which were originally considered by Stock to be the mandibular dentition of his species *Yumanuis woodringi*, the type of which was a partial upper dentition. According to Gazin, this type is a synonym of *Washakius*, as discussed above. However, Gazin considered the jaw fragments distinctive and therefore coined the name *Stockia* for their reception. From Gazin's figures and discussion, it is clear that *Stockia* resembles both *Utahia* and *Hemiacodon*. Russell, Louis, and Savage (1967) consider that *Stockia* is very close to *Hemiacodon*. To a relative outsider, as far as the taxonomic arrangements of the California Eocene primates are concerned, it would seem that there is a high probability that further generic synonyms for them will be determined.

Ourayia (See Figure 60)

Ourayia was named by Gazin in 1958; originally its species type had been called *"Microsyops" uintensis* (see Osborn, 1902). It is another form seemingly related to *Hemiacodon* but is younger and at least 15 to 20 per cent larger in comparable parts. The type comes from the Upper Eocene White River pocket, near Ouray in the Uinta Basin, Utah. It is generally like *Hemiacodon* but clearly differs in lower molar outline and construction. In *Hemiacodon* molar and premolar cusps are typically more conical and divergent from the body of the tooth. The posterolateral tilt of the hypoconid, along with the high, lingually placed metaconid, gives M_{1-2} of *Hemiacodon* an almost W-shaped appearance in crownview. Thus, *Hemiacodon* never shows the rounded molar outline seen particularly in M_2 and characteristic of *Ourayia*.

In 1961, I described an excellent palatal and mandibular dentition of *Ourayia* in the Princeton collections from the same White River Beds in Utah from which the type of this species was recovered. The determination that this specimen was *Ourayia* was originally made by Robinson and then concurred with by myself, by Gazin (1958), and by others. Recently, Robinson (1968) has suggested the transfer of this nearly complete Princeton dentition to a new species of *Hemiacodon* that he concedes is phyletically intermediate between *Hemiacodon* and the type specimen of *Ourayia uintensis*, which he leaves as the sole representative of that species. The Princeton specimen is from the same horizon and geographic area as the type, is of similar size, and differs only in that the paraconid of M_2 is poorly expressed in the type but clearly present in the lower molars of the Princeton dentition. Examination of a series of *Hemiacodon* jaws shows a high degree of variation in position and degree of expression of the paraconid, and the same could well be true for species of *Ourayia*. Robinson's discussion and figures are enthusiastic in emphasizing ties between the Princeton specimen and

Figure 60 Comparison of the lower and upper dentition of a generalized mammal, *Ptilocercus* (A and B) with that of *Ourayia* (C and D), an Eocene prosimian. *Ourayia* has been collected from late Eocene deposits in the *White River* pocket near Ouray in the Uinta Basin, Utah. Scale (A, B) × 4.5 and (C, D) × 3.1. (Drawing by Martha Ericson.)

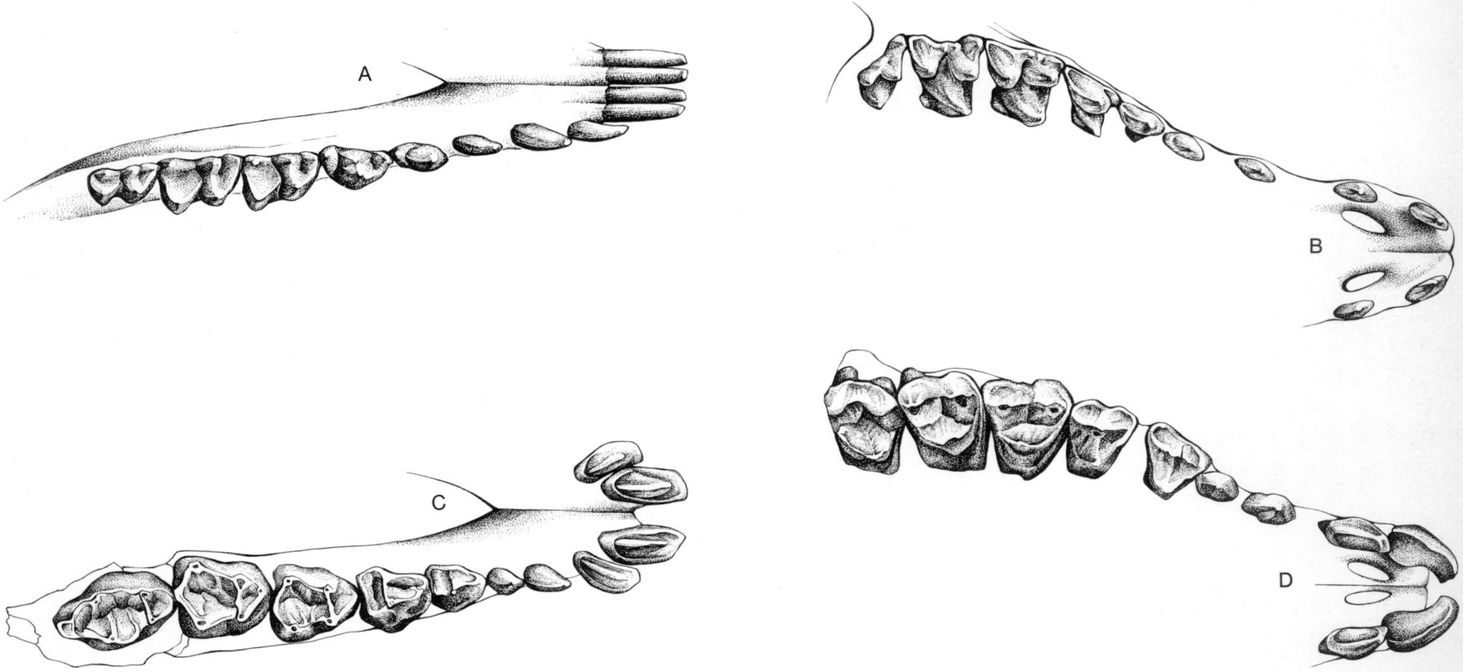

Hemiacodon. In fact, if this specimen represents a species of *Hemiacodon*, then so does the type of his *Mytonius hopsoni*, according to recent observations of Szalay, with whom I agree. Robinson stressed the lesser development of the cristid obliqua on M_{1-2} of the type of *Ourayia*, but this is a heavily worn area in that individual—unworn, the crest would have been more distinct. He also makes diagnostic of the supposed new species "tooth enamel crenulate" and speaks of the smoothness of the teeth of *Ourayia*. His figure of the type of this species shows practically no indication of crenulation. Interestingly, Gazin (1958, Plate 13) figures the same specimen with more crenulation indicated on P_4-M_2 than exists in the Princeton specimen (see Simons 1961b) supposed to be different and more crenulate than the type. This digression as to the taxonomic placement of the Princeton *Ourayia* has been necessary because it is an important find documenting dental anatomy among omomyines. Were it just another variant of *Hemiacodon*, its scientific value might be less. As far as I can see, *Mytonius*, described by Robinson in the same paper, is also a synonym of *Ourayia uintensis*.

The remaining portion of the snout in the Princeton find of *Ourayia* is crushed so that little can be determined about the palate. Nevertheless, almost all of the right premaxilla is preserved, and the suture between it and the maxilla can be seen on both sides. As in both *Aegyptopithecus* and *Rooneyia*, which are only a little younger than *Ourayia*, the ascending flange of the premaxilla is large and broad, indicating that there had been little if any retreat of the nasal apertures. Between these well-developed ascending premaxillary wings what remains of the anterior ends of long nasal bones can be seen. Something of the rim of the right orbit remains in this specimen (the orbital opening is filled with matrix). The jugal is missing and the rim is weathered and broken, but the definite impression is given that the orbit was quite large relative to the size of the snout. Moreover, the vertical depth of the snout above the canine was clearly greater than the front-to-back distance for the edge of the nasal opening to the border of the orbital cavity. Thus, this find, like the skull of *Rooneyia*, gives evidence that at least some omomyine possessed short, relatively deep snouts, even when the premaxillae were large.

Rooneyia

The primate genus *Rooneyia* has a type species, *R. viejaensis* (Figure 61), that in turn is known from a single nearly complete cranium recently discovered by J. A. Wilson in West Texas. No mandibles were found. In addition to its uniqueness as a single specimen, the discovery comes from a time and place in which primates are very poorly known. The skull was found in a stratigraphic zone of the Chambers Tuff formation, Presidio County, Texas, for which there are K/Ar dates both above and below the level of the cranium. These geochemical dates fix its age at about 35 million years.

The only other primates in North America that survived beyond

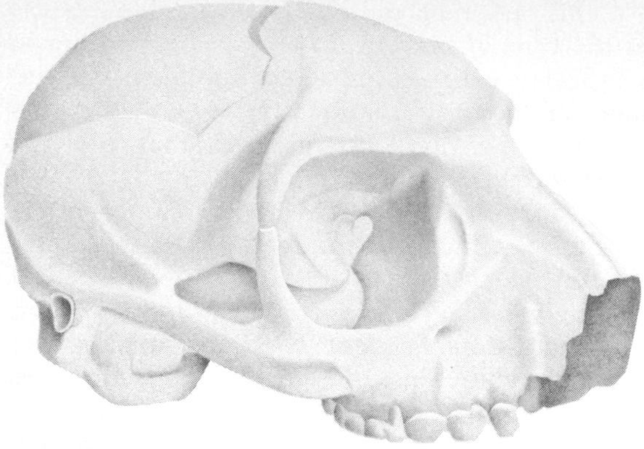

Figure 61 Cranium of *Rooneyia*. This is the only Oligocene primate skull ever found in North America. Scale × 2.0 approximately. (Drawing by Carl Wester, Yale Peabody Museum.)

the onset of Duchesnean times (latest Eocene) are *Chumashius* of the latter age, perhaps about 40 million years old, *Rooneyia* and *Macrotarsius* of the earliest Oligocene, and *Ekgmowechashala* of early Miocene times, about 25 million years old. None of the other three late-surviving omomyines are known from published upper dentitions, but their lower dental patterns are such that they would seem to have little affinity with *Rooneyia*. The newly described early Oligocene platyrrhine *Branisella* from Santa Cruz age deposits in Bolivia also shares few dental features with *Rooneyia*, at least no more than can be found in the even more distantly distributed and surely remotely related early Oligocene Old World monkey *Apidium* from the Fayum, North Africa.

This cranium shows a combination of features typically considered "advanced"—or, more properly, like Anthropoidea—such as an ossified auditory tube and incipient postorbital closure, together with resemblances to a variety of large-eyed Eocene prosimians and some unique structural conditions as well.

The dental formula of *Rooneyia* presents some problems of interpretation because externally the maxillary–premaxillary suture runs between two single rooted more-or-less equal sized and apparently caniniform teeth. On the palatal surface this suture runs alongside and partly anterior to the more forward tooth. Thus it seems difficult to assert that this tooth is entirely located or rooted in the premaxilla, as Wilson (1966) does. On the palatal surface the premaxillary–maxillary suture meets this tooth near the anterior end, so that a good part of its root at least must lie close to if not in the maxilla. The ascending branch of the premaxilla is unusually broad for a primitive primate and possibly superficially overlaps the anterior end of the maxilla. In any case, interpretation of this tooth as an incisor would give the animal three upper incisors, a condition unknown in any other primate and hardly possible for a mid-Tertiary species. Furthermore, *Rooneyia* resembles earlier omomyines in several different ways, and all students have agreed it is best considered an omomyine. In all cases where lower canines are known in omomyines they are small, almost premolariform, upper canines (where known) in *Hemiacodon* and *Ourayia* are also small, an unusual condition among primates but also found in *Rooneyia*.

The *Rooneyia* skull is by far the most complete omomyine skull ever found and one of the most complete fossil primate skulls known from the New World. Wilson (1964) has described it very thoroughly. It presents a rather unique combination of features consistent with its being a representative of a distinct family and is not particularly close to the early Eocene cranium of the anaptomorphid prosimian *Tetonius*, found in the Bighorn Basin of Wyoming in 1881. Unlike all other New World primates except *Plesiadapis*, *Rooneyia* has a tubular external auditory meatus. This is probably an acquisition that arose in parallel with that of its European partial contemporaries the microchoerines. Inasmuch as the earliest catarrhine skull, that of *Aegyptopithecus*, a form only a little younger than *Rooneyia*, lacks this tube, and inasmuch as the New World monkeys have never acquired it, ancestors of Anthropoidea clearly did not have such a meatus in early Oligocene times. A distinctly prosimian feature of *Rooneyia* is the extension of the lacrymal onto the face, with the lacrymal foramen lying outside the orbit. This is somewhat like the condition seen in the Eocene adapid *Pronycticebus* but is a greater facial extension of the bone than typifies either *Adapis* or *Notharctus*. Relative to skull length, the breadth across the orbit is great. On the right side of the skull, the ventral and dorsal insertions of the postorbital bar are preserved in *Rooneyia*. This makes it possible to restore the postorbital bar and estimate the orbital breadth. Applying the orbital-breadth–skull-length index of Walker (1967a), *Rooneyia* plots out with the nocturnal forms among Malagasy lemurs, falling almost exactly between *Chirogaleus medius* and *Chirogaleus major*. It is therefore most interesting that Hofer and Wilson (1967) quite independently came to the conclusion that the cerebral hemispheres of *Rooneyia* resemble more closely the stage of development characteristic of the prosimians with the most greatly expanded visual systems. Although the posterior orbital region is open, the ventral side of the dorsal insertion of the postorbital bar is produced downward and the posterior border of the maxilla is recurved in such a manner as to suggest that the malar, maxilla, and frontal may have had flanges restricting the size of the opening between the orbital and temporal fossae. Closure is developed to a greater extent than in *Necrolemur*, where broadening of the postorbital bar internally is also seen. In the basicranium *Rooneyia* shows bulbous auditory bullae, reminiscent of those of *Tarsius* and *Necrolemur*. The auditory bullae extend further ventrally than in either of these two kinds of primates, but unlike them there is no apparent inflation of the mastoid outward. The foramen magnum of *Rooneyia* is probably a little more ventrally directed than in *Necrolemur*, suggesting that *Rooneyia* was more likely a hopping form than a quadruped, a possibility compatible with the long calcaneum and navicular of *Hemiacodon*, the only omomyid for which the structure of the hindlimb is known. Another "progressive" feature is that the opening for the internal carotid artery is a little further forward than in *Necrolemur* and is located farther toward the front of the bulla than is typical of lemurs. *Rooneyia* resembles only *Tarsius* among prosimians in this regard. In overall general appearance the skull of *Rooneyia* most closely resembles those of *Necrolemur* and *Pronycticebus* among fossil prosimians, but is clearly quite distinct and different in many dental and cranial features.

After studying the natural endocranial cast of *Rooneyia*, so far as it is exposed by bone that has been broken away, and with the help of X-rays, Hofer and Wilson (1967) managed to report in some detail on its brain structure. They were able to show that the olfactory bulbs were relatively larger than is typical of members of Anthropoidea, but more reduced than in prosimians of similar size, except for *Tarsius*, where the olfactory system is even more de-emphasized. They conclude: "As a whole the brain of *Rooneyia* has the morphology of a prosimian brain with a highly developed visual system, but in having small olfactory bulbs and a large neopallium, especially in the occipital poles, it is approaching a level of early simian brain development."

Ekgmowechashala (See Figure 62)

The type species of the genus *Ekgmowechashala*, *E. philotau* was named by MacDonald in 1963 on the basis of the completely unexpected find of jaws of a North American early Miocene primate. The type and other jaws have been recovered from the Rosebud formation in Western South Dakota. Because of its highly crenulate and polycuspidate $P_4–M_3$, together with its occurrence 10 million or 12 million years after the supposed disappearance of early Tertiary prosimians in the United States at least, MacDonald met some initial resistance to the idea that *Ekgmowechashala* was even a primate. Nevertheless, the broadening of cheek teeth, the crenulation, the loss of the paraconid, and the development of a pronounced metastylid seen in *Ekgmowechashala* are all foreshadowed among Eocene omomyines, to which group MacDonald assigned his new primate.

MacDonald's name is as strange as is the late occurrence of this primate. Because it was found in Sioux Indian country, he chose

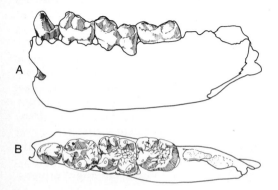

A

B

Figure 62 Mandible of *Ekgmowechashala*, an exotic primate species that occurs in Miocene deposits of the Dakota badlands. (*A:* External view. *B:* Occlusal view.) It is the latest-surviving North American prosimian. Scale × 3.0. (After J. Reed MacDonald, 1963.)

to name it after the Sioux Indian term for "cat man": "*ekgmo*"—cat, "*wechasha*"—man, and "*la*"—a diminutive suffix. The recommended pronunciation of the name is "Ígg-uh-moo-wee-cháh-shah-la." As in earlier omomyids, the lower dental formula is $\frac{2.1.3.3.}{}$.

TARSIIDAE

Various placements for the subfamily Microchoerinae (sometimes accorded family status as the Michrochoeridae) have been adopted throughout the years. A considerable amount of knowledge of the craniology of this group is provided by about a dozen skulls of *Necrolemur* found in the middle Eocene Quercy phosphorites of South-Central France. From study of these it is possible to relate this subfamily in "vertical" taxonomic association with the living tarsier rather than to classify the group "horizontally" with some group contemporary with it. Resemblances between various necro-lemurines and the tarsier have been noted throughout the history of study of fossil primates and have probably been the main basis for the traditional practice of dividing the early Tertiary primates into lemur-like and tarsier-like groups—that is, because North American *Tetonius* and members of this particular subfamily, especially *Pseudoloris* and *Necrolemur*, definitely showed numerous specific resemblances to the present-day Southeast Asian form.

   Microchoerus, the latest-surviving microchoerine, was originally described by Wood in 1846, but its relatedness to other primates was long overlooked. Lydekker (1887) separated it out as typifying a distinct family of mammals, in which he also included *Hyopsodus*, and suggested that the group was related to the hedgehogs and their allies. It remained for Wortman (1903, 1904) to point out the possibility that *Microchoerus* was related to *Necrolemur* and to stress that both were allied to *Tarsius*. Only one skull of *Necrolemur* was known to Wortman, and consequently his conviction that there were early Tertiary primates with special phyletic relation to *Tarsius* rested principally on the anatomy of the 1881 Bighorn Basin skull that he had found and Cope (1872b) had originally assigned to *Anaptomorphus*. Matthew (1914) later transferred this skull to *Tetonius*. After Stehlin (1916) had much more extensively described and figured the four genera currently placed in this subfamily, Teilhard de Chardin (1921) and Gregory (1922) noted the closeness of *Pseudoloris* to *Tarsius* and its dissimilarity to lorises. Stehlin also was the first to clearly associate the genera *Nannopithex*, *Necrolemur*, and *Microchoerus*. Unlike all other groups of early Tertiary primates, we know nearly complete upper and lower dentitions of all the genera of microchoerines, either from the teeth themselves or in the case of some incisors from their sockets alone. There is no doubt that all share the same dental formula above: $\frac{2.1.3.3.}{}$, as in *Tarsius*. The lower dental formula differs from *Tarsius* and is harder to interpret. Stehlin considered it to be $\frac{}{0.1.4.3.}$, but alternatively the canine could be considered lost and the lower dental formula be written as $\frac{}{2.0.3.3.}$. Both of these formulas differ from *Tarsius*, which has $\frac{}{1.1.3.3.}$. The solution of the microchoerine lower dental formula seems provided by acceptance of the lower dental formula recently determined for *Tetonius* by Szalay, which is $\frac{}{2.1.(2.\ or\ 3).3.}$. The microchoerines, being younger in age, have lost a variable premolar number and presumably share the lower dental formula $\frac{}{2.1.2.3.}$, which differs from both of the earlier interpretations. The question of what is the lower dental formula in this group is of some interest, because supposed differences in it have been used by some students to disassociate this particular stock from the vicinity of the ancestry of *Tarsius*. Nevertheless, the amount of variation in anterior dental formulas in early Tertiary primates suggests that considerable plasticity is to be expected rather than the greater uniformity of shape and number of these teeth seen in the canalized and often relict surviving prosimian stocks. In any case the only microchoerine that could have been ancestral to or near the ancestry of *Tarsius* is *Pseudoloris*, and no lower jaw of it is complete enough to prove how many anterior teeth it had.

However, it cannot be stressed sufficiently that the phyletic interpretation of these front lower teeth has to take second place in classification to the extensive and thoroughgoing dental craniological similarities to *Tarsius* seen in this group. Relative lack of resemblance to lemurs and lorises can easily be confirmed among microchoerines (= necrolemurines or Necrolemuridae of Hürzeler, 1948, and Simons, 1961). In species of all four genera of the group there is enough of the orbital region preserved to show that the eyes were greatly enlarged. They were probably all crepuscular or nocturnal forms like *Tarsius*. In correlation with this, the snout is relatively short and narrow and the space between the orbits is reduced. In consequence, the upper dentition has a bell-shaped outline, and the jugal bones of the cheek do not reach far enough across the ventral rim of the orbit to contact the bone that bears the tear duct. In all four genera the orbits have flaring rims, and in *Necrolemur* there is evidence that, as in *Tarsius*, expansion of the postorbital bar was beginning to close in the orbital cavity. In the base of the skull, of *Necrolemur* at least, the foramen magnum is shifted forward and the face is somewhat bent downward on the basicranial axis. The bullae are inflated with tubular ectotympanics and the carotid foramen is located ventromedially. The pterygoid wings broadly overlap the bullae, and the frontals fused before maturity—all special features of *Tarsius* among living prosimians.

In the group represented by *Microchoerus* the teeth are broadened by large hypocones and are flattened and polycuspidate, suggesting a trend toward more exclusively herbivorous feeding.

Nannopithex

The name *Nannopithex pollicaris* was proposed by Stehlin in 1912 for a species that had earlier been named *Necrolemur filholi* on the basis of finds from the middle Eocene in France. Stehlin's specimen

Figure 63 Crushed skull of *Nannopithex* from the middle Eocene brown coal deposits of Germany. (Upper dentition on right). (Photo courtesy of G. Krumbiegel.)

came from a locality in Switzerland near Egerkingen. In these forms the hypocone of the upper molars is more distinctly set off from the protocone than in younger *Necrolemur* and *Microchoerus*, and the posterior face of the protocone shows the characteristic *Nannopithex*-fold running back toward the cingulum. Stehlin believed that *Nannopithex* was not particularly close to *Necrolemur*, but my studies, as well as the conclusions of Hürzeler (1948) and Gregory (1922), all suggest that *Nannopithex* may well have been ancestral to *Necrolemur*.

In the middle 1930s two species from the middle Eocene brown coal deposits near Halle an der Saale in East Germany were described as *"Pseudoloris abderhaldini"* and *"Necrolemur" raabi*. My studies (Simons, 1961a) indicated that both these "species" belong in *Nannopithex*, as *Nannopithex raabi*. In this species the dentition above and below is completely preserved, as well as a crushed skull (see Figure 63). Together with this cranium, some parts of a left hindlimb were preserved. This constitutes the oldest-known partial skeleton of an Old World primate, other than that of *Plesiadapis* from the Paleocene of France. Weigelt (1933) reported that this skeleton showed distal fusion between tibia and fibula, seen among living primates only in *Tarsius*, but my observation did not confirm this. There is no indication that a splinter of bone lying across the left tibia could have been attached to it, or even that it is part of the fibula. Nevertheless, the calcaneum is elongate, suggesting that this species like others of its subfamily was a hopping form. The orbits are large compared with skull size.

Necrolemur

Necrolemur antiquus (Figure 64) is one of the best-known fossil primates of any age, knowledge of it being based on about a dozen skulls of Middle Eocene occurrence recovered from the Quercy phosphorites of South-Central France. Most of them are relatively undistorted, so that aspects of cranial anatomy can be studied in almost the same detail as in modern skulls. Study of these led Stehlin, Gregory, and others to postulate early that it is structurally much closer to the living *Tarsius* than to the lemurs and lorises, even though its dental anatomy is divergent enough to make clear that it has no living descendant. The cogent reasons for this association have already been outlined in the discussion of subfamily Microchorinae. It was therefore a somewhat surprising departure for Hürzeler (1946, 1948) to have concluded that *Necrolemur* is like lemurs and not like tarsiers in significant cranial features. This led to a reaction among scientists about the study of early primates. If opinions could differ so widely in the case of *Necrolemur*, which was well known cranially, then in no case would it really be possible to decide whether any early Tertiary form was closer to lemurs or to tarsiers. The basis for such an implication deserved analysis because of its widespread significance if true. It turned out on re-examination that Hürzeler's principal basis for associating *Necrolemur* with *Adapis* and the modern Malagasy lemurs was that he believed the tympanic ring to resemble that of these forms and

Figure 64 Reconstruction of the right three quarters' view of a skull of *Necrolemur* from the middle Eocene Quercy phosphorites of South-Central France. Scale × 3.0. (Drawing by Ellen Cole.)

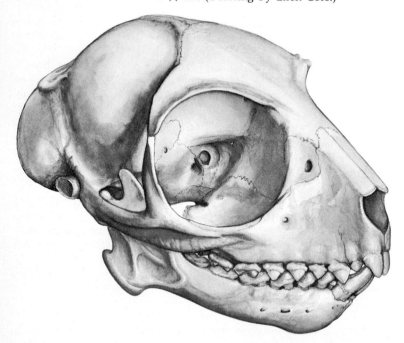

Figure 65 Reconstruction of the possible facial appearance of *Necrolemur*, a European Eocene prosimian. Scale × 1.5. (Drawing by E. L. Simons.)

not that of *Tarsius*. My own study of the ear region of a skull of *Necrolemur* in the British Museum showed that it has a tympanic ring that does resemble the tympanic ring of *Tarsius*. It is drawn out into a tube and does not stand within the bulla as a free ring, as in the vast majority of living and fossil lemurs. Hürzeler cited a resemblance between the tympanic bone of *Necrolemur* and the giant extinct fossil Madagascan lemur *Megaladapis*, but my examination of the two satisfied me that their auditory regions are about as dissimilarly constructed as one could expect to find among members of one order.

Clearly it was a mistake to assign the microchoerines to the Lemuriformes as Piveteau (1957) did when he also placed all the varied but generally less tarsier-like North American omomyines in the Tarsiiformes. This difference of opinion about the phyletic relationships of *Necrolemur* is instructive, because it shows the fallacy of reliance on the evidence or supposed evidence of one or a few characters, in preference to consideration of the whole mosaic of features represented by a fossil as well-known craniologically as *Necrolemur*.

The Quercy phosphorites have also yielded specimens of fused tibiofibulae of a proper size to belong to *Necrolemur*. If they do, this detail of hindlimb construction is significant, as *Tarsius* is the only present-day primate showing such fusion. We know that the associated heel bones of *Nannopithex* (the probable ancestor of *Necrolemur*) were elongate, and the large orbits, globular cranium, and forward-shifted foramen magnum of *Necrolemur* all suggest that it was a hopping form that may frequently have held the body in othograde postures. Figure 65 shows a hypothetical reconstruction of the face of this animal.

Microchoerus

The type species of the genus *Microchoerus*, *M. erinaceous*, was in 1844 one of the first five or six fossil primates to be described, but, as has been mentioned already, it was long unrecognized as a primate. The type came from later Eocene deposits at Hordwell, on the southern coast of England, opposite the Isle of Wight. This prosimian is common there, but is also known from many mandibles found in France and Switzerland. The type of *M. erinaceous* constitutes an upper and lower dentition. Most parts of the maxillae and mandibles of this individual were found, and in another collection there is a frontal bone of this species that confirms that it had enlarged orbits, a narrow interorbital septum, and frontal fusion. *Microchoerus* species continue the trend toward polycuspidation of cheek teeth seen incipiently in *Necrolemur*. Lobate ridges also branch from the principal cusps in the most advanced species, *M. ornatus*, almost in the manner seen in teeth of the orangutan. It seems clear that *Microchoerus* (which is partly younger than *Necrolemur*) could have been derived from an early species of the latter genus or of *Nannopithex*. The flattening and polycuspidation of the trigonid basins, loss of lower molar paraconids, and molarization of the premolars, together with deepening of the anterior mandible and vertical deepening and relative enlargement of the mandibular angle, are acquisitions that parallel developments seen more clearly among Anthropoidea; even if not ancestral to anything now living, this late Eocene primate clearly demonstrates that trends toward conditions we find among Higher Primates were by then underway.

Just as can be seen in the brown coal skull of *Nannopithex* and several *Necrolemur* skulls, the type palate of *Microchoerus* appears to show the premaxillary–maxillary suture behind the second upper incisor pair; in some this suture is absent; the upper canine is larger than P^2 but is reduced in crown height relative to most modern primates, as is also the case for such other omomyids and anaptomorphids for which canines are known.

Pseudoloris

The species *Pseudoloris parvulus* was originally described by the French paleontologist Filhol in 1890 as a new species of *Necrolemur*. The type and other specimens came from the middle Eocene Quercy phosphorites of South-Central France.

Stehlin (1916) recognized that this animal belonged in a distinct genus and coined the name *Pseudoloris*. He took the view that the animal was related to the lorisids. Teilhard de Chardin (1921) reviewed new and better material and concluded that the phyletic relationships of this species were with *Tarsius* and not with the lorises. The dentition is extraordinarily like that of the living tarsier (see Figure 66) and can hardly indicate only a parallelistic resemblance. Simpson (1940) remarked: "So far as the dental evidence goes, this genus stands considerably closer to *Tarsius* than does any

Figure 66 (opposite)   *Stereoview.* Comparison between the maxillary and mandibular dentitions of *Pseudoloris* (top) and of *Tarsius* (center). (In the bottom view, A is *Pseudoloris* and B is *Tarsius*.) The resemblance between these two animals is greater than is the case between any other early Tertiary primate and a modern form. Scale (top and A) × 5.0 and (center and B) × 3.0 approximately. (Photos courtesy of A. H. Coleman, Yale Peabody Museum, and D. E. Russell.)

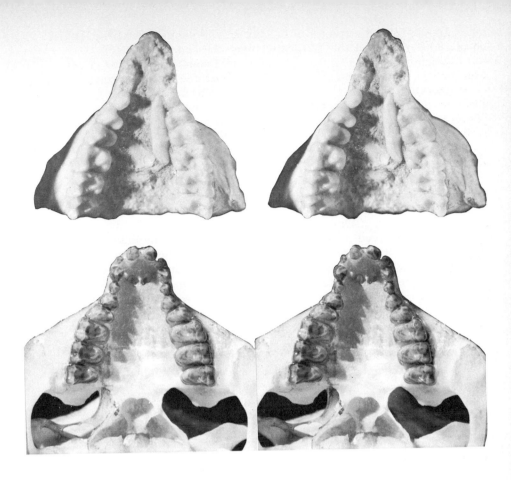

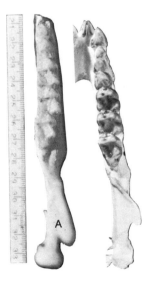

other known from the Paleocene or Eocene, and should perhaps be placed definitely in the Tarsiidae." Simpson seemed reluctant to associate *Pseudoloris* with *Necrolemur*, although Teilhard de Chardin had remarked on their similarity. In fact, the resemblance is so close that Weigelt (1933) later confused specimens of *Nannopithex*—the probable ancestor of *Necrolemur*—with *Pseudoloris*, which resulted in his describing the invalid form *Pseudoloris abderheldini* (a junior synonym of *Nannopithex raabi*). Simpson felt that perhaps *Pseudoloris* was related to the omomyines and *Necrolemur* to the paromomyines, but gave little reason for such associations. It would seem that all the microchoerines form a fairly compact group and that their ancestry is uncertain. If *Pseudoloris* is related to early Eocene *Teilhardina*, then it possibly has the same lower dental formula: $\frac{2.1.4.3.}{}$. One of the specimens Teilhard de Chardin reported on preserved either the sockets or crowns of the entire upper dentition, the floor of the orbits, and part of the frontals. The general outline of the relatively enlarged orbits and the bell-shaped margin of the palate with circular terminal nares, a short compressed snout, and flaring orbital margins, as well as similar frontals, are all close craniological similarities to *Tarsius*. The large lachrymal foramen is located outside the orbital margin. Two features of difference from *Tarsius* that Teilhard de Chardin noted were not confirmed by me. He reported two large posterior fenestrations or openings in the floor of the palate such as occur in some Insectivora. Examination of the margins of these under high magnification shows that they are not natural openings but clearly spots where the palatal bone has been broken away on this particular fossil. Secondly, Teilhard de Chardin reported that there were three upper incisors, but again careful examination of the premaxillae of *P. parvulus* shows that there are sockets for only two incisors; hence the upper dental formula is the same as that for *Tarsius*: $\frac{2.1.3.3.}{}$. The anterior teeth were clearly a little more procumbent than in the modern form, the mandible a little shallower anteriorly, and the coronoid process more posteriorly directed and with a higher condyle relative to the tooth row

Pseudoloris was approximately half the size of a tarsier, and because of the size of the orbits relative to the snout it could have been crepuscular or nocturnal. The hindlimb ascribed to this genus belongs to *Nannopithex*, not *Pseudoloris*. My examination of the tibia of the specimen indicated that there was no tibiofibular fusion as in *Tarsius*. Nevertheless, because of the large eyes this animal was probably much like *Tarsius* in its way of life.

LORISIDAE

Because the least altered or "advanced" of living prosimians now survive on the island of Madagascar, it had commonly been conjectured that lemurs or lemur-like prosimians would ultimately be recovered in the Tertiary deposits of Africa, as Africa seemed the most likely corridor through which they could have reached Madagascar. However, with more extensive recovery of fossils this pattern of distribution has not been confirmed, because (as the mammalian microfaunas of the Miocene of East Africa have become known) only loris-like or lorisid primates have been found. In the Oligocene deposits of North Africa only basal monkeys and apes occur. The absence of lemurs or their forebears from these deposits cannot be attributed to the nonrecovery of fossils of small mammals of all sorts, including lemurs, owing to unfavorable depositional conditions for small vertebrates; other, smaller mammalian jaws, for instance of rodents, occur in these sites in some abundance.

It had also been hypothesized that mid-Tertiary prosimians might be located in the Tertiary of Africa that would be intermediate between, or a common stock for, the modern lemurs and lorises. However, the Miocene East African prosimians do not represent such a common stock but are sufficiently close to the modern lorises, pottos, and bushbabies to be placed in the same family with them: Lorisidae.

The first-recovered African Miocene lorisid find was reported from Songhor, Kenya, by MacInnes (1943), who diagnosed the sole initial mandible as a new form, *Progalago dorae*. MacInnes considered the probability that *Progalago* was close to the ancestry or a direct forerunner of present-day galagos, a view that Le Gros Clark and Thomas (1952), who reviewed additional material of the genus, found little to disagree with. Their later-recovered lorisids came both from various sites on Rusinga Island, Kavirondo Gulf of Lake Victoria, and from Songhor on the mainland. These finds consisted of mandibular and maxillary fragments that, on grounds of size and morphological difference, indicated the presence of at least three species. In addition a partial cranium with natural endocranial cast was recovered. Initially, these authors considered the African lorisid finds to be of early Miocene age (= European Burdigalian provincial age), but now that numerous K/Ar age dates have been determined it is evident that Rusinga and Songhor are of early middle Miocene age, about 18 million to 20 million years old.

Le Gros Clark and Thomas (1952) saw a number of features in the suite of material available to them that they considered more primitive than in comparable parts of living galagines. Not unreasonably, they treated the cranium as belonging to *Progalago dorae*. Nevertheless, this skull (Figure 67) was later placed in a new genus *Komba* by Simpson (1967). It is more primitive than are modern galagines in showing more flattened-out cerebral hemispheres, relatively smaller and shorter temporal lobes, and a greater degree of exposure of the cerebellum posteriorly. However, the degree of advance toward modern forms was considerably beyond that of such Eocene prosimians as *Adapis*, which had relatively much smaller frontal lobes and a cerebellum almost completely uncovered by the occipital lobes of the cerebral hemisphere. On mandibles of *Progalago dorae*, Le Gros Clark and Thomas further observed that the canine was relatively less assimilated into the toothcomb, be-

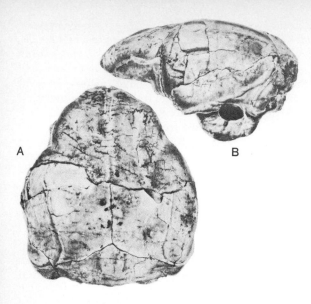

Figure 67 Cranial fragments and natural endocast believed to belong to the Miocene East African prosimian *Komba. A:* Top view. *B:* Side view. Scale × 1.9. (From Le Gros Clark and Thomas, 1952, plate 1.)

cause broken roots showed it to be relatively larger and separated more distinctly from the incisors by a gap. They also suggested that the apparent higher angle of the incisor root sockets might indicate that these teeth were less procumbent than in modern galagines. Nevertheless, because in the modern prosimians the forward tilt of the procumbent incisors is accomplished almost entirely by an angulation of the crown, it is not possible to determine the degree of incisor procumbency of lorisiforms from the roots alone.

Le Gros Clark and Thomas also noted that the auditory bullae are larger and more inflated in the calvaria of *Progalago* (now considered as belonging to *Komba robustus*) than in any other lorisiform other than *Galago*. The tympanic bone contributes to the lateral wall of the bulla, as is the case in the Lorisidae generally. The entire arrangement of the foramina in the skull base is just as in modern lorisids—for instance, there is no evidence of the posterior carotid foramen characteristic of the lemurs.

Four years later, Le Gros Clark (1956) published a detailed description of another much more complete skull found in 1952 in the Kiahera series on Rusinga Island associated with fossil fruits and seeds. Subsequent finds and comparative studies, principally that of Simpson (1967), have shown that this skull, which held a nearly complete upper dentition and the alveoli of missing teeth, does belong to *Progalago dorae* (see Figure 68D–E). As a consequence,

Figure 68 (opposite) Comparison of maxillary teeth of *Progalago dorae* (A), cf. *Progalago songhorensis* (B) with *Komba robustus* (C). Skull of *Progalago* (D, E, and F). Scale (A, B, C) × 4.0 approximately and (D, E, F) × 1.7. (A, B, and C from Simpson, 1967. D, E, and F from Le Gros Clark, 1956, plate 1.)

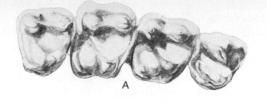

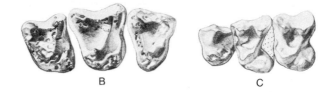

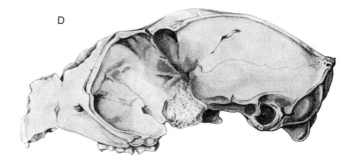

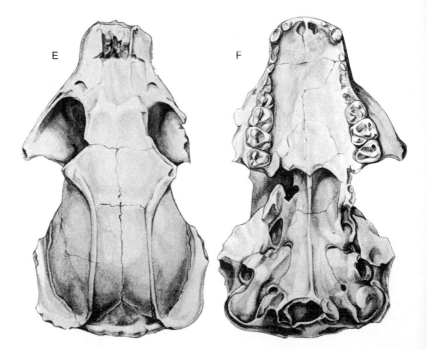

the remarks of Le Gros Clark and Thomas (1952) about the cranium of *Progalago* should be recognized as actually referring to *Komba*, whereas Le Gros Clark (1956) is making reference to *Progalago*. This is why the two calvarial descriptions of Le Gros Clark differ in so many details. In fact, Le Gros Clark (1956) suspected that the two fossil lorisid skulls were generically distinct. In general, the skull of *Progalago* seems closer to that of *Perodicticus* or *Nycticebus* than to that of *Galago*. As in *Progalago,* the auditory bullae are not expanded and the facial part of the skull is shortened. Laterally, the petrosal forms the margin of the auditory opening, with the tympanic ring attached to its edge but still distinctly set off by sutures. The tympanic does not appear to contribute as much to the ventral wall of the bulla as in modern lorisids. The palate is relatively broader and the brain case is comparatively smaller than in modern forms of the same size. The upper dentition of *Progalago dorae* broadly resembles that of the potto (*Perodicticus*), but its third molars are relatively larger. Of course, this slight difference could be explained if the modern potto is an animal undergoing reduction in cheek-tooth area—a trend that has frequently occurred among other primates. The P^4 of *Progalago* lacks the partial molarization seen in *Galago*, and in this it again resembles *Perodicticus*. The upper incisors are spaced widely apart, indicating the presence of a fully developed lorisiform toothcomb below.

Other fossil lorisid material accumulated, and was followed by the description by Leakey in 1962 of a further genus, *"Mio-euoticus"* [sic], from the Miocene of Uganda, based on a partial skull, *M. bishopi*, with most of the dentition. Then, in 1967, Simpson produced a further review. He felt that *Mioeuoticus* was probably not valid and stated that he would not have proposed it. Simpson also failed to find even a single special resemblance to modern *Euoticus*. Recently, Walker (1970) has transferred *"Mioeuoticus"* to *Progalago* as a synonym of the latter genus. Simpson (1967) also decribed a new genus and species, *Propotto leakeyi*, based on three half-mandibles with several of the lower teeth represented. He considered the tooth structure somewhat degenerate, a feature that seemed to relate the form to the potto. However, Walker (1969) has recently shown convincingly that these mandibles belong to a fruit bat and should be assigned to the order Chiroptera. This conclusion is now accepted by Simpson. After these transfers and synonyms, the following species for Miocene lorisids (see Figure 68A–C) appear to be valid (the authors of species who originally placed them in other genera are, by taxonomic convention, set in parentheses):

Progalago dorae MacInnes, 1943.
Progalago bishopi (Leakey), 1962.
Progalago songhorensis Simpson, 1967.
Komba minor (Le Gros Clark and Thomas), 1952.
Komba robustus (Le Gros Clark and Thomas), 1952.

Simpson was of the opinion that the Miocene lorisids were almost as diversified as the modern members of the group and that none stood in a clear-cut ancestral relationship to modern species. He considered lorisids to be neither generalized mammals nor generalized primates and stressed that the Miocene forms already possessed the unusual specialization of the anterior teeth into a toothcomb below and exhibited the unique (among prosimians) middle ear construction of the lorises. (That is, the tympanic ring is annular but fixed in the lateral wall of the bulla.) Simons (1962b) suggested that the similar position of the ectotympanic of *Pronycticebus* in the lateral wall of the bulla around the auditory aperture might suggest a relationship to the lorises. However, it should be remembered that none of the species presently assigned to the Adapidae, along with *Pronycticebus*, in which the anterior teeth are known, show any indication whatever of a tendency toward formation of a toothcomb apparatus. In fact, in *Adapis*, supposed to be closely related to *Pronycticebus*, symphyses fused with age—a phenomenon usually associated with nipping and relatively vertically planted incisors. Simpson concluded that the Miocene lorisids do not really help to close the morphological gap between Eocene and Recent prosimians, because they are so much like the modern forms.

In his recent informative study, Walker (1970) has allocated (on grounds of differences in size) the considerable number of lorisid postcranial remains from the East African Miocene sites. He concludes that they probably represent skeletal parts of all five of the accepted species of *Progalago* and *Komba*. Although these five species show diverse resemblances to all of the living lorises and galagines, seen in various combinations in their dental and cranial anatomy, the skeletal remains do not show them to have been similarly diversified in locomotor habits. There are no limb remains that would indicate the slow-climbing locomotor system of the lorises, but rather all show the vertical clinging and leaping system seen in the modern galagos. In fact, practically the only skeletal feature that is distinctly different is the less elongate calcaneum, which nevertheless is more lengthened than in any present-day arboreal quadruped. Walker tends to favor the view that this evidence suggests the possibility that in Miocene times the ancestors of the living slow-climbing lorisids may still have been vertical clingers and leapers. It is apparently possible to interpret the biochemical evidence of affinities among the slow-climbing lorisids, *Perodicticus, Arctocebus, Loris,* and *Nycticebus* as suggesting that the lorisines are not a natural group separate from the galagines of genus *Galago*. The two subfamilies have been drawn largely on the morphological differences consequent to their locomotor behavior. If slow climbers have evolved from active forms in this group more than once, then one or another of the lorisine genera may actually be much closer to *Galago*, the sole retainer of the original locomotor pattern, than it is to the others. There are also considerable differences within genus *Galago* not reflected by the current grouping of all the extant species into one genus. Nevertheless, behavior, pelage patterns, and the otherwise unique specializations of the index finger and second toe that pottos and lorises share belie their separate origin.

8 The Earliest Monkeys

CEBOIDEA

As we have already seen, the monkeys of the Old and New Worlds have been divided into two separate infraorders, the Catarrhini and Platyrrhini, terms coined by the French naturalist Geoffroy Saint-Hillaire in 1812. Such evidence as is provided by the fossil record indicates that both these infraorders have, since they first differentiated, been restricted to the respective hemispheres in which they now occur. For many years paleontologists have questioned the nature of the beginnings of these two diversified groups, specifically calling into doubt whether they need have arisen from the same basal stock of prosimians. It was postulated that the complex similarities that have caused scholars to call them "monkeys" have arisen in parallel—that is, their similarities might be features of independent acquisition rather than structures shared as a common heritage. This question now appears to have been settled by the various biochemical techniques summarized by Goodman (1967) and also dealt with more recently by Sarich (1968). These show that in the various substances—blood albumins, DNA, transferrins, etc.—that have so far been studied all the Anthropoidea show similarities when contrasted with various prosimians. Alternatively, the Old and New World Anthropoidea could have evolved from a single prosimian group that was not closely related to the living prosimian stocks.

Platyrrhini contains but one superfamily, Ceboidea, in which a more-or-less expanded tympanic bulla is always present. The tympanic ring is fused laterally around the auditory meatus but does not extend outward as a bony tube, as in catarrhines; the postorbital plate is composed posteroexternally of the jugal, which reaches the temporal fossa where it contacts the parietal; the orbitotemporal foramen is relatively large; and each upper and lower jaw holds three premolars, and among marmosets third molars are typically lost. Almost nothing anatomically informing is known about early ceboids, although a few Tertiary fossils, which will be considered below, have been found—principally in this century. It is clear from shared similarities that all ceboids are the products of a single adaptive radiation.

The fossil record of the platyrrhine monkeys is not very impressive and is presently restricted to a few Oligocene, Miocene, and quite recent Pleistocene or subfossil discoveries from South America and Jamaica. In general, these monkeys do not appear to be suitable candidates for the ancestry of any of the surviving species of the Ceboidea. A point of principal interest is that none of the Tertiary monkey mandibles recovered so far show the rounded or U-shaped symphysis typical of most living cebids, but instead they exhibit anteriorly converging or V-shaped tooth rows. This also appears to be the case generally among known Oligocene and Miocene catarrhines of the Old World. Such anterior convergence is a prosimian or "primitive" feature. Perhaps this negative evidence suggests that the U-shaped dental arcades of the cebids have arisen independently since the Miocene.

It had been thought that because the ceboids do not have a tubular tympanic ring extending laterally beyond the bulla as a protection for the auditory canal, because the opening between the eye socket and temporal fossa is larger, and because they have not lost $P^2_{\bar{2}}$, that their separation from the common ancestral stock of Higher Primates must have been very early. These suppositions no longer hold much weight, because the early catarrhines of the Fayum Oligocene resemble platyrrhines in having fairly large orbitotemporal fenestrae and in lacking a tubular ectotympanic. In some cases (*Apidium* and *Parapithecus*), they also possess $P^2_{\bar{2}}$.

Now that we have fairly good evidence of the shape and relative proportions of jaws and teeth in the dental arcades of five fossil platyrrhines (*Homunculus, Cebupithecia, Neosaimiri, Stirtonia*, and *Xenothrix*), it would be wise to consider their meaning in functional terms and in relation to dietary preferences. One should also consider the degree and significance of the relative size differences between teeth in various parts of the tooth row. Mandibular depth and robusticity should relate to stresses affecting various parts of the ramus, as stresses are apparently reflected by degree of procumbency and size of the incisors. Some of these questions are dealt with in part by Hershkovitz (1970), but much more work of this sort needs to be done on the South American fossil monkeys. Hershkovitz tends to correlate all the differences in dental function to be seen in these ceboids directly with differences in their absolute size, but nothing as complex as a primate dental mechanism could have such a simple correlation. In fact, as he shows, the best interpretation of the jaw and teeth of *Xenothrix* is that it is analogous to that of the Malagasy aye-aye (*Daubentonia*). This, in turn, implies a diet-adapted mandible that is the way it is, not because of its size, but because of some special feeding function, perhaps grub eating.

Perhaps a major hitch in interpreting the relation of diet to tooth shape and size and jaw mechanics among platyrrhines is that not enough behavioral data have been compiled for the present-day South American monkeys. Nevertheless, as the only comprehensive review of the South American fossil monkeys, Hershkovitz's recent paper serves well as an introduction to the subject, and (apart from the following discussion of the newly discovered genus *Branisella*) his positions on fossil platyrrhines will be outlined and followed here.

Branisella

The recently described primate *Branisella boliviana* consists of an upper left maxillary fragment from a locality near Salla, Bolivia, that has been studied by Hoffstetter (1969) in Paris (see Figure 69). Apart from its definite distinctiveness, its greatest interest is that it documents the presence of primates in South America at a much earlier date than was heretofore known. The type and only specimen was recovered by Branisa of La Paz at a Deseadan horizon (early Oligocene) and is definitely dated to that stage by an extensive associated fauna.

The discovery shows that primates reached South America at about the same time as the hystricomorph rodents, which are present along with *Branisella* at Salla, Bolivia. Thus the rodents and primates, which were the only incursive elements into South America in mid-Tertiary times, evidently got there as a result of the same favorable conditions for dispersal. Such dispersal between adjacent continents has been discussed by Simpson (1953). Because the incoming elements were so few and the primates at least were arboreal, it would seem that these two groups might have first reached South America from Central America on rafts of floating vegetation.

There are few early Oligocene primates outside South America with which *Branisella* could be compared: two species from North

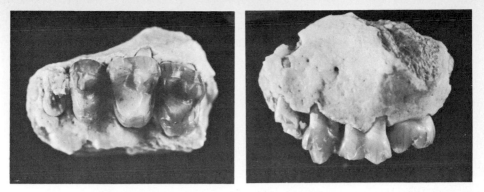

Figure 69   Left maxillary fragment with P³ through M² of *Branisella* from the early Oligocene of Bolivia. This is the oldest South American primate. Scale × about 4.9. (Photo courtesy of Robert Hoffstetter.)

America, *Rooneyia viejaensis* found in Rifle Range Hollow, Presidio County, Texas, and *Macrotarsius montanas* from Pipestone Springs, Jefferson County, Montana. Inasmuch as the latter is known only from a lower jaw, it is not strictly comparable with *Branisella*. Eurasia is a complete blank as far as Oligocene fossil monkeys are concerned, but in the Fayum of North Africa both upper and lower dentitions of *Apidium* and *Parapithecus* of that age have been recovered.

Perhaps the greatest resemblance of *Branisella* to another primate is to *Apidium phiomense*, in that both show extension of a shelf forward around the hypocone with development of a distinct pericone cusp. In *Rooneyia* the hypocone decreases from M¹ to M² and is hardly present on M³. Nevertheless, both *Parapithecus* and *Apidium* are advanced over *Branisella* and *Rooneyia*, in that among the last two forms P² is small, single-rooted, and not extended transversely from inside to out, whereas in the first two genera this tooth is transversely expanded.

Hoffstetter's (1969) discussion is the only presently available source of information on *Branisella*. Among the points he makes about it are that the palate is apparently less arched than in typical modern platyrrhines. However, the maxilla is vertically shallow, as in many prosimians as well as in *Callimico* and to an even greater extent in *Aotus*. Of course, the shallow maxilla of *Aotus* is due to the enormous expansion of the orbits in correlation with the nocturnal habits of this, the owl monkey.

In the presence of at least a suggestion of a pericone cusp on M¹ lingual to the protocone, *Branisella* resembles *Saimiri*, but the valley between the protocone and hypocone is much more incised and deeper than in modern *Saimiri* and *Callimico*. Unlike *Parapithecus*, which retains the paraconule, this cusp is lost in *Branisella*. In contrast, *Apidium* shows an even larger metaconule than *Branisella*.

The outline of the molars is subtrapezoidal in *Branisella*—a difference both from the more quadrate molars of cebids and cercopithecoids and from the more triangular molars of marmosets and many prosimians. As in *Rooneyia*, *Apidium*, and *Parapithecus*, M^3 in *Branisella* was evidently smaller than M^1 or M^2. These differences can be summarized, as Hoffstetter has, in terms of similarity on one side to modern South American monkeys and on the other to Eocene primates, which have to be considered as representative of an earlier stage. These differences can be tabulated, after Hoffstetter, as follows:

A. *Characters resembling Eocene primates*
   1. P^2 small and not transversely broad.
   2. Well-developed labial styles of molars, even more developed on premolars.
   3. Molar outline subtrapezoidal.
   4. Hypocones shifted lingually in relation to protocones.
B. *Characters resembling Higher Primates*
   1. Molars lack external cingulum.
   2. Paraconule eliminated, metaconule reduced.
   3. Molar crowns a little less brachyodont than in modern platyrrhines.
   4. Cusps less acute.

Another feature, the presence of deep troughs at the base of the labial cusps and between hypocone and protocone, appears to be a difference from both the early prosimians and the modern ceboids. Hoffstetter prefers the conclusion that the marmosets with their triangular molars are not primitive but are the result of a trend toward dwarfing, along with tendencies to M^2–M^3 reduction and simplification of molar design, with loss of the hypocone occurring late. In his opinion, *Branisella* could be related to *Rooneyia* and to the North American omomyids and would serve as an adequate model for the primitive platyrrhine dentition. There are special dental similarities to North American Eocene *Washakius*, for instance.

Dolichocebus

Dolichocebus gaimanensis was described by Kraglievich in 1951 from sediments of latest Oligocene age (Colhuehuapian provincial age) in Patagonia. This makes it the second oldest of the South American fossil monkeys. The find consists of a much broken and distorted cranium. Most of the surface bone of the face as well as the entire upper dentition are broken off, but judging from the roots the upper dental formula is apparently $\frac{2,1,3,3}{}$. Affinities seem to be with *Homunculus*, but considering the condition of the find little can be said of its relationships. The dolichocephaly that gave rise to the name could have been due to the distortions during fossilization that this skull obviously suffered, as well as to the ceboid trend toward a large, long brain case as in *Saímiri*.

Homunculus

Homunculus was named on the basis of an imperfect lower jaw from Patagonia, *H. patagonicus*. Later, Bluntschli (1931) reviewed this and other specimens first described by Ameghino from Santa-cruzian sediments near the mouth of the Rio Gallego, Santa Cruz, Argentina. These later finds he referred to a new species, *H. ameghinoi*, which Hershkovitz (1970) prefers to keep as a separate species, although he is willing to consider it also as a possible synonym of Ameghino's prior species. The Rio Gallego material is more informative than the type. It consists of a mandible with horizontal rami preserving part of the left ascending ramus and most of the lower teeth, as well as a facial fragment with left canine and upper premolars. Near this was found a complete right femur. In partial length of tooth row (C–M_2), *Homunculus* is, according to Hershkovitz, about two thirds the size of a young adult female howler monkey.

The horizontal rami of the mandible in Bluntschli's *Homunculus ameghinoi* (Figure 70) converge toward the symphysis in a V-shape characteristic of most pre-Pliocene Anthropoidea, both in the Eastern and Western Hemispheres. As with *Apidium*, the canines are short and small relative to the other teeth, and the two front premolars (P_{2-3}) are much less transversely broad than in the older Fayum monkeys, discussed below.

M_1 and M_2 in *Homunculus ameghinoi* are subequal in size, whereas, like the condition in most ceboid monkeys, M_3 is slightly smaller than the front molars but not as reduced as in some other fossil

Figure 70 A mandible of *Homunculus ameghinoi* from Miocene deposits near Santa Cruz, Argentina. Scale $\times$ 2.0 approximately. (From Hershkovitz, 1970.)

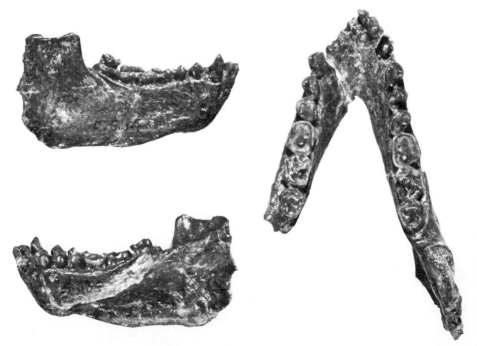

monkeys of South America, to be discussed below. The molars of this find also show heavy wear.

Posteriorly, the mandibular rami may be somewhat deepened compared with many other platyrrhines, and this is one of the features that led Stirton (1951) to associate *Homunculus* with *Alouatta*. The ventral borders of the horizontal rami show a sigmoid outline, with a downward bulge at the symphysis and then an upward curve followed by a deepened area under the molars.

The M_{2-3} curve upward above the plane of the other cheek teeth to a greater degree than characterizes other Ceboidea, living or fossil. Among Hominoidea this flexure is known as the curve of Spee. It is thought to be a functional rearrangement whereby the load arm of the anterior teeth is reduced and the mechanical advantage of the dental mechanism is increased. Other features of interest in this mandible are the pronounced alveolar elevations on the outer symphyseal surface, originally noted for *Homunculus ameghinoi* by Stirton (1951), plus the fact that there is a shelf that conceals the digastric depression from view when examined from below. Hershkovitz has demonstrated that the angle of the anterior face of the symphysis from the horizontal is about 50°—a fairly advanced condition for a platyrrhine (see Figure 71).

Figure 71 Arrangement of the symphyseal angle and plane of crowns of postcanine teeth in living and fossil South American monkeys and one lemur—all brought to the same scale. (From Hershkovitz, 1970.)

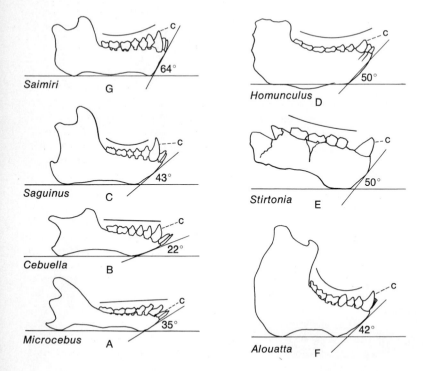

Hershkovitz concluded that Stirton was wrong in associating *Homunculus* with the Alouattinae, but he himself diagrammed it as morphologically antecedent to *Alouatta*. His dictum is incorrect that "whichever the canine–incisor relationships, the V-shaped mandible with highly-specialized truncate and constricted symphyseal region cannot give rise to the U-shaped mandible with the incisor–canine relationship present in the living platyrrhines and catarrhines." Almost all of the most archaic placental insectivores as well as most early primates have V-shaped dental arcades with symphyseal regions unlike those of later Anthropoidea. Clearly, animals with the former type of dental arrangement have given rise repeatedly to the U-shaped arcade more commonly seen among the later Anthropoidea.

An almost complete skull of this genus was discovered by Harrington in 1931 at Scanava, Chubut Territory, Patagonia. This became the type of *Homunculus harringtoni* described by Rusconi (1933). An extensive description of this skull is to be found in Hill (1962, pp. 146–156).

Stirtonia

In 1951, Stirton described a new species of late Miocene primate from the La Venta fauna, collected in the Honda Formation of Central Colombia, South America. This he named *Homunculus tatacoensis*. Hershkovitz (1970) determined that this mandible was dissimilar to those of *Homunculus* and deserved a new generic designation, which in honor of Stirton he chose to call *Stirtonia*. The type specimen consists of most of the horizontal rami of both sides of a mandible with (on one side or both) canines and all cheek teeth. The dental formula is $\frac{2.1.3.3}{2.1.3.3}$. This is the largest of the fossil platyrrhines; if body parts correspond with jaw size, it would have been about the size of a large male cebus monkey (see Figures 71 and 72). Apparently, the horizontal ramus of *Stirtonia* did not deepen significantly to the rear as in *Alouatta*, but as in howlers the symphyseal angle is fairly high (50°). Unlike *Homunculus ameghinoi*, the digastric fossae are directed ventrally. The canines are comparatively large in relation to *Homunculus*, but the incisors are small and laterally compressed. The rami diverge markedly to the rear. Hershkovitz reports that the distance across the outer alveolar borders of M_{2-3} is about four times the distance across the incisor alveoli. In other forms with posteriorly divergent rami, such as Egyptian Oligocene *Aeolopithecus chirobates* or modern *Alouatta caraya*, this spread is only three times the breadth across the incisors. The incisor alveoli are arranged in a forward-bowing arc. The symphyseal cross section appears to be about 15 per cent deeper than long, and it seems that the snout may not have been as foreshortened as in modern ceboids.

Stirtonia is about a quarter larger than *Homunculus ameghinoi*, but, in the opinion of Hershkovitz, it is not at the same evolutionary grade, there is little evidence of the curve of Spee, the jaw does not deepen posteriorly, and the P_{2-4} show more distinct paraconid

Figure 72 Views of the mandible of *Stirtonia* from the late Miocene La Venta fauna recovered from the valley of Rio Tatacoa near Huila, Colombia. Scale × 1.5. (From Hershkovitz, 1970.)

cusps than are to be found in *Apidium* or *Parapithecus*. In possession of such paraconid cusps it appears also to differ from other platyrrhines.

Hershkovitz also believes that the uncompleted eruption of M_3 in *Stirtonia* (even after the adult canines were erupted and considerably worn) indicates that a trend toward reduction or loss of M_3 common in South American monkey groups also characterized the lineage represented by *Stirtonia*. Dissatisfied with the idea that it is closely related to any of the modern ceboid subfamilies, he has proposed a new subfamily, Stirtoninae, for its reception.

Cebupithecia

Stirton and Savage in 1951 described the genus *Cebupithecia* of La Venta, late Miocene, and considered it related to *Pithecia*, a view that Hershkovitz finds little to substantiate. The fragments of maxillae, basicranium, and lower teeth were combined in an elegant plaster reconstruction of a *Pithecia*-like skull, but apparently the supposed features of resemblance to pithecines are not to be found. Hershkovitz is of the opinion that the seeming pronounced degree of procumbency of the upper central incisor root is due to distortion during fossilization, but even were the orientation correct, similar procumbency is also seen in howler monkeys. For similar reasons the lateral splaying of the canine also appears due to crushing.

Cebupithecia also lacks the extreme enamel wrinkling and hollow canines of pithecines. Moreover, there is no M_3 reduction in pithecines, and their upper canines are triangular in basal cross section, not rounded. Having disassociated *Cebupithecia* from the pithecines, Hershkovitz (1970) advocates its placement in a separate ceboid subfamily, Cebupithecinae.

The holotype individual of *Cebupithecia* also includes many parts of the postcranial skeleton.

Neosaimiri

With *Neosaimiri fieldsi*, named by Stirton in 1951, we seem on safer ground. This species is so far represented by a mandibular fragment with most of the teeth in place that is near modern *Saimiri* in both size and morphology, as Stirton pointed out (see Figure 73). Nevertheless, the mandibular rami are more divergent posteriorly than in the modern squirrel monkeys, and somewhat as in *Homunculus* the incisors are small and crowded, and even more pro-

Figure 73 *Neosaimiri* (A) from the Miocene of Colombia compared with a modern South American squirrel monkey, *Saimiri* (B). Scale × 1.9. (From Hershkovitz, 1970.)

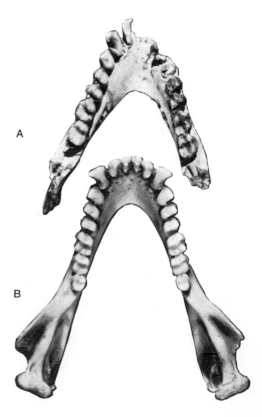

cumbent. This would appear to be a primitive feature to be expected in a Miocene form, in view of the posteriorly divergent rami seen in Miocene catarrhines. The present-day squirrel monkey has expanded and more vertically implanted incisors and a U-shaped mandible. This is evidently due to a shift toward more front-of-the-mouth feeding.

Xenothrix

Xenothrix has proved to be perhaps the most enigmatic of all the South American extinct monkeys, even though it comes from subrecent deposits in Long Mile Cave, Trelawney Parish, Jamaica. The discovery, made in 1920 by H. E. Anthony, was described in 1952 by Williams and Koopman. The material consists of an incomplete mandible preserving the symphysis, the left horizontal ramus, and the anterior half of the right ramus. On the left, M_{1-2} alone are preserved, but the alveoli of all the other antemolar teeth are preserved intact (see Figure 74). The dental formula indicated $(\frac{2.1.3.2}{})$ is that of the callithricids, but the jaw size is that of a much larger animal, even thicker and more robust than is the jaw ramus of such forms as *Pithecia* or *Callicebus* of similar proportions. The molars are even more developed relatively and are as large

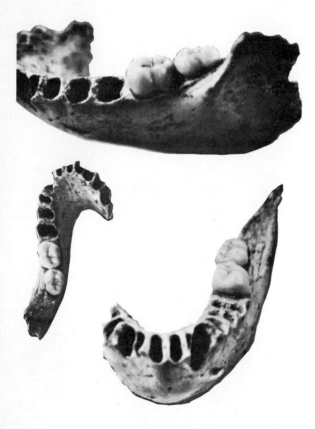

Figure 74 Type mandible of *Xenothrix*, a strange, extinct Jamaican monkey from Pleistocene or subrecent deposits in Long Mile Cave, Jamaica. Scale × 1.75 and crown view × 1.0. (Photo courtesy of Philip Hershkovitz.)

as those of larger cebids such as *Lagothrix* or *Ateles*. Hershkovitz (1970) is impressed by the bunodont, puffy molar crowns, which suggest to him a possible adaptive resemblance to the specialized Malagasy lemur *Daubentonia*, the aye-aye. He considers this mandible as a strong indication that there had existed as an insular relic in Jamaica a distinctive stock of Middle American primates with an unusual dietary specialization perhaps enforced by the limitations of an island habitat. These curious monkeys were apparently exterminated in the relatively recent past, perhaps by pre-Columbian man. Hershkovitz (1970) has therefore proposed that this single mandible of *Xenothrix macgregori* be taken as representing the type genus of a new platyrrhine family: Xenothricidae.

CERCOPITHECOIDEA

Catarrhines from the Oligocene and Miocene have been found only in Africa. There are so many sites in Eurasia that cover well this whole period from about 33 million to about 12 million years ago but have never yielded any monkey fossils that it seems they were not yet in Eurasia. Therefore, I have to differ strongly with Napier (1970) regarding his theory that certain African monkeys are derived from stocks that spent mid-Tertiary times in Eurasia. There is no evidence for this, but only evidence to the contrary. Only the Barbary macaque seems to have such a derivation, and it appears to have differentiated in Europe within Pleistocene times.

It is odd that monkeys are not better known from Miocene localities in Africa, but the fact is that in these numerous sites fossil apes are about twenty times commoner than are monkeys. In an African forest today this proportion would be reversed. The striking differences in abundance in the Miocene may be due to one or a combination of the factors listed below:

1. The earliest Old World monkeys were adapted to live principally in rainforests wetter than East Africa in Miocene times.
2. Miocene apes could outcompete Miocene monkeys.
3. Collectors have concentrated on collecting ape fossils at the expense of a search for monkeys.
4. Miocene monkeys were in general very small, and consequently their bones were more often eaten, were less often buried, and are harder to find as fossils.
5. Miocene African monkeys were in general adapted to a drier climate and more terrestrial way of life than was available in the East African Miocene.
6. Miocene African monkeys consisted of only very few species. Like bovids and ursids, their adaptive radiation was yet to come.

Of these possibilities, the last would seem to me to be the most likely on present evidence. The first can only be proven when much larger faunas from definite rainforest environments are found, perhaps in the Congo. The second alternative is belied by much greater abundance of parapithecines compared with apes in the Fayum Oligocene deposits. The third and fourth alternatives seem unlikely also, because many small rodents, including numerous complete skeletons, come from the Kenyan Miocene localities. Because most present-day African monkey species are arboreal, the fifth possibility is also doubtful, unless one believes that the Cercopithecoidea are secondarily adapted to tree living.

In sum then, as far as the Oligocene of the Old World is concerned, the whole of our knowledge of Anthropoidea up to the present time comes from the Fayum of Egypt.

The two parapithecine genera *Apidium* and *Parapithecus* each have two described species—*A. phiomense* and *A. moustafai*, *P. fraasi* and *P. grangeri*. Along with these four species there are species of four genera of apes, but there are no known Fayum prosimians. Thus, in the Old World, studies of members of this order perforce shift from the primitive suborder to the advanced.

Apidium

Apidium was the first Oligocene monkey to be discovered and described, by Osborn in 1908, but he was not certain even of its ordinal affinities (see Figure 75). The name is presumably a diminutive of Apis, the sacred bull of the Ptolemaic Egyptians, which suggests that at least when the name was coined he considered it an artiodactyl. The type specimen was found by Richard Markgraf in the upper Fossil Wood Zone of the Jebel el Qatrani Formation, but the exact locality was not recorded. Our extensive prospecting

Figure 75 *Stereoview*. Reconstruction by the author of the face of *Apidium*, a primitive catarrhine from the Oligocene Fayum deposits of Egypt. (Photo courtesy of A. H. Coleman, Yale Peabody Museum.)

0 cm   1   2

at that level has convinced me that the upper horizons of this formation are so sparingly fossiliferous except for the areas of Quarries I and M, in both of which *Apidium phiomense* occurs, that the type probably came from one or the other of these quarry areas. Quarry M is not far to the northwest of the 1906–1907 field camp of the American Museum at Quarry A, and that is what the original field label says—"NW of Quarry . . . new genus. ?primate, Feb. 17, 1907, collr. R. Markgraf."

Simons (1962b) described a smaller and older species of *Apidium*, *A. moustafai*. It is known from a few dozen jaws found in Quarry G, located stratigraphically between the two fossil-wood zones. During the several Yale expeditions, *A. phiomense* proved to be the commonest mammal found at Quarry I. The materials we now have include many limb bones, scores of teeth and mandibles, three partial frontals, petrosals, and several maxillae. Preliminary cranial and postcranial studies suggest that *Apidium phiomense* had a short, rather marmoset-like face with small canines relative to those of *Parapithecus* and similar to those of *Callithrix*. The postcranials indicate that the hind feet were adapted for springing. The olecranon process is not retroflexed, but rather the ulna is bowed forward as in highly arboreal primates. *Apidium phiomense* was apparently about the size of the present-day owl monkey, *Aotus trivirgatus.*

The affinities of *Apidium* were much discussed by scientists when there was but one specimen. It seemed to some condylarth-like, but condylarths have not otherwise been found in Africa. Hürzeler (1958) took the position that *Apidium* was not a primate but was related to phenacodont condylarths.

Simons (1960) stressed that in its polycuspidation and possession of a lower molar centroconid *Apidium* resembles *Oreopithecus* from the late Miocene of Tuscany, Italy. Since then, several upper dentitions of *Apidium* have been found. *Oreopithecus* has been recovered at Fort Ternan, Kenya, and another oreopithecine genus *Mabokopithecus* was named by von Koenigswald (1969) for a single tooth from Maboko Island in Lake Victoria, Kenya. Hürzeler (1968) had gone on record that *Apidium* is not a primate, giving as reasons the facts that the molar tooth structure resembles that of non-primates and that the mandibular ramus is low or shallow, a non-primate characteristic that he also observes in "*Moeripithecus*." Nevertheless, he has admitted a "striking resemblance" between *Apidium* and *Oreopithecus*. Simple inspection of either the type of "*Moeripithecus*" or of *Apidium* will show that each is a juvenile; both show characteristic juvenile striated bone. There is practically no wear on the M_{1-2} of *Moeripithecus*, and the type of *Apidium phiomense* has M_3 unerupted. This indicates that these animals were immature and is the reason for the shallowness of the horizontal rami of these mandibles. They would have deepened with increasing age, and all that is needed to know that this is so is awareness of the way in which mammals grow up, coupled with direct observation of the two specimens described long ago. Scores of jaws of *Apidium* and *Parapithecus* have been found in the Fayum by the recent Yale expeditions, but Hürzeler had evidently not seen the preliminary reports on them (Simons, 1962b, 1963a, 1966). These new materials resolve without doubt the affinities of *Apidium*. In January of 1967, I found at Quarry I in the Fayum an associated group of cranial fragments of *Apidium phiomense* together with palatal fragments and upper teeth. One of the fragments of this find is a partial frontal bone preserving the interorbital septum. The frontals are completely fused, showing no trace of the metopic suture between bilateral frontals commonly present in prosimians and nonprimates. Furthermore, this frontal fragment is exactly like that from the Fayum described by Simons (1960), and consequently the latter more complete frontal, which gives evidence of the presence of post-orbital closure, must now be assigned to *A. phiomense*. All parts of the mandible of *A. phiomense* are presently known, and several of these go past the midline, proving that symphyseal fusion at a very early age characterized *Apidium*. The dental formula of *Apidium* is $\frac{2.1.3.3.}{2.1.3.3.}$ as in some platyrrhines, and this formula is now confirmed in at least a dozen specimens. Numerous adult mandibles of *A. phiomense* in the new collections demonstrate that with maturity the jaw was deep relative to the height of tooth crowns. The upper teeth of *Apidium* (see Figure 76) are anteroposteriorly short and have well-delineated separate cusps with distinct paraconule and meta-conule. These teeth admit the possibility, just as the lower teeth do, of a topological conversion into those of *Oreopithecus*, particularly because those of *Oreopithecus* (unlike any other later member of the Catarrhini) retain well-defined paraconule and metaconule cusps. Nevertheless, 10 million to 15 million years separate Oligocene Egyptian *Apidium* and Tuscan *Oreopithecus*. The analogies in their upper (and lower) tooth structure may thus be parallelisms, primitive retentions, or indications or real phyletic affinity. Basically, two things of importance have been discovered in the last decade: (1) both *Oreopithecus* and *Apidium* have been demonstrated as un-

Figure 76 Maxillary dentition of *Apidium phiomense* from the Egyptian Oligocene. (Photo courtesy of A. H. Coleman, Yale Peabody Museum.)

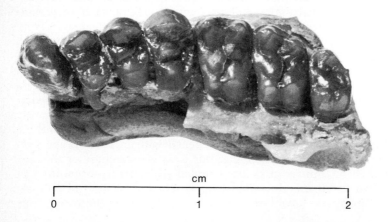

cm

0   1   2

doubted primates, and (2) *Oreopithecus*-like teeth have been found at Fort Ternan, Kenya (Leakey, 1968a,b), and on Maboko Island, Lake Victoria, Kenya (von Koenigswald, 1969).

Both of these latter occurrences point toward an African origin for the Oreopithecidae. This is a probability which gains further strength from the peculiarly limited range of *Oreopithecus* in Eurasia (only in North Italy and Southern Russia), which of itself suggests an origin outside that great land area.

A further observation that seems worth stressing is that *Apidium* and *Parapithecus* are the two commonest African Oligocene primates. If one includes isolated teeth, there are nearly two hundred finds of *Apidium* and about a fifth as many of *Parapithecus*. All the Fayum ape specimens put together do not tally as high a number as those of *Parapithecus* alone. Certainly, the rest of the African continent in Oligocene times represents an enigma, but it does seem unlikely that such abundant and adaptively successful primates as *Apidium* and *Parapithecus* were aberrant side branches, doomed to eventual extinction.

Parapithecus

Parapithecus fraasi, named by Schlosser, was the most complete type specimen of all the African Oligocene primates described in the early part of this century. It consisted of a mandible that preserved both horizontal rami and considerable parts of the ascending branches of the jaws. In this particular dentition were preserved a pair of central incisors, and posterior to these seven teeth on the left, and six on the right—one premolar had fallen out. As long as the type was the sole specimen of *Parapithecus*, it remained a bone of contention. This was because the dental formula was subject to various interpretations, and the problem was not enhanced by the fact that morphology of the cheek teeth was somewhat unlike anything else among Primates. Apart from a vague and distant resemblance to the contemporary Fayum ape *Propliopithecus*, little talk of affinities was possible—other than that this was definitely a primate dentition. Nevertheless, the specimen was endlessly discussed, and associations ranging from ties with the modern prosimian *Tarsius* to an ancestral relationship for present-day man were proposed.

It might be that if the effort and money expended to publish opinions on the sole specimen of *Parapithecus* in scores of scholarly journals and textbooks during a period of 60 years had long ago been spent in the attempt to find only one or a few additional specimens in the field, more pertinent understanding of this animal might have been secured. Thus it stands as an object lesson in what ought to have been done, but, in fact, was not done.

The mandible that became the type of this particular genus and species was recovered by Richard Markgraf in 1908 in the Egyptian Fayum and later forwarded by him to the museum at Stuttgart, Germany. The first record of it in the Stuttgart accession journal was as a "?marsupial."

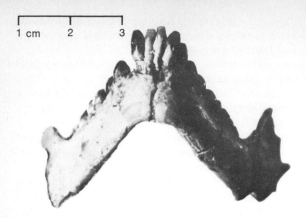

Figure 77 Anterior face of the symphysis of the type mandible *Parapithecus* from the Fayum of Egypt. (Photo courtesy of J. Hürzeler.)

As alluded to above, a long-term debate—even concerning the exact identification of tooth type and number—arose over this discovery after 1911, when Schlosser published a full description. The problems of its interpretation could never have been settled without recovery of additional specimens. No one could have guessed that there was a basic imperfection in this seemingly complete initial find! At the midline in the front of this mandible, what were indisputably two small central incisors remained, and lateral to them were two much larger teeth that were variously interpreted as a pair of large lateral incisors or alternatively canines. However, most students worked with crown-view photographs of this dentition, and few if any who wrote about it had recourse to the original specimen in the Stuttgart "Natur Kabinett"; photographs from above did not reveal the extreme size disparity between the two seemingly most anterior pairs of lower teeth. Had this discrepancy been grasped early, the problem of what were the canines of this animal would have been solved before new finds were made. In writing the original description of this mandible, Schlosser wavered somewhat as to whether the dental formula is $\frac{}{1.1.3.3.}$ as in the living tarsier or $\frac{}{2.1.2.3.}$ as in the present-day catarrhines. This set the stage for the two principal interpretations of *Parapithecus*: (1) that it was a tarsioid prosimian or (2) that it was a higher primate. Gregory (1920) even went so far as to suggest it for hominid ancestry.

Actually, neither of these interpretations holds up because neither of the dental formulas given above were correct. Our many new finds of *Parapithecus* and *Apidium* from the Fayum show them to be closely related forms, but generically distinct. Moreover, all the jaws that preserve part of the symphyseal region show sockets for two pairs of lower incisors. What had happened in the case of Schlosser's specimen was that the delicate alveolar border in the symphyseal region had been broken up at, or before, the time of collection and the two horizontal rami as well as the two central incisors were glued together in such a way as to indicate that the specimen did not have lateral incisors. This in turn led to the errors that continued to be perpetrated right up to and including Kälin's (1961) monograph on the Fayum primates. First there was misinterpretation of the dental formula. Also, it was believed that the symphysis was unfused—because of the damaged area that had destroyed evidence of the incisor alveoli the two central incisors were simply glued onto the front of the mandible (see Figure 77). And because the horizontal rami were glued together with a central fragment missing, they diverged markedly to the rear. This pronounced V-shaped arrangement of the tooth rows was taken to be a tarsioid resemblance. Actually, the new jaws, with their fused symphyses, are slightly more U-shaped.

Most of the new *Parapithecus* finds are 15 to 20 per cent larger than the type of *Parapithecus fraasi*, which was evidently found at a lower level than Quarry I, where the new species occurs. This new parapithecine has been named *Parapithecus grangeri* (Simons, 1972).

Parapithecus has comparatively small canines, and like *Apidium* it has three pairs of premolars, above and below. In the larger species the canines are relatively robust. Judging from the size of the mandibles (which are comparable), *P. grangeri* (see Figure 78) would presumably have been about the size of the smallest of modern African monkeys, the swamp monkey, *Miopithecus talapoin*. This is, of course, working on the assumption that postcranial proportions are also comparable in the two species. The similarity between the teeth of *Miopithecus* and *Parapithecus* is remarkable, but may be due to parallel evolution. In any case, *Apidium* and *Parapithecus*, with symphyseal and frontal fusion and with postorbital closure, have reached the anthropoid grade and qualify to be considered monkeys.

Figure 78 Comparison of mandibles of *Parapithecus* (above) from the Egyptian Oligocene and *Miopithecus* (below), the living African swamp monkey. The *Parapithecus* specimen is a juvenile from Quarry I. (Photo courtesy of A. H. Coleman, Yale Peabody Museum.)

Victoriapithecus

The oldest East African monkey is *Victoriapithecus leakeyi*, described by von Koenigswald in 1969. The type of this species was first figured and discussed by MacInnes (1943). The specimen reported by MacInnes was a lower right mandibular ramus with fourth premolar through third molar that may have been recovered on Rusinga Island in Lake Victoria, Kenya. Van Couvering and Miller have recently (1969) dated the principal sites of Rusinga Island primates to about 18 million years, by the K/Ar dating method. MacInnes referred his primate to cf. *Mesopithecus* sp., but his discussion makes clear that the form would probably prove to be generically distinct. This species that von Koenigswald named *Victoriapithecus* appears to show at least one primitive feature in the lower teeth; that is, the fourth lower premolar is externally somewhat anteriolaterally extended. This phenomenon is seen also in *Parapithecus* and *Prohylobates*. As MacInnes originally remarked, P_4 "is fairly sharply oblique to the axis of the tooth row, whilst in the modern form (*Colobus*) the longer axis of the tooth continues the line of the molar series." Von Koenigswald recognizes two species, a smaller *Victoriapithecus macinnesi* as its type, and a larger *Victoriapithecus leakeyi*. He does not mention the evidence that Maboko Island is of a different and younger age (on grounds of a different faunal composition) than is Rusinga. Therefore, the type of *Victoriapithecus macinnesi* is not the same age as the referred material and might be at least 4 million years older. All of the material of the larger species has apparently been recovered from Maboko Island, but von Koenigswald also seems unaware that Kiboko Island is another name for Maboko Island. Typical cercopithecoid bilophodonty in the upper molars may not have then been fully developed, and some of the primitive details of the trigon can still be detected. Five upper molars are described by von Koenigswald and are figured at the end of the text. In one of these teeth a lingual cingulum extends around the protocone and onto the hypocone, but in the other four specimens no cingulum is present. *Victoriapithecus* also shows considerable variation in the size of the hypocone among the different specimens. Two of the upper molars show clear-cut evidence of a crest running from the apex of the protocone down to and joining a crest descending anteriorly from the apex of the metacone. This is the so-called crista obliqua. Von Koenigswald makes much of this primitive feature and concludes that the cercopithecoid monkeys on the basis of this evidence must have been derived from a species with a distinct trigon and hypocone. Nevertheless, because nearly all the early Tertiary primates possess distinct trigons and hypocones, I am somewhat mystified as to why he gives this conclusion such emphasis. Without having studied personally the new material of them, he discards *Apidium* and *Parapithecus* from ancestral relation either to monkeys or to *Oreopithecus* and proceeds further to the conclusion that *Pliopithecus* from the European Miocene should be excluded from the Hylobatinae. He further conjectures that the form "probably might be a last survivor of the original group, which gave rise to the bilophodont Cerco-pithecoidea which have tails . . . ." The idea that *Pliopithecus* has anything to do with Cercopithecoidea is quite unlikely. As dis-cussed elsewhere in this text, the craniology and postcranial skele-ton of *Pliopithecus* show many specific and precise resemblances to the modern gibbons, and the structures that *Pliopithecus* possesses that do not conform with the modern gibbons invariably constitute primitive structures that any Miocene ancestor or collateral relative of the gibbons would have been most likely to have possessed. Finally, there is a discussion of the proximal part of an ulna of a size properly to belong with *Victoriapithecus*. The olecranon process is said to be relatively longer than similar-sized ulnae of *Mesopithecus* from the Pontian of Greece. However, this process and the shaft of the ulna are almost straight. If this portion of the ulna is proxi-mally retroflexed, it usually indicates terrestrial locomotor habits, as can be seen clearly in the ulnae of baboons or of patas monkeys. On the other hand, if the proximal part of the ulna is curved dorsally, it reflects the condition seen in arboreal forms such as most lemurs, South American monkeys, or *Pliopithecus*. The straight proximal ulnar shaft of *Victoriapithecus* possibly indicates quad-rupedal and semiterrestrial habits. It certainly does not show the degree of convexity of this bone typical of modern Old and New World arboreal monkeys.

The only other African monkeys that may be of Miocene age are *Prohylobates*, discussed below, and a single lower third molar from Ongoliba in the Congo described by Hooijer (1963). This tooth has a well-developed third lobe and was referred by Hooijer as follows: "cf. *Macaca* c.q. *Mesopithecus* sp." This tooth appears to be typically cercopithecoid. Arambourg (1959) described a species "*Macaca flandrini*" from the upper Miocene of Oran, Algeria. As von Koenigswald points out, the same fauna from which *Macaca flandrini* comes contains *Hipparion* and *Hyaena*, which by most standards would make the fauna both Pontian and Pliocene. He further observed that *Macaca flandrini* appears to be a composite of two or more different species.

Prohylobates

The species *Prohylobates tandyi* was described in 1918 by the French geologist Réné Fourtau. It was one of a series of species of Miocene vertebrate fossils collected principally from the ridges north of Hatayet al Moghara, on the northwest side of Wadi Moghara, Egypt, U.A.R. In addition to the type specimen of *Prohylobates tandyi*, Fourtau described two other mandibular fragments under the name *?Dryopithecus mogharensis*. Through the assistance of Dr. Darwish el Farr, Director of the Geological Museum, Cairo, I recently had the opportunity to study the originals of these three specimens, and the results of that study are published in Simons (1969b). Analysis of these three finds shows that they are not apes, but all have the mandibular anatomy of cercopithecoid monkeys. It seems reasonable to conclude further that they all belong to the same species because the size disparity is not great, they come from the same general locality and age, and—insofar as they can be compared—there seems to be no anatomical difference between the three. *Prohylobates tandyi* has page priority as a name over *?Dryopithecus mogharensis*, and thus it has to be sustained as an unfortunate but taxonomically valid name for what seems to be (if early Miocene in age) the oldest monkey described to date. In recent years, Remane (1965) and Le Gros Clark and Leakey (1951) have recognized in one way or another that the molars of the three Wadi Moghara primates resemble those of cercopithecoid monkeys, but not having seen the originals their remarks are cautious.

Initially, Remane (1921), who did consider at some length the significance of Fourtau's Miocene Egyptian primates, was impressed with the idea that *Prohylobates* was rather closely related to *Propliopithecus* and that the possibility of this relationship had been entirely missed by Fourtau, who made no reference to Schlosser's important work (1911) on North African Oligocene mammals, including primates such as *Propliopithecus*.

Remane (1921) was the first to point out that the entire set of characteristics by which Fourtau attempted to relate *Prohylobates* to *Hylobates* was not taxonomically important and did not indicate in any way that the two held an ancestor–descendant relationship.

On the other hand, Remane himself, working from Fourtau's poor photographic plates, did not realize that the external border of the mandible had been broken away anteriorly so that the mesial alveolus and root of the P_3 had been lost. Concluding, instead, that P_3 of *Prohylobates* was single-rooted, he considered the form quite distinctive, because this feature (single-rooted P_3) is found commonly elsewhere among Higher Primates only in *Homo*.

Many of the features of resemblance that Remane early saw between *Propliopithecus* and *Prohylobates* are such common features among primates, like the evidence for a triangular-shaped and apparently distinct hypoconulid or rounded outlines of the teeth, that they indicate no special affinity, and by 1965 he had reversed his position that *Prohylobates* was related to the ape *Propliopithecus*. Instead he concluded that the affinities might lie with the colobines.

Simons (1969b) presented evidence for the possibility that *Victoriapithecus* (= cf. *Mesopithecus* sp., MacInnes) and *Prohylobates* could be related to a different Fayum genus, *Parapithecus*. All have anterolaterally oriented P_4 protoconids, relatively small *Cercopithecus*-like M_3, somewhat hypsodont molars, and incipient tendencies toward quadritubercular or quadricuspid molars with heavy flat wear. The decreasing degree of wear on the cheek teeth posteriorly in *Prohylobates* is striking.

Other than the finds of Miocene African monkeys discussed above, nothing more is known at present except for two specimens from Napak, Karamoja, Uganda (see Pilbeam and Walker, 1968). These constitute a frontal bone with completely fused metopic suture from Napak Site IX that is believed to resemble colobines most, and an upper M^1 or M^2 that came from Site V and appears to more closely resemble cercopithecine molars. Pilbeam and

Walker took these two finds as suggesting the probability that separation of the two subfamilies of Old World Monkeys might have taken place prior to the time of the 19 million to 22 million years ago K/Ar dates associated with the Napak sites.

Mesopithecus

Only the fourth extinct primate to be brought to the attention of scientists was *Mesopithecus pentelici*, described by Wagner in 1839 on the basis of finds made in deposits of the earliest Pliocene (Pontian or Pikermian provincial ages) occurring near Athens, Greece. This monkey is somewhat puzzling, for although it occurs with a fauna that indicates open-country grassland conditions, giving evidence that the primate must have been terrestrially adapted, the cranium of *Mesopithecus* (see Figure 79) closely resembles those of arboreal colobine monkeys. Actually, the paradox is not so great as it might seem, for considering that we know that colobine monkeys had to have migrated out of Africa in order to reach their present-day distribution in Southeast Asia, then a terrestrially adapted species is the most obvious channel for such a migration. A fully arboreal colobine such as *Colobus polykomos* seldom ventures away from forests and when on the ground prefers to walk on fallen branches. It seems improbable that continuous forest ever extended all the way from Central Africa to Southeast Asia. It is therefore likely that part of the migration of colobines to that region was terrestrial.

Numerous skulls of *Mesopithecus*, perhaps twenty or more, and a large number of postcranial bones have come from the Pontian of Attica. These show that there was slightly more sexual dimorphism, in this species expressed in larger skull, snout, and canines in males, than is typical of the African colobines. In this case, the resemblance is to such genera as *Nasalis* or *Rhinopithecus*.

Mesopithecus occurs in a broad distribution in the Pontian of Europe and the Near East, but apparently is not found in the

Figure 79 Skull of *Mesopithecus* (male), the earliest Eurasian colobine monkey, from early Pliocene deposits near Athens, Greece. Scale × 0.75. (Photo courtesy of E. Delson.)

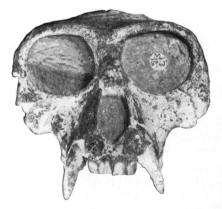

Pontian of the Far East. *Mesopithecus* has been reported from the vicinity of Kalimanci, Bulgaria; near Tiraspol, Russia; Saloniki and Pikermi, Greece; Titov Veles, Yugoslavia; and Maragha, Iran.

As in quadrupedal monkeys, the hindlimbs of *Mesopithecus* were clearly longer than the forelimbs. However, they did not equip the animal to "run backwardly more rapidly than forwardly," as indicated by one student a few years ago. The comparatively long phalanges, if they can be properly associated with limb bones of full adult size (because of disassociated recoveries they may not have been), could indicate an arboreal adaptation. Since the olecranon process of the ulna has a low posterior inclination, it may be that a semiarboreal adaptation similar to that of the African vervets or Indian hanuman monkeys is indicated. Nevertheless, in comparison with present-day monkeys the long bones of *Mesopithecus* seem rather thick and stocky for a tree-dwelling species. Vogel (1968) has reaffirmed the craniological resemblance of *Mesopithecus* to *Colobus* and *Presbytis,* as do also the indexes calculated by Verheyen (1962). Moreover, in addition to these indications is the standard one that in cercopithecines the parietals and alisphenoids are typically in contact whereas in colobines it is the squamosal and temporal bones that are contiguous. In this detail *Mesopithecus* resembles colobines.

In view of its early and wide distribution in Europe and the Near East, it would seem possible that *Mesopithecus* does not represent an extinct side branch, but more likely is a species near the basal ancestry of the Asian colobines.

Fossil macaques

Fossil finds indicate that the genus *Macaca* was European or perhaps circum-Mediterranean in origin. Today it has achieved what appears to be the most widespread distribution of any Old World monkey—ranging in discontinuous distribution from Gibraltar and North Africa across India and Southeast Asia, and on to the northern island of Japan, where the Japanese macaque (*Macaca fuscata*) is adapted to the most rigorous environment tolerated in the wild by any living nonhuman primate.

Moreover, species of *Macaca* show a long time-duration for the group, if all published descriptions of their occurrence are accepted. Arambourg (1959) named a species of this genus from Miocene-Pliocene lignite deposits in the department of Oran, Algeria. This fossil site must be some 6 million to 8 million years old, which would make this one of the oldest documented occurrences of a species belonging to a living genus of primates. Although Arambourg's discussion seems cogent, none of the specimens from Oran are very complete. Over forty primate specimens have been recovered there, but most are isolated teeth. In fact, von Koenigswald (1969) has suggested that "*M. flandrini*" consists of at least two different species. Stromer (1913) described a primate, *Aulaxinus libyca,* from the Wadi Natrun, Egypt, where *Libypithecus* (which Stromer also named) was recovered.

Ristori (1890) showed that *Aulaxinus* is a junior synonym of

Macaca. To my knowledge, direct comparisons that would demonstrate whether *M. libyca* is a species distinct from other early members of the genus have not yet been made, but these species are currently under study by Delson.

As long ago as 1859 the French scientist Gervais named *Macaca prisca* from a jaw fragment of the latest Pliocene near Montpelier, France. Owen (1865) named a species of this genus, *M. pliocaenica*, from English middle Pleistocene deposits, but Kurtén (1968) emphasizes the view that the middle Pleistocene form is probably conspecific with the modern Magot or Barbary macaque, *Macaca sylvanus*. He also believes that the early Pleistocene species *Macaca florentina* (see Cocchi, 1872) from the Val d'Arno and Villafranca d'Asti, Italy, as well as from various localities in France and Holland, is the ancestor of *M. sylvanus*. Early and middle Pleistocene macaques reported from outside Europe and North Africa may not belong in the genus.

?*Macaca sivalensis* was described by Lydekker (1878) from middle or early Pliocene sediments of Dhok Pathan age near Hasnot in the Salt Range, West Pakistan. The type of this species, which consists of two maxillary fragments, is hardly adequate for strict generic determination. These two specimens along with three others from near Hasnot constitute the oldest monkey remains from India. Pilgrim (1910) placed the Hasnot monkey in *Semnopithecus* (now *Presbytis*) but later for no presently appreciable reason transferred his 1910 "*Semnopithecus*" *asnoti* to the genus *Cercopithecus*—an occurrence of this genus never documented elsewhere in Eurasia. My studies indicate that his grounds for this transferral were quite inadequate, and the characters of the Hasnot monkey, which he cites as being diagnostic of *Cercopithecus*, actually occur in Indian *Presbytis*, both living and fossil.

Dolichopithecus

A new genus and species of Pliocene monkey was described by Depéret in 1897 under the name *Dolichopithecus ruscinensis* (see Figure

Figure 80 Partial skull of *Dolichopithecus* from France. Scale × 0.66. (Photo courtesy of E. Delson.)

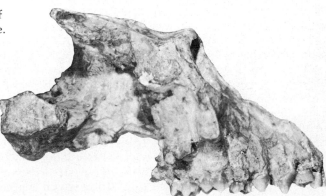

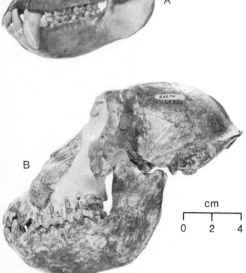

Figure 81 Skull of *?Procynocephalus* (B) from France (cast). Once considered a species of *Dolichopithecus*, this find from near Senèze in the Arvergne region of France is more like a large macaque (A) than like a colobine. (Photo courtesy of A. H. Coleman, Yale Peabody Museum.)

80, page 197) from finds made at sites near Perpignan, France. Together with fairly complete skulls of both sexes, many of the limb bones (including some phalanges, humerus, ulna, radius, and femur) were recovered.

The affinities of this species appear to be with colobines, but according to Jolly (1967) the stocky limb bones are clearly macaque-like. In spite of the long face, Depéret placed the genus among the colobines (= semnopithecines). Jolly (1967) supported this view, because *Dolichopithecus ruscinensis* skulls resemble *Colobus* in showing short, broad nasals, and the cheek teeth have comparatively high cusps with a strong development of transverse crests. Like other colobines, the angular region of the jaw is large and the incisors are relatively smaller than those of cercopithecines which have posterior teeth the absolute size of those of this species.

Much later, Depéret (1929) published a second species of this genus, *D. arvernensis*, from a Villafranchian (early Pleistocene) site near Senèze, France. The description was based on a nearly complete female skull, which is the specimen most often figured in texts as an example of *Dolichopithecus*. Nevertheless, this second species is actually referable to the Cercopithecinae and should not have been assigned to a colobine genus (see Jolly, 1967, and Vogel, 1968). It seems rather to have been an oversized derivative of the earliest radiation of *Macaca* outside Africa, which adaptively if not phyletically resembles the Celebes black ape, *Macaca nigra*—one of the largest of present-day macaques (see Figure 81).

Procynocephalus

Knowledge of the true affinities of the second supposed species of *Dolichopithecus* came with the description by Schlosser in 1924 of *Procynocephalus wimani* from Pleistocene Nihowan (= Villafranchian) age deposits in various parts of China. This material, like that of *D. arvernensis*, indicates a species or geographically widely distributed group of species of large Eurasian terrestrially adapted macaques. Teilhard de Chardin (1938) described various limb bones that, according to Jolly (1967), show clear evidence of terrestrial adaptation. The ulnar olecranon process is reflected backward. In the more arboreal monkeys the maximum breadth of the distal articular facet of the humerus is close to that across the two distal condyles. In the more terrestrially adapted monkeys the facet is narrow relative to the condyles. In this regard, *Procynocephalus* resembles the terrestrial baboons. The similarities between the Chinese and French members of *Procynocephalus* become more understandable in terms of paleogeographic distribution when the two supposed baboons (*Papio*) from the Pleistocene of India are considered. These are the basis for the widespread misconception that the genus *Papio* once occurred in Eurasia.

The second fossil primate ever to be described was *Cynocephalus subhimalayensis* (see Figure 82), a species first reported by Baker and Durand (1836). This consists of a right female maxilla—judging by the small canine—that is of presumed Pleistocene age and is closely similar to the maxillae of Depéret's (1929) "*D. arvernensis*" female. Moreover, speaking on Depéret's behalf, it should be pointed out

Figure 82 Comparison of Indian (*A*) and French (*B*) specimens of *?Procynocephalus.* The upper palatal fragment was found in Pleistocene deposits in India in the 1830s. (Photo of casts courtesy of A. H. Coleman, Yale Peabody Museum.)

that he almost certainly was not aware of the analogies to be found between the Senèze monkey and the find in India that Baker and Durand had reported almost a century earlier. Later, Lydekker (1878) reported a nearly complete *Papio*-like mandible, which he named *Cynocephalus falconeri* and which also came from a Pleistocene Indian site. Although of a smaller individual than the 1836 find, this specimen also resembles closely the French and Chinese materials, all of which may eventually prove to belong to Schlosser's 1923 genus *Procynocephalus*. It would appear that these comparatively large terrestrially adapted macaques were even more successful in their early penetration of India and China than was *Macaca*, sensu-stricto. This may have been because they achieved a full terrestrial adaptation at an even earlier period than did species of *Macaca*. Perhaps the latter initially lived in a largely arboreal manner as does the Wanderoo macaque, *M. silenus*.

Another evidence of a similar large form was provided by Necrasov *et al.* (1961), who reported on a macaque-like monkey from Pleistocene deposits in Rumania. This they named *Paradolichopithecus geticus*. Their description was necessarily influenced by study of Depéret's second robust species of *Dolichopithecus*—a form now seen to belong close to or within *Procynocephalus*. The large absolute size of the Rumanian find, coupled with a close overall similarity to the French and Chinese finds, particularly because of its comparatively large incisors, suggests that it should also be grouped with these large terrestrially adapted macaques.

Libypithecus

The unusually complete skull that was made the type of *Libypithecus markgrafi* was found about 1910 by the intrepid German fossil collector Richard Margraf in Pliocene deposits at Gar Maluk in the Wadi Natrun of Northern Egypt and was made the type of a new genus and species of primate by Stromer (1913) (see Figure 83). The large and long canines suggest that it is a male. At the

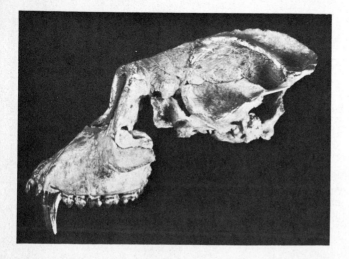

Figure 83 Skull of *Libypithecus*, left lateral view. The specimen is apparently a male and may represent a variety of terrestrial colobine from the Pliocene Wadi Natrun deposits of Northern Egypt. Scale × 0.5. (Photo courtesy of E. Delson.)

same site, specimens assignable to *Macaca* were recovered. For decades, Wadi Natrun remained the only Pliocene faunal site in Africa, but its exact age has not been well determined. The other animals from this spot give a circum-Mediterranean rather than sub-Saharan impression. Associated ostrich and mastodon suggest open country nearby. As far as the Wadi Natrun primates are concerned, such faunal ties have some significance, because *Libypithecus* has always been difficult to interpret in relation to African monkeys, even though Stromer considered it to have "semnopithecine" (that is, colobine) ties, principally because of the tall conical molar cusps. The large and long snout suggested to students of the literature that it might have been a baboon-like animal related to or belonging in genus *Papio*. This was particularly noted because of the low hafting of the snout below the orbits, which resembles mainly the baboons. In 1938, Edinger studied an endocranial mold of the brain but found little that was primitive about it. Actually, the original of this find at Munich was little studied directly after Edinger's work, particularly because an erroneous story was circulated that it had been destroyed by bombing in the early 1940s. The original find is preserved today almost intact in the Institute for Paleontology and Historical Geology, Munich. A principal observation that direct study of this find provides is that it is much smaller than some have thought. It is the size of a patas monkey and is certainly not as large as a typical savanna baboon. In the opinion of Jolly (1967), *Libypithecus* appears to stand closer to the type species of *Dolichopithecus ruscinensis* and may in fact be conspecific or congeneric with it.

Theropithecus (= Simopithecus)

Theropithecus gelada, one of the most intriguing species of living monkey, has also equally interesting extinct relatives that were formerly classified under a separate genus, *Simopithecus* (Andrews, 1916; see Jolly 1972). As has been discussed in Chapter 5, modern *Theropithecus* is the most terrestrially adapted of the living baboons. It seldom climbs into trees, and most of its present range is above the timberline in the highlands (High Semyen) of Ethiopia. The work of Jolly and others has shown that this must almost certainly have been the case with extinct members of this genus. A giant female individual has been found at Olduvai Bed IV preserving much of an associated skeleton. This find poses interesting questions, because the forelimbs are definitely longer than the hindlimbs and the body is gorilla size. This may be the largest monkey species that ever lived (see Figure 84). In spite of its huge size, the phalanges are no longer than those of a male *Papio* but are much more robust. This, together with its size, the associated savanna environment, and the demonstrated habitat of the related living form in Ethiopia, indicates that the Olduvai Bed IV *Theropithecus* (± *Simopithecus*) must have been highly adapted to a ground-living way of life. Although the intermembral index is high in the modern gelada baboon, it has not reached the condition found in the giant fossil form, but the feeding and locomotor behavior of present-day geladas suggests

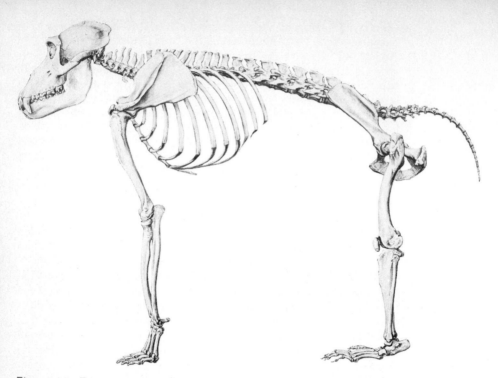

Figure 84 Reconstruction of the skeleton of an extinct giant species of
Theropithecus (= *Simopithecus*) found at Olduvai Bed IV, East Africa.
Note that in this huge, terrestrial monkey, the forelimbs are distinctly
longer than the hindlimbs. Scale $\times \frac{1}{9}$ approximately. (Jay H. Matternes,
© National Geographic Society.)

that long forearms may have been selected for among animals who
feed while sitting. Geladas feed at one spot and then rapidly "bot-
tom-scoot" or duck-walk forward to another spot, gathering small
dietary items on which they feed. Indeed, besides the ischial callosities, they have another pair of pads to facilitate their constant
sitting. Forelimb elongation as a ground adaptation may also relate
to the fact that this would tend to shift the center of gravity backward. Such a shifting of the weight load may be of advantage for
gorilla-sized primates. As is mentioned in Chapter 4, there are
several theoretical reasons for development of long forelimbs besides the traditional one that correlates it with arm swinging.

If extinct species of *Theropithecus*—of which there are several,
representing the time-successive stages, *T. darti*, *T. oswaldi*, *T. leakeyi*
(perhaps = *T. johnathani*)—were terrestrial open-country feeders,
there should be evidence of this in their teeth and in their paleoecol-
ogy. Indeed, Jolly has recently presented eloquent evidence that
this was the case. He has shown that if one compares the surface
area of M_3 calculated in relation to P_4, then in successively younger
populations of extinct *Theropithecus* the molar surface area gets larger

and larger. Moreover, enamel infolding and cuspidation increase in frequency. All this better fits the animal to grind up seeds, grass sprouts, grass corms, and grains.

If *Theropithecus*, in the past, shared the open-country way of life with the modern species, one would expect it to occur in waterside areas where seasonal rainfall fluctuations were great. When such fluctuations occur, lakes dry up annually, giving rise to grassland margins, and seasonal overbank flooding may also cause grasslands by drowning out trees.

Table 3, modified from Jolly (1972), shows clearly that the fossil occurrences of extinct *Theropithecus* indicate that it lived in a waterside habitat.

A final question one could consider is what evidence is there for the antiquity of the savanna baboons? Immunochemically, *Mandrillus, Papio,* and *Theropithecus* are indistinguishable. Moreover, there are those taxonomists who would place all the open-country baboons as well as forest *Papio,* drill, and mandrill in one genus.

As is mentioned below in reference to *Parapapio,* it is possible some species of *Parapapio* contains forms ancestral to members of the modern genus *Papio,* which is about the same absolute size and from which *Parapapio* can hardly be distinguished. Patterson's (1968) discovery of a partial mandible of *Parapapio* at Kanapoi, Turkana, Kenya, at a site now dated (Patterson *et al.* 1970) as older than 4 million years, together with his recovery of a *Theropithecus* tooth (subgenus *Simopithecus*) in the upper deposit from nearby Lothagam that is dated at a similar age (perhaps slightly older), strongly suggests that the forebears of modern *Papio* and *Theropithecus* have been separately evolving lineages for at least the last 5 million or 6 million years. This is the farthest back that the separation of any two groups of African monkeys has been documented to date. Of course, on grounds of much more radical differences in behavior and anatomy, we can be sure that the common ancestries of most other African monkey genera are at least this old or even more ancient. One should bear in mind that there is little fossil evidence other than *this* from Turkana, Kenya, and that of the East African Miocene sites that would indicate *anything at all* about the time of the basal radiation of African cercopithecines.

Parapapio

The genus *Parapapio* was described by Jones in 1937, and the type species was based on a damaged skull from Sterkfontein, Transvaal, South Africa. A principal characteristic of the genus *Parapapio,* and one seen in both sexes, is the absence of any forward projection of the brow ridges, an absence particularly noticeable in the males. The temporal lines in both sexes are prominent as they leave the external margins of the brow ridges and cross posteriorly past the postorbital constriction of the frontals, where they almost immediately fade out. In both sexes the cheek bones are comparatively slender. A principal characteristic of the skull in both sexes is that, seen from the side, the top of frontal and nasal bones

	Theropithecus	*Papio and Parapapio*	*Cercopithecoides*	*Gorgopithecus*	*Dinopithecus*	*Hippopotamus*	"Waterside" Rodents
I. Waterside sites:							
Hopefield	A	–	–	–	–	X	
Olduvai I and basal II	A	–	–	–	–	X	
Olduvai Upper II	A	B	–	–	–	X	
Olduvai Upper IV	A	B	–	–	–	X	
Kaiso	A	–	–	–	–	X	
Omo	A	–	–	–	–	X	
Kanjera	A	–	–	–	–	X	
Olorgesailie	A	–	–	–	–	X	
Koobi Fora	A					X	
II. "Dry" sites:							
Taung	–	A	X	–	–	–	
Makapan	B	A	X	–	–	X	X[1]
Sterkfontein	–	A	X	–	X	–	
Bolt's Farm	–	A	X	–	–	–	X[2]
Gladysvale	–	A					
Swartkrans	B	A	X	–	X	–	X[2]
Kromdraai	–	A	–	X	X	–	[1]*Pelomys*
Laetolil	–	A	–	–	–	X	[2]*Dasymys*

Statuses: *Theropithecus, Papio,* and *Parapapio:* A: Only or most common monkey

B: Present, but less common than other form

Other monkeys, rodents, and *Hippopotamus:* X: Present

Data for monkeys from Freedman (1957); for other fauna from Cooke (1963) and R. Leakey (personal communication).

Figure 85 Comparison of an extinct variety *Parapapio* (*A*) from South African Pleistocene deposits with *Papio* (*B*). The former often occurs in association with *Australopithecus*. Note that the profile of the nasal bones in *Parapapio* is much less concave than in *Papio*. Scale × ⅓ approximately. (Photo of casts courtesy of A. H. Coleman, Yale Peabody Museum.)

form a straight line, or an only slightly concave curve, from the nasal opening to the interorbital septum (see Figure 85).

As in most baboons, the sexual dimorphism in *Parapapio* is usually marked, but the differences relate more to size than to morphological distinctions. There are size differences between the sexes in the canines and in P_3, but the remaining teeth are approximately the same size, and these in turn are morphologically very close to the teeth of species of genus *Papio*. Some three hundred to five hundred specimens of *Parapapio* are known from South African sites, which include Sterkfontein, Makapansgat, Bolt's Farm, and Taung. Specimens of the genus have also been reported at Swartkrans and Kromdraai, but the amount of material documenting this is very small. Studies so far have divided *Parapapio* into four species, *Parapapio broomi*, *Parupupio jonesi*, *Parapapio whitei*, and *Parapapio antiquus*. According to Freedman (1961), it is not always entirely possible to decide which of these species an individual specimen belongs to. Freedman (1961) also notes that the straight dorsal profile of the muzzle is not always present, and the line may vary from a straight one to one having a fairly steep drop in the interorbital region. Such individuals more closely resemble *Papio*, but the absence of clear sexual dimorphism in the molars of *Parapapio* remains, in the opinion of Freedman, the most significant feature separating *Parapapio* and *Papio*. Nevertheless, it seems possible that one or another of the species of *Parapapio* may have been ancestral to the modern savanna baboons of genus *Papio*. New evidence that *Parapapio* species may have been most abundant in the late Pliocene and early Pleistocene is indicated by the increasing evidence of an early date (more than 2 million years) for the Sterkfontein deposits. In further support of this is the recent description by Patterson (1968) already mentioned of a *Parapapio* mandible from the Kanapoi Beds, Turkana, Northwest Kenya, which comes from a level that is about 4 million years old.

Dinopithecus

Dinopithecus was established in 1937 by Broom as a genus of a very large extinct baboon. This genus, unlike *Parapapio*, shows sexual dimorphism to a considerable degree. Broom's type specimen was recovered at Skurweberg, Transvaal, South Africa, and was named by him *Dinopithecus ingens*. Arambourg (1947), when describing a number of new fossil mammals from the Omo Valley, Ethiopia, identified one as *Dinopithecus* and proposed a new species name, *Dinopithecus brumpti*, for this find. However, later it turned out that the Omo discovery was better referred to *Simopithecus*, itself treated here as a subgenus of *Theropithecus*. Several dozen specimens of *Dinopithecus* have been recovered from Swartkrans, South Africa. These finds indicate that the skull was very large and rugged, and in the female at least there was a rather long muzzle somewhat reminiscent of the chacma baboon, *Papio ursinus*. Maxillary fossae are lacking. The female upper tooth row is arranged in a U-shaped outline narrowing somewhat to the rear. The male may have been similar but with less posterior narrowing. The tooth morphology of *D. ingens* most closely resembles that of *Gorgopithecus major*, but the latter species apparently shows little or no sexual dimorphism in tooth size. In fact, teeth of *Gorgopithecus* are definitely smaller in all measurements than are those of female *Dinopithecus ingens*. Cresting on the skull of *Dinopithecus* is pronounced. Both sexes show a large nuchal crest, and the temporal lines are strong. The males have well-developed sagittal crests and large postglenoid processes. The large molars often show many accessory cuspules, and the genus is characterized in general by a tendency to show large, broad cheek teeth coupled with a relatively short lower front premolar possessing a particularly large anterior fovea.

Gorgopithecus

The one species belonging to the genus *Gorgopithecus* was originally described by Broom in 1940 as a species of *Parapapio, P. major*, but together with Robinson in 1949 Broom elevated it to generic level as *Gorgopithecus*. The type unhappily consists of only two teeth, an upper second and third molar that are considerably worn and of unidentifiable sex. However, as far as the South African fossil monkeys go, there seems to be no other species that falls into the same size range as *Gorgopithecus*. In this genus skulls are about the size of those of male *Papio ursinus*. Freedman (1957) points out that the type of *Gorgopithecus* is a particularly unfortunate specimen because of its incompleteness, but concludes that two other Kromdraai specimens upon which most of the diagnosis of this animal are based presumably belong in the same species as the type. *Gorgopithecus* appears to be restricted in occurrence to the Kromdraai site. Compared with modern *Papio ursinus*, the muzzle of *Gorgopithecus* is short and the brain case is rather longer. Another significant difference is that in *Gorgopithecus* the anterior insertion of the zygomatic processes has an almost vertical face, whereas that of the modern *Papio ursinus* slopes backward. This gives the impression of a shorter snout in *P. ursinus* than would otherwise be apparent. Even so, with the muzzle starting more or less directly under the orbit in *Gorgopithecus*, the snout appears short. This feature is combined with a vertically high and transversely narrow rostrum. In short, *Gorgopithecus* appears to show its closest resemblances to *Dinopithecus ingens* on the one hand and the chacma baboon on the other. According to Jolly (1967), Freedman is now of the opinion that both *Dinopithecus* and *Gorgopithecus* are related to *Theropithecus*.

Material formerly allocated to another genus and species, *Brachygnathopithecus peppercorni*, has proven to belong in part to *Dinopithecus*, in part to *Gorgopithecus*, and in part to "*Simopithecus*" (see Freedman, 1957).

Cercopithecoides

The genus *Cercopithecoides* was established by Mollet in 1947 for the species *Cercopithecoides williamsi*, which was based on a damaged skull and mandible of an old male that had been recovered in the dumps of the limeworks at the entrance to Makapan Valley, Transvaal, South Africa. Since that find, further specimens from Makapan, a considerable number from Sterkfontein, and one each from Taung and Cooper's sites have been found. Perhaps the most remarkable feature of the skull in both sexes is the very short muzzle. The snout is perhaps even shorter in the male relative to the overall length of the skull than it is in the female. In males the nasal aperture seems larger and is buttressed on the side by the large eminences of the canine roots. The maxilla slopes downward abruptly toward the alveolar border. Unlike the genus *Paracolobus*, to be discussed in the following section, the ascending branch of the mandible in *Cercopithecoides* is directed somewhat backward, much as in *Papio*. The orbits are large, there is an unusually large interorbital septum, and the top of the brow ridges seems to be directed upward. Behind this torus is a transverse depression followed by the domed frontal area of the skull. The brain case is globular, and the temporal lines are particularly pronounced. There is no sagittal crest. A feature of considerable functional significance is that the zygomatic processes of the maxillae are located relatively far forward, at about the level of M_2. After considerable discussion as to its affinities, it has become apparent that *Cercopithecoides williamsi* is most closely allied with the colobine monkeys. It would be interesting if more were known of the postcranial skeleton, for it would seem from the general ecology of the South African *Australopithecus* cave sites that the area was one of savanna type—an environment that does not match the typical colobine habitat.

Paracolobus

The type of the genus *Paracolobus*, *P. chemeroni*, was recently described by Richard Leakey (1969) from a find of a remarkably well preserved skeleton in the Chemeron beds west of Lake Baringo, Kenya (see Figure 86). K/Ar dates from this succession indicate

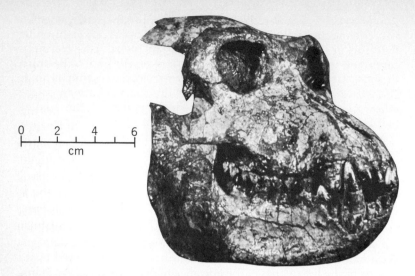

Figure 86 Skull of *Paracolobus,* a newly described extinct colobine monkey from late Pliocene deposits in the Baringo Basin, Kenya. (Photo courtesy of W. W. Bishop.)

that the skeleton is about 4 million years old. This could be considered a late Pliocene age. Among Proboscidea, *Ancodus, Deinotherium,* and a primitive elephant have been collected at the same site. This unusually complete specimen of a primate is an auspicious indication of what may later be recovered in these Pliocene deposits. If hominoid primates as well preserved can be found there, they could be of overwhelming significance.

Paracolobus is a comparatively large form that shows definite ties with the colobine monkeys, as the name implies. Projected estimates of skull length are that it probably exceeded 6.5 inches, and length of the hindlimb from the ball of the femur to the distal extremities of the toes would have been approximately $2\frac{1}{2}$ feet. These measurements exceed those of any surviving African colobine, and are compatible with the general gigantism of mammals (particularly herbivores) that existed in East Africa about the time of the transition from the Pliocene to the Pleistocene Epoch.

The olecranon process of the ulna is curved anteriorly to a line drawn through the long axis of the remaining shaft, which, together with a humerofemoral index below 100, could suggest that this was an arboreally adapted species. Nevertheless, a similar low index can be found in the patas monkey, a terrestrial form.

Considering dental function, mandibular anatomy of *Paracolobus* corresponds well with what would be expected of a large herbivorous monkey. In *Paracolobus* the horizontal line of the tooth row is dropped well below the basicranium, and the direction of the ascending mandibular ramus is at right angles to the horizontal rami. Moreover, the ascending ramus is high, and, as in herbivorous feeders, the molars increase in size posteriorly. The lower canines, which are relatively undamaged in the type and only specimen, have a comparatively low-caliber cross section at the base from front to back and from side to side, although they are quite high, suggesting that the individual may be a male.

In the right angle presented between horizontal and ascending mandibular rami, in the deep face, and in the long pointed canines, as well as in the relatively large size of M_3, *Paracolobus* resembles *Colobus* males. It differs from the latter cranially in having a longer snout. However, the face has a smoothly rounded outline that is little like that of *Papio*. Another difference from most modern *Colobus* is that the nasal aperture is transversely quite narrow and vertically unusually high. R. E. F. Leakey (1969) appears to believe that in general South African *Cercopithecoides* is more similar to modern *Colobus* than is *Paracolobus chemeroni*. The postcranial skeleton of this unusual find still awaits comprehensive analysis.

In concluding this consideration of the fossil Old World monkeys it should be pointed out that knowledge of their relationships is currently in a state of flux. Studies by Delson on Miocene and circum-Mediterranean forms, by Freedman on South African fossil cercopithecoids, and by R. E. F. Leakey on those of East Africa should go a long way to revise our understanding of their evolutionary history.

Amphipithecus and Pondaungia

These two primates were described from late Eocene deposits of the Pakokku district Burma (see Pilgrim, 1927). Both are good examples of two common limitations in the study of fossils; they are very fragmentary, and few students that have discussed them have studied the original fossils. The question of their affinities is dealt with further in Simons (1972) and other references cited therein; at present nothing definite can be said about their placement.

Pondaungia cotteri is known from a left maxillary fragment with M^{1-2} and from the posterior horizontal rami of both mandibles containing left M_{2-3} and right M_3, probably of one individual. On the basis of tooth structure, *Pondaungia* could be related to *Pelycodus* or *Notharctus*, but in the enlargement of the lingual halves of the upper molar teeth, it also resembles Fayum primates and the Hominoidea generally.

The type of *Amphipithecus mogaungensis* consists of a left mandibular ramal fragment with roots of canine, P_2, and part of M_2. Crowns of P_3, P_4, and M_1 are preserved. The jaw is unusually deep for so ancient a primate, which suggests that it had symphyseal fusion; the teeth are compacted together from front to back and the more anterior teeth seem to be relatively small and vertically implanted. The presence of three premolars in an Old World early Tertiary form is a resemblance only to Fayum primates. The deep jaws, apparent fused symphysis, and M_1 structure (resembling African *Oligopithecus*) are all advanced features. *Amphipithecus*, therefore, could qualify as the oldest known catarrhine.

9 Tertiary Apes, Oreopithecids, and Hominids

PONGIDAE

Oligopithecus

With reference to its original description, *Oligopithecus savagei,* seemed at the time suggestive of a relationship with Old World monkeys (see Simons, 1962a). Since then, other animals that resemble monkeys more, species of *Apidium* and *Parapithecus,* have become known from scores of new finds in the Egyptian Oligocene, as has been discussed above. However, species of the latter two genera still retained three premolars on each side above and below, and because the single known jaw of *Oligopithecus* clearly had lost all but two premolars, this advanced condition evoked a reassessment of its relationships, (see Figures 87 and 92.) If *Apidium* and *Parapithecus* represent Oligocene Cercopithecoidea, then *Oligopithecus* might perhaps be nearer the apes, although the slightly bilophodont arrangement of protoconid–metaconid and entoconid–hypoconid (in the absence of other knowledge), suggested a possible tie with monkeys. In any case, Dr. P. M. Butler of the Royal Holloway College soon thereafter pointed out to me that *Oligopithecus* might be considered as more similar to the most primitive known apes than to the parapithecines or the cercopithecines.

The single left jaw ramus that became the type of *Oligopithecus* was found at Fayum Quarry E in December 1961 by Dr. D. E. Savage, paleontologist of the University of California at Berkeley and then a member of our expedition. As such, it represented the first find of a primate recovered from Oligocene deposits in the Old World in more than half a century. It was a most welcome sight that night by a gasoline lantern in our cold desert tent. Quarry

Figure 87 *Oligopithecus* from the Fayum of Egypt. *A:* Internal view of mandible. *B: Stereoview* showing the characteristic honing action and wear facet of P$_3$. (Photos courtesy of A. H. Coleman, Yale Peabody Museum.)

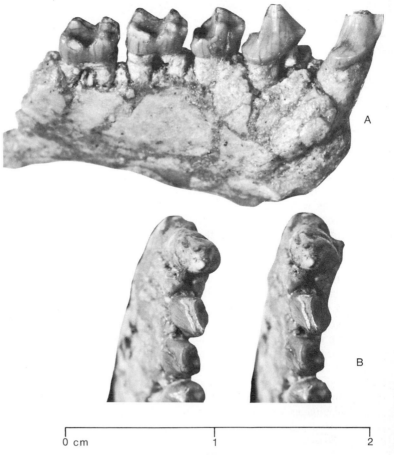

A

B

| 0 cm | 1 | 2 |

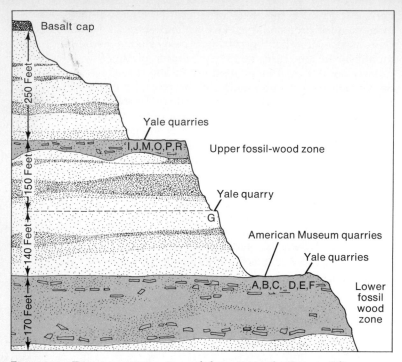

Figure 88 Diagrammatic section of deposits in the Fayum Oligocene of Egypt. Quarry sites A to R lie at various levels in the fossil-rich deposits of unconsolidated gravels, sandstones, and mudstones. (After Simons, 1967. Copyright © 1967 by Scientific American, Inc. All rights reserved.)

E in the Fayum depression lies in the upper part of the lower fossil wood zone (see Figure 88). The occurrence of *Oligopithecus* at this level makes it the oldest documented find of a primate from the Oligocene Epoch in Africa.

All finds of primates before the date of its discovery in the Fayum are of uncertain age because the early collectors noted only that the fossils came from north of Lake Quarun. This was an uninformative notation because we now know that the fossil localities in the section of cliffs exposed there run in age from some 45 million up to 25 million years old.

Oligopithecus was a small animal. Resembling that of omomyines, the canine was comparatively small. If jaw size correlated with body size in the manner typical of monkeys, then the creature was probably about the size of the South American squirrel monkey (*Saimiri*). *Oligopithecus savagei* is unlike the other Fayum primates that are near its approximate size range (*Parapithecus fraasi, Propliopithecus haeckeli,* and *Aeolopithecus chirobates*) in a number of significant features. Firstly, all the latter three are somewhat larger. It differs from *Propliopithecus* and *Parapithecus* in that P_3 is elongate and bladelike with a distinct, large wear facet on the top and front indicating that a sharp-edged upper canine was honed against it. This is an exclusive characteristic of Anthropoidea, and definitely serves to place *Oligopithecus* with higher primates—even though, like omomyins, it shows a barely distinct primitive protoconid cusp on M_1. This is not present on M_2. Equally different from *Propliopithecus* and *Parapithecus* are the details of morphology of the first two molars, which distinctly differ from *Parapithecus* in particular and which resemble early Tertiary primates of the subfamily Omomyinae or even the earliest relatives of *Notharctus*, such as species of the genus *Pelycodus*, which at the beginning of the Eocene were not very different from their earliest omomyine contemporaries. Although *Aeolopithecus* (discussed below) was of only slightly larger size, it differs from *Oligopithecus* in a number of ways, principally in the possession of extremely large canines with thick, cigar-like roots. Inasmuch as both *Oligopithecus* and *Aeolopithecus* are genera with only one species and only one specimen each, a fruitful discussion of their possible ranges of variation cannot now be carried forward. It is much to be hoped that further work in the field in Africa will clarify their relationships as well as those they bear to other Fayum primates. Relative to absolute size of teeth, the jaw of *Oligopithecus* is much deeper than that of *Aeolopithecus*, the canines are much smaller, and the geological horizon that the former comes from is distinctly older by perhaps as much as 5 million years. As far as can be concluded on present evidence, both may be primitive dryopithecine apes. In the loss of all but two premolars, of which the front one is a sectorial hone, both are advanced above nearly all earlier primates, and there is no reason at present to suppose that either is to be grouped with the monkeys or with the prosimians, in preference to placement with the pongids.

Propliopithecus

The type specimen of *Propliopithecus haeckeli* was found in 1908 by the remarkable professional collector Richard Markgraf in the Egyptian Fayum and sold in the same year to the Natural History Museum in Stuttgart, Germany. Its initial description in 1910 and a later and fuller diagnosis in 1911 were carried out by Max Schlosser of Munich, whose incisive and thorough analysis of the creature deserves careful study.

The original find consisted of two horizontal jaw rami (Figure 89), which Schlosser believed were of one individual. Although they do not actually contact, considerations of absolute size, morphological similarity, and the same dental age would suggest that his information was correct. The left jaw ramus originally contained P_3 through M_3 and on the right the symphyseal region with incisor alveoli and C through M_3. Nothing exactly like this individual find has ever been discovered in the Egyptian Oligocene by subsequent expeditions (with one exception—a M_2 from Yale Quarry G at about the middle of the 600-foot-thick section of Oligocene land-deposited rocks exposed in the Fayum, U.A.R.). Because the original site of discovery was not recorded by Markgraf,

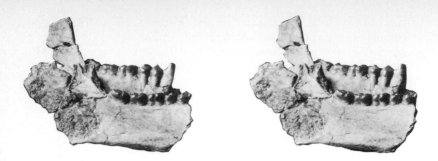

Figure 89 *Stereoview.* The mandibles of the type specimen of *Propliopithecus haeckeli* from the Fayum. Scale × 1.0. (Photo courtesy of Staatliches Museum für Naturkunde, Stuttgart.)

we may never know exactly where in the rock sequence this occurred, but the best bet would be about the time of deposition of Quarry G, perhaps about 30 million years ago. Schlosser (1911) concluded that *Propliopithecus* was most probably in the ancestral line of the gibbons, but he suggested other alternatives as well, including the idea that it might also have been in the ancestry of "*Pithecanthropus*" and consequently of man as well.

Gregory (1916) and most subsequent textbooks have continued the idea of relatedness to the lesser apes. Nevertheless, alternative views do exist. Simons (1963a) suggested the possibility that *Propliopithecus* might be nearer the ancestry of Hominidae than the other Fayum apes because of its relatively small vertically implanted canines, similar-sized or homomorphic premolars, and subequal-size, low-crowned molars. Schlosser (1911) also observed that the sockets for roots of incisors are more vertically oriented than is typical of apes. Nevertheless, these characteristics could alternatively be only parallelisms to Hominidae that are due to its having been small and short-faced or primitive features of the Higher Primates. Recently, Pilbeam (1967) more strongly suggested that *Propliopithecus* lay near the base of Hominidae. Since then, a dramatic increase in our understanding of the basic functioning of the hominid dental mechanism—together with continued failure to find anywhere in Africa in early or middle Miocene deposits evidences of such a dentition—has led to our shelving this possible point of view. As is discussed below, the supposed 20-million-year-old hominid widely touted by Leakey (1967, 1968a) is an unlikely candidate. The pieces all belong to various different species of Miocene apes, and none shows hominid features. Le Gros Clark and Thomas (1952) discussed the similarities that exist between *Propliopithecus* and *Limnopithecus* from the middle Miocene of East African (discussed below). The East African form, in turn, resembles closely *Pliopithecus* recovered from several European sites of Miocene age. Zapfe's (1960) useful monograph discusses all these similarities, and some of his graphs at least partially express the degrees of variation in tooth length to be found in all these gibbon-like forms. Possibly, *Aeolo-*

pithecus, also from the Fayum, is more closely related to hylobatines. It may well be that *Propliopithecus* species wholly or in part are earlier than or ancestral to *Aegyptopithecus zeuxis* from the uppermost levels in the Fayum. In this case it does fit fairly well as a generalized basal dryopithecine.

Aeolopithecus

The type and only specimen of the small Oligocene primate *Aeolopithecus* was discovered by me in the fall of 1964 at Quarry I in the upper fossil wood zone of the Jebel el Qatrani formation. The fragments of the small jaw had been exposed the night before its discovery by a windstorm, and so it seemed appropriate to name the creature in honor of *Aeolus,* Greek god of the winds. In fact, it was this and several nearly simultaneous discoveries that led us to the Fayum wind-excavation technique that was to prove so profitable for the recovery of the jaws and teeth of primates as well as other small animals. *Aeolopithecus* (Figure 90) has a typical catarrhine dental formula of $\frac{2.1.2.3}{2.1.2.3}$. It is intermediate in size between *Propliopithecus* and *Oligopithecus* or *Parapithecus.* It is only about half the size of *Aegyptopithecus.* The lower canines are comparatively large and the root is extraordinarily thick for so small an animal. In addition, the heteromorphy of the premolars is extreme for Oligocene primates, being even greater than that of *Aegyptopithecus,* which has comparatively large canines for a primate of its size. Robust lower canines and the anteroposterior P_3 hones imply that this animal possessed quite large upper canines, somewhat unusual in what must have been a very short-faced animal. This seems likely because the mandibular rami diverge posteriorly at a very high angle, in fact, exceeding that known in any other hominoid primate. In a recent work, Leakey (1968a) has argued at considerable length that such a high angle of posterior ramal divergence is a feature

Figure 90 Type mandible of *Aeolopithecus* from the Fayum Oligocene of Egypt. (Photo courtesy of A. H. Coleman, Yale Peabody Museum.)

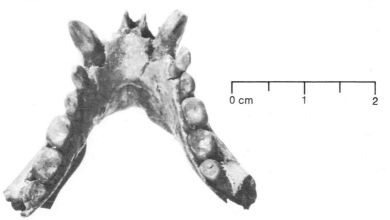

that characterizes hominids. On the contrary, it typifies all known extinct apes. The incisor sockets of *Aeolopithecus* suggest that these teeth were relatively large and rather procumbent. Comparatively enlarged front teeth among primates correlate with arboreal, principally frugivorous feeding and in this case are an adaptive resemblance to gibbons.

Another feature quite different from *Aegyptopithecus* is the very deep genioglossal pit at the back of the symphysis separating well-defined distinct superior and inferior transverse tori. In *Aegyptopithecus* the inferior torus (so-called simian shelf) is directed more downwardly or, in other words, is poorly developed. This is much as in the Miocene East African apes of genus *Dryopithecus* (subgenus *Proconsul*). The horizontal branches of the mandible in *Aeolopithecus* shallow posteriorly, this a difference from *Propliopithecus*. The third molars are clearly smaller than the first or second, and this is a resemblance to some modern *Hylobates* species where third molar reduction is evident. At least one of the European Vindobonian finds of *Pliopithecus*, the second individual from Sansan (Gers), France, also shows small M_3, but, as far as I know, this feature is not to be found in the East African Miocene gibbon-like form *Limnopithecus*. This M_3 reduction may be a correlate of a gibbon-like short face. Because *Aeolopithecus* was a very small ape, it is not surprising that like the smallest monkeys the face is short. Hershkovitz (1970) has argued that the New World monkeys represent a sort of sliding scale of form and that their facial, dental, and cranial proportions are governed by their absolute size. If *Aeolopithecus* is a test case of this (being as small as a marmoset in jaw size) from an independent source group, it does not tend to confirm his position. Unlike the marmosets with relatively small canines compared with those of the larger ceboids, *Aeolopithecus* has canines that are probably larger compared with jaw and cheek-tooth size than in any other primate. It would appear that the differences are due to dissimilar feeding and living adaptations. It may be that *Aeolopithecus* lived as a frugivorous exploiter of the small-branch niche in the canopy, whereas marmosets perhaps depend more on insect feeding.

Aegyptopithecus

The first evidence of the existence of *Aegyptopithecus* was a much damaged and wind-eroded jaw collected in Egypt by Olson of the American Museum in 1906 but not described until 1963 (see Simons, 1965b).

In 1964, several further specimens of this largest of Oligocene dryopithecine apes were found, and recent knowledge of it culminated with the discovery of a nearly complete skull by my research associate G. E. Meyer in 1966 (see Figure 91). *Aegyptopithecus* is a remarkable fossil among primates, for it truly represents a connecting link between primitive Paleocene–Eocene primates and the mid-Tertiary apes of the Miocene of East Africa. It is the only early Tertiary primate that we presently know well enough to

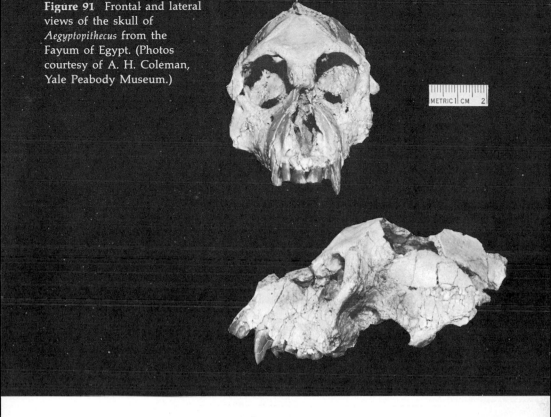

Figure 91 Frontal and lateral views of the skull of *Aegyptopithecus* from the Fayum of Egypt. (Photos courtesy of A. H. Coleman, Yale Peabody Museum.)

demonstrate clear-cut relations with later Tertiary hominoids as well as with more ancient forms. The skull is particularly important because to date only two skulls of extinct apes have ever been found: Grant Meyer's discovery of *Aegyptopithecus* and the less complete cranium of *Dryopithecus africanus* found in 1948 by Mary Leakey in middle Miocene deposits on Rusinga Island, Lake Victoria, Kenya.

Taken altogether, *Aegyptopithecus* presents what might seem something of a puzzle in its combination of advanced and primitive features, but actually these are just what would be expected in a "connecting link," to use Charles Darwin's term.

It is also a remarkable coincidence that both *Aegyptopithecus zeuxis* and *Dryopithecus africanus* can be shown from cranial and dental studies to be plausible stages related to or in the ancestry of the modern chimpanzee. Inasmuch as the chimpanzee is possibly the closest relative of man among animals, the implications of these relationships are obvious. Somewhere along a line of ancestry in or near this one, the first hominids branched off. We cannot be certain when this was, but the oldest undoubted hominids are much younger than either of these two skulls. Thus the possibility exists that one or both of them represent a stage in human ancestry.

Perhaps more important is the fact that even if neither is a direct human ancestor, they remain informative to students of human evolution as representative of general grades or stages of hominoid evolution at about 20 million and 30 million years ago, respectively.

Aegyptopithecus jaws are about a quarter larger than is the type of *Propliopithecus* in most measurements that can be compared. Unlike the latter, canines and M_{2-3} are relatively enlarged. The premolars are also much more heteromorphic. Although it is much smaller than any of them, *Aegyptopithecus* approximates toward both small and larger East African middle Miocene dryopithecines in showing pronounced lower molar size increase posteriorly ($M_1 < M_2 < M_3$). In *Propliopithecus*, molars are subequal in size, and the lower canine appears smaller and more vertically implanted and shows a pronounced upper canine to lower canine wear facet, whereas in *Aegyptopithecus* canine wear is upper canine to lower canine $+P_3$. On the third lower molars the entoconid and hypoconulid are joined by a distinct crest, whereas in most dryopithecines the strongest crest in the area is between hypoconid and hypoconulid. The lower molars have restricted central foveae, and the molar teeth as well as their individual cusps have a more rounded, puffy appearance than is typical among *Dryopithecus* and *Pliopithecus*, or in *Propliopithecus*. The symphyseal cross section most closely resembles that of *Dryopithecus africanus* rather than that of *D. nyanzae* and *D. major*, where the superior transverse torus appears to be enlarged at the expense of the inferior transverse torus so that the symphyseal cross section is more triangular in outline. The ascending ramus or branch of the mandible is much broader from front to back (relative to mandibular depth as M_3) than in *Propliopithecus* and *Dryopithecus*. This implies large, powerful chewing muscles. When the skull was found, this was confirmed, for the temporal muscles were so large that they met at the midline to form a sagittal crest. Figure 92 compares lateral views of the P_3–M_1 of *Aegyptopithecus* and *Oligopithecus*, showing that, in both, premolars are heteromorphic and similar.

In fact, it is the skull that shows most clearly the distinctiveness of the genus. Unlike all later Hominoidea, the snout is long and the nasals are projected far forward. Rather than being diminished and shifted backward as in *Dryopithecus* (along with the nasal aperture itself), the ascending part of the premaxilla is so broad from front to back that it exceeds in relative size the proportions of this bone in most if not all Eocene primates. The orbits are large and fully directed forward, and the postorbital plates of frontal, jugal, and maxilla give proof of postorbital closure between the orbital and temporal fossae to about the extent seen typically in the platyrrhine monkeys.

Compared with the facial component of the cranium, the brain case itself is surprisingly small. It is clearly relatively smaller than in any living monkey, and this together with the long snout gives the creature an almost lemur-like aspect. Yet in dentition and in postorbital closure it has advanced far beyond any prosimian in

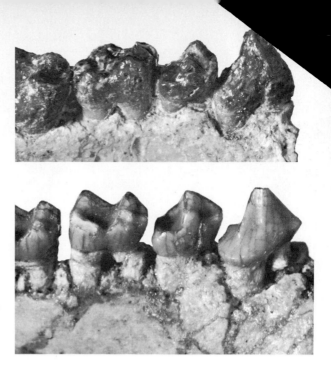

Figure 92 Comparison of the P_3 through M_1 of *Aegyptopithecus* (top) with *Oligopithecus* (bottom). Scale (top) × 4.0 and (bottom) × 5.7. (Photos courtesy of A. H. Coleman, Yale Peabody Museum.)

the direction of the higher hominoids, and these are some of the reasons why it should be considered a basal dryopithecine.

Figure 93 shows the upper dentition of *Aegyptopithecus*, which can be compared with that of the 10 million years younger East African species *Dryopithecus africanus*. Actually, the palate of *Aegyptopithecus zeuxis* is only about two thirds the size of that of *D. africanus*. As the figure clearly shows, there is a close resemblance between the two, but where they differ, *Aegyptopithecus* as a good connecting link should, differs in the direction of Eocene forms.

How did *Aegyptopithecus* live and move? Unfortunately, the Fayum Oligocene river channel deposits from which it comes almost never contain associated skeletal parts. Because these Egyptian exposures are the only known continental Oligocene from which fossil mammals have been recovered in all of Africa, we perforce, have to be concerned with what can be recovered there. *Aegyptopithecus* only occurs in the upper level (horizon of Quarry I) and localities I and M in the Jebel el Qatrani formation. From Quarry I we have recovered a few primate toe bones, including the proximal phalanx of the big toe, that on grounds of appropriate large size and occurrence at the same site most probably belong to *Aegyptopithecus*. Napier (personal communication) reports that these bones are strikingly like the same bones in *Dryopithecus africanus*—a view that is in complete agreement with the evidence of affinity seen in the dental similarities. From Quarry I we have also recovered some large tail vertebrae that appear to be primate. If so, they may belong to *Aegyptopithecus*, a possibility made consistent by Ankel's (1965)

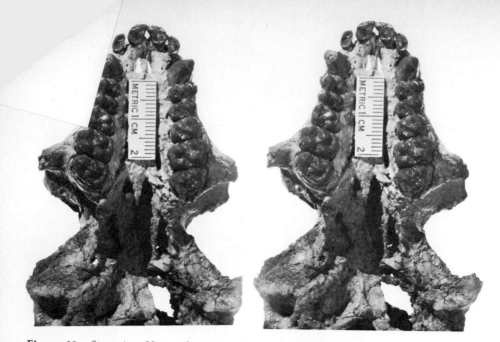

Figure 93 *Stereoview.* Upper dentition of *Aegyptopithecus* from the African Oligocene (incisors found separately). (Photo courtesy of A. H. Coleman, Yale Peabody Museum.)

discovery that *Pliopithecus* was a tailed ape. The humeral retroflection of *D. africanus* considered together with the presence in *Dryopithecus* of straight-shafted femora that preserve on the back side of the femoral neck a primitive, slight eminence of bone may, in the view of Le Gros Clark and Leakey (1951) and Napier (1963b), be evidence of springing and leaping capacities greater than those of similar-sized present-day apes. An associated humerus and femur of *Dryopithecus* from the Miocene of Maboko Island, Lake Victoria, Kenya, are as long as those of present-day chimpanzees but are much less robust. The evidence for East African Miocene *Dryopithecus* locomotor behavior (with the possible exception of *D. major,* on grounds of its large size) would indicate that it was probably a quadruped with considerable locomotor plasticity showing tendencies toward both brachiation and knuckle walking and yet retaining a lightly built skeleton effective in leaping. Probably such an animal would still profit from retention of a tail, and in fact we have no definite evidence that *Dryopithecus* did not have a tail, because no sacrum of it is known. The foregoing digression from *Aegyptopithecus* to *Dryopithecus* has been necessary in order to speculate on the anatomy of *Aegyptopithecus,* as the near identity, except for size, of the toe bones with those of *D. africanus* hints at the possibility that the rest of *Aegypotopithecus* might be similar. If so, then it may well be that *Aegyptopithecus* had reached or might even have passed the level of locomotor sophistication and versatility of movement seen today in the spider monkeys (*Ateles*) of South America. Incidentally, this versatility exceeds anything that the catarrhine monkeys ever attained. This is why I am of the opinion that what evidence there is from both Oligocene and Miocene African and European finds does not show us animals that were postcranially monkeys. *Ateles* is not postcranially a typical monkey but is adaptively like an ape. Oligocene and Miocene ape bones are a mosaic of primitive and advanced features many of which specifically resemble modern apes alone, whereas other features are usually spoken of as monkey-like, as Le Gros Clark and Thomas (1952) have stressed. They also pointed out that the first to notice this resemblance was the French scholar Charles Depéret (1887), who described a first metacarpal bone found with a mandibular fragment of *Pliopithecus* at a site in the Rhone Basin. Depéret drew the conclusion that if this bone really belonged to *Pliopithecus,* then (translation): "it becomes necessary to admit that during the period of the middle Miocene there existed a catarrhine with the hands of a langur or macaque and the molars of an ape."

In spite of all this, none of the studies on Tertiary ape postcranials including those of Le Gros Clark and Leakey (1951), Le Gros Clark and Thomas (1952), Napier and Davis (1959), Zapfe (1960), Walker (1967b), Day (1969), and Pilbeam (1969) really give evidence that these animals were just like monkeys postcranially; rather, there is increasing evidence that many of the postcranials resemble those of modern apes, but with primitive features just as ancestors should have. These primitive features might just as well be spoken of as lemur-like. As a consequence of this, I doubt that all fossil apes known need to be called "dental apes." What it is to be an ape was then emerging postcranially as well as cranially and dentally. Also, all known studies of the biochemical affinities of the higher hominoids confirm that they are monophyletic. There is one basal family Pongidae, from which in later Tertiary times one divergent family Hominidae emerged.

In sum, it would seem likely that *Aegyptopithecus* was an agile canopy dweller with a dentition that certainly indicates a basically herbivorous, perhaps frugivorous, adaptation. In support of this some paleoecological inferences may also be drawn. The Fayum river channel deposits contain thousands of tree trunks, many over 100 feet long, strongly suggesting that there was gallery forest along watercourses (if not everywhere). Fossils of turtles, tortoises, crocodiles, false gavials, upside-down catfish, and lung fish are abundant in these deposits, and they attest to a wet environment, as do fossil seed pods recovered that are related to plants that today grow in standing water.

The numerous mammals from these sites include the most primitive known forebears of the elephants, anthracotheres (related to modern *Hippopotamus*), a variety of large and small hyraxes, the giant extinct four-horned monster *Arsinoetherium,* elephant shrews, bats, and a few primitive creodont carnivores, rodents, and, of course, the primates. None of these strongly indicate that there was open-country habitat near the Oligocene Fayum rivers.

Pliopithecus and Limnopithecus

As is the case with several other groups of fossil primates, the question arises with these small apes as to whether more than one genus is represented. The abundant kinds of lesser apes from East Africa have been divided into two species of Pliopithecus (subgenus Pliopithecus) and one each of Pliopithecus (subgenera Epipliopithecus and Plesiopliopithecus). From North Africa in the Wadi Moghara deposits west of Alexandria, Egypt, Fourtau (1918) described the supposed lesser ape Prohylobates tandyi. Simons (1969b) has demonstrated that this animal, now based on parts of three lower jaw rami originally assigned to two different species, is in fact a cercopithecoid monkey. The fossil record of lesser apes from Asia is much less satisfactory. One supposed species from near Ertempte, Mongolia, Pliopithecus posthumus, was described by Schlosser in 1923, but this single very worn tooth has been considered not to be a primate by a number of authors including Hürzeler (1954) and Piveteau (1957). I recently studied a cast, and agree it is not a primate. The specimen from Haritalyangar, India, that Pilgrim named Hylopithecus hysudricus was put forward by a few authors as being a gibbon relative or related to Pliopithecus. Recent inspection of the type specimen in question indicates to me that it is no more than a fourth milk molar of Dryopithecus—similar in all morphological details to Dryopithecus milk molars from the Swabian Jura in Germany. The single known tooth of Hylopithecus is embedded in an ironstone concretion that by sheer coincidence resembles a mandibular fragment by reason of an elevation in front of the anterior margin of the tooth. Interpreting this as the ascending base of the coronoid process, some have looked at the partly broken tooth the wrong way round, and consequently it has been mistaken for a small (gibbon-sized) third molar. The name Hylopithecus hysudricus should certainly be abandoned, for even when it was described Pilgrim wrote "I am conscious that my material (the type and only specimen of "Hylopithecus hysudricus") is quite insufficient for diagnosis." "Bunopithecus" sericus of supposed Pliocene age was described by Matthew and Granger (1923) from a site near Wan-hsien, in Szechuan Province, China. Later it turned out that this site is Pleistocene, perhaps even late Pleistocene. The jaw fragment contains only M_{2-3}, which are about the size and shape of those of the hoolock gibbon. This find probably belongs to one of the modern species of gibbon—which are themselves unclearly discriminated in the literature. Thus the Szechuan find principally serves to extend slightly in time and farther geographically the known range of Hylobates. Recently, the Yale–Punjab University group working at Haritalyangar, North India, located a single upper left third molar (in 10- to 12-million-year-old sediments) that is strikingly like that of Hylobates. Associated at the same precise site (within 1 or 2 cubic yards of matrix) were other forest animals including *Dryopithecus*, a small tragulid, and *Ramapithecus*. This occurrence establishes the presence of hylobatids in Asia before the appearance of monkeys just as in the case of the Miocene sequence in Europe.

The first specimen of *Pliopithecus* was found near Sansan (Gers), France, in 1837 by Edouard Lartet and was only the third fossil primate to be described (see Figure 94). It was named *Pithecus antiquus* by de Blainville in 1840, but was placed in a new genus *Pliopithecus* in 1849 by Gervais. The genus *Pithecus* was later suppressed by the International Commission. Hürzeler (1954) considered the deposits at Sansan to be of late Vindobonian age and discussed the two principal finds of *Pliopithecus* made there. The type of *Pliopithecus antiquus* consists of a mandible with all the teeth preserved; the tip of the right canine and the end of left lateral incisor are missing. Much of the ramus below the front teeth has been broken away—otherwise the find is remarkably complete. The jaw is clearly of a lesser ape about the size of a gibbon and distinctly smaller than the siamang. Principal differences from modern *Hylo-*

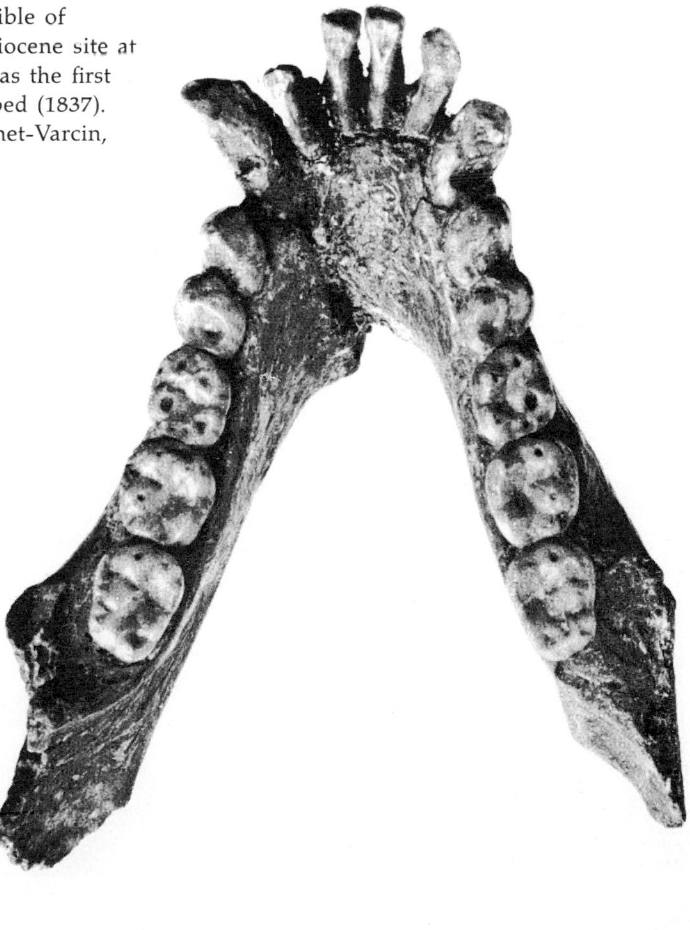

Figure 94 Type mandible of *Pliopithecus* from the Miocene site at Sansan, France. This was the first fossil ape to be described (1837). Scale × 2.0. (From Genet-Varcin, 1969.)

bates are that the Miocene ape had deeper horizontal rami and a comparatively larger chin region—judged by the cross section at the symphysis.

In the view of Hürzeler (1954) *Pliopithecus* appeared first in Europe in the early Vindobonian of Touraine (say about 16 million years ago). Deriving from a primitive species, *P. piveteaui,* varieties of *P. antiquus* finally gave rise to the Pliocene form *?Pliopithecus brancoi* from the "bohnerz" site at Salmendingen, Germany. The latter species is known from only one lower molar. However, it closely resembles that of the Vallesian age apes from Spain, which have usually been classified as *Dryopithecus.* Unfortunately, of these three species only *P. antiquus* is really well known, the first species being based on two finds: a jaw fragment with M_{2-3} and a single M_3. As I have pointed out elsewhere (Simons, 1968), such fragmentary remains should not be made species types. Hürzeler's (1954) study was published before that on the remarkable finds of cranial and postcranial remains of *Pliopithecus* (*Epipliopithecus*) reported by Zapfe (1958, 1960) from Neudorf an der March, C.K.S (see Figure 95).

In the 1930s, along with the discovery of fossil great apes in Kenya, East Africa, lesser apes were found on Rusinga Island, Lake Victoria, Kenya. Hopwood, whose expedition to Kenya had enlarged the material of these apes, described a species of a new genus *Limnopithecus, L. legetet,* in 1933. In the quarter century following this description, many jaws and facial and cranial fragments of *Limnopithecus* were found in East Africa, and a second larger species, *L. macinnesi,* was named (see Figure 96). The latter approximates toward living *Symphalangus* in size. Apart from the size differences, *L. legetet* is much commoner at the mainland sites of Songhor and Koru, which are sites in ash falls on the slopes of volcanoes, whereas the principal localities at Rusinga are lower-laying lacustrine or

Figure 95 Comparison of the maxillary dentition of European *Pliopithecus* (*A*) and East African *Limnopithecus* (*B*). Scale × 1.0 approximately. (Photos courtesy of E. Delson [*A*] and P. Andrews [*B*].)

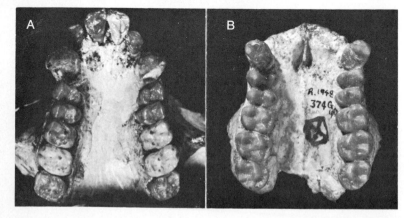

fluviatile deposits. As yet, there are no publications on cranial remains of *Limnopithecus*, apart from fragments of skulls that include the palate and face as far up as the ventral border of the orbit.

An important association of the postcranial bones of several different individuals was found in 1948 by Leakey near Hiwegi on the eastern side of Rusinga Island. Finds of *Limnopithecus* made up to 1948 are discussed by Le Gros Clark and Leakey (1951) supplemented by Le Gros Clark and Thomas (1952), who reported on the associated postcranial bones of *Limnopithecus macinnesi* from near Hiwegi, Rusinga. Later, working in Paris, Ferembach (1958) presented the contention that *Limnopithecus* in East Africa was only a small variety of *Dryopithecus* (subgenus *Proconsul*) and that its species bore no relation to the modern gibbon and siamang. Nevertheless, most authors have suggested that one species or another of *Pliopithecus* or *Limnopithecus* is likely to be in or close to the ancestry of gibbon and siamang (Le Gros Clark and Thomas, 1952; Simons, 1963a). This would be consistent with the evidence that there was never very much diversity among the extinct dryopithecines ancestral to *Gorilla*, *Homo*, *Pan*, and *Pongo*, or alternatively that if there was great diversity it has not been proven (see Simons and Pilbeam, 1965).

Taking up the position of Ferembach that the lesser Miocene apes differ in no principal way but that of size, it is clear from comparison with the chimpanzee-sized humerus from Maboko Island, Lake Victoria, Kenya, and the similar-sized central part of the shaft of a humerus from the vicinity of Klein Hadersdorf near Vienna, Austria, that the humerus in large dryopithecines differed distinctly from that of *Pliopithecus*. The dryopithecine humerus is flexed, not straight shafted as in *Limnopithecus*. Although much less elongate than in modern *Hylobates*, the *Pliopithecus* humeri from Czechoslovakia, as well as those of *Limnopithecus* from site R. 3A near Hiwegi on the eastern side of Rusinga Island, Lake Victoria, Kenya, are straight shafted. Both the larger (chimpanzee-sized) humeral fragments are assumed to be those of *Dryopithecus*. In any case, both are more robust than the only site-associated find, the subadult *Dryopithecus* humerus found at Saint Gaudens before 1857. The two agree in morphology with the retroflexed humerus of *Dryopithecus africanus* associated with other forelimb bones at the Gumba, Rusinga, site. These large fossil ape humeri are not straight but show the same backward flexion of the proximal third of the bone that can be detected in the humerus of the associated juvenile forelimb of *Dryopithecus africanus* described by Napier and Davis (1959). As these authors show, a retroflexed proximal humerus occurs in the more quadrupedal primates, regardless of whether they are arboreal or terrestrial.

The humeri of *Pliopithecus* and *Limnopithecus* are straight shafted and, although more robust than in living gibbons, are already shifted in the direction of the brachiating, hanging-feeding adaptation of the modern hylobatines. Clearly, the humeri of *Pliopithecus* and *Limnopithecus* are distinctly different from those of the similar-

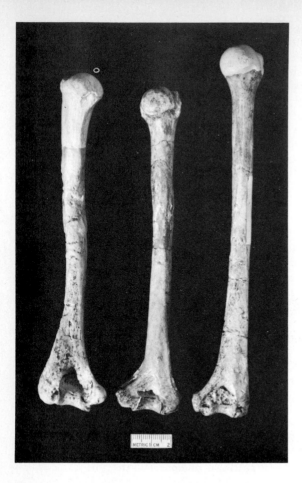

Figure 96 Comparison of the humeri of *Dryopithecus africanus, Pliopithecus vindobonensis,* and *Limnopithecus macinnesi.* Although the caliber of the three shafts is similar, that of *Limnopithecus* is longer and narrower distally. (Light areas are restored.) (Photo of casts courtesy of A. H. Coleman, Yale Peabody Museum.)

sized *D. africanus* juvenile from Gumba, Rusinga (see Figure 96). These differences are greater than those that separate many clear-cut modern primate genera, and when taken together with the many easily recognized dental differences between pliopithecines and dryopithecines they fully refute the position taken by Ferȩmbach.

Distinct differences in the humerus do exist between *Limnopithecus* and *Pliopithecus.* The *Limnopithecus* Hiwegi humerus is about 11 per cent longer than that of *Pliopithecus* from Neudorf even though the robusticity of both near the center of the shaft is about the same. An index derived from distal condyle breadth times 100 divided by total humeral length shows these two animals to be more different than man and gorilla or man and chimpanzee. The much greater breadth of the distal condyles and the shorter shaft in *Pliopithecus* show that it was much less adapted for suspensory activities than *Limnopithecus macinnesi.*

Similar intermembral indexes and versatile arboreal climbing, swinging, and hanging are seen today in the howler monkey (*Alouatta*) and related spider monkey (*Ateles*) of South America.

With the discovery of Ankel (1965) that *Pliopithecus* had a moderately long tail, the relevance of the analogy between the spider monkey and *Pliopithecus* in interpretation of the origin of the modern hylobatines gains strength.

As Le Gros Clark wrote long ago,

> The striking resemblance between some of the details of the fossil limb bones (of *Limnopithecus*) and those of *Ateles* is particularly interesting for it is well recognized that the spider monkey of the New World shows certain structural modifications which parallel the line of development followed by the gibbon of the Old World. Thus if, as now appears, *Limnopithecus* is to be regarded as a gibbon "in the making," it is not surprising that it should display these resemblances to the spider monkey.

Turning to the question of the need for keeping *Pliopithecus* and *Limnopithecus* as distinct genera, the latest monograph of Zapfe (1960) somewhat steps aside from the issues, for although he notes many similarities between the two, the possibility that they were congeneric is not really discussed. The following table indicates such measurements as are comparable in the two lots of postcranial materials (measurements are from Zapfe, 1960, and Le Gros Clark and Thomas, 1952):

	Pliopithecus vindobonensis	*Limnopithecus macinnesi*
HUMERUS		
Epicondylar width	34.8	31.8
Anterior trochlear width	9.0	9.4
Anterioposterior diameter at midpoint of shaft	10.6	10.5
Transverse diameter at midpoint of shaft	11	10
FEMUR		
Total length	206–217	214 (est.)
Anterioposterior diameter of shaft	11.6, 10.5	12.4, 10.3, 10.0
Transverse diameter of shaft	11.7, 11.5	12.0, 10.0, 11.0
Pilastric index	89, 90	89.2

The above estimates and measurements suggest considerable similarity in size and proportion of the long bones. Estimated intermembral indexes for species of genera *Pliopithecus* and *Limnopithecus* appear to differ. The femoral shaft in both genera is thin, long, and cylindrical, with practically the same dimensions and indexes in each. It must be remembered that not all parts of the skeletons of these two primates are comparable. Those that are, are similar apart from the longer humerus in *Limnopithecus*. Both show clearly recognizable resemblances to the gibbons in particular, but naturally (being some 16 million to 20 million years old) they could not possibly be like their modern descendants, if gibbons are their derivatives, considering the facts of the evolutionary process.

First, we should remember that these Miocene lesser apes from Europe and Africa are of almost the same absolute size as modern hylobatids—about that of modern gibbon or siamang species. Most of the earlier authors who worked with the original materials of pliopithecines were impressed with their "primitive" as well as the "advanced" features. What has perhaps been glossed over, to a certain extent, is perception of what is the meaning of the "different"—that is, conventionally speaking, the "primitive" —features of *Pliopithecus* and *Limnopithecus*. An assessment of what literature there is to date would suggest that many of the structures that have been observed to resemble those of Old World monkeys are merely holdovers from the past that can still be found today in platyrrhine monkeys and even among lemurs. In fact, the loss (in the one known specimen) of an opening through the internal part of the lower end of the humerus in East African *Limnopithecus*— the so-called entepicondylar foramen—together with a greater estimated humeral length gives evidence for sustaining a generic separation between this form and European *Pliopithecus*. At Neudorf an der March, C.S.R., at least, *Pliopithecus* still shows the entepicondylar foramen present in the two known individuals. Such an opening occurs very infrequently in modern man, but we do not know the reason for its retention in *Pliopithecus*, when in apes contemporary with it it was lost. One fact is that it is a characteristic of primitive mammals generally to possess this foramen. There are so few Miocene ape humeri that it is completely impossible to be sure whether or not the opening was variably present in the species that we do know, and equally we cannot judge whether its presence or absence was taxonomically significant.

The postcranial features of *Pliopithecus* and *Limnopithecus*, particularly characteristics of the long bones and feet, have frequently reminded those who have studied them of the spider monkey (*Ateles*), the most perfected arm swinger among the South American monkeys. In addition, it must be remembered that the changes in the forelimb of *Hylobates* in contrast with those of the hindlimb are much greater, working on the assumption that the living gibbon and siamang are derived from a form such as *Pliopithecus* or *Limnopithecus*. Femora of *Hylobates* and the Czechoslovakian *Pliopithecus* are almost identical in shape and robusticity. The long bones of the forelimb differ much more in these two animals, but the difference is basically related to lengthening. This would increase the efficiency of the basic movements of brachiation.

Lastly, it cannot be overemphasized that the modern genera *Hylobates* and *Symphalangus* have achieved a divergent pattern of life and social behavior that can in no way be considered typical or "simple" among the anthropoids. Because of this, they clearly deserve to be in a distinct subfamily. These animals are unusual for diurnal primates in that they exist in very small social groups—usually an adult pair with offspring—within a very restricted home range. Advanced brachiation seems to be a good way of getting about locally but is not so efficient for long-distance travel.

In general, those who have considered the unspecialized anatomy of *Pliopithecus* (Remane, 1965; Schultz, 1968) as separating it from the modern gibbons seem to have missed the main point. *Pliopithecus* and *Limnopithecus*, as we currently understand them, are ideally structured to be forebears of these modern apes. Granted that the gibbons had Old World ancestors and that the present-day gibbons are not like the typical or basal primates, then they have undoubtedly come to be what they are through evolutionary stages unlike those that they now exhibit.

Remane (1965) summarized this movement, which I find hard to understand, toward the rejection of *Pliopithecus* and *Limnopithecus* from the vicinity of the ancestry of the gibbon. The process was begun in the curious paper by Ferembach (1958), which contained much assertion but little demonstration that *Limnopithecus* was just a smaller version of East African *Dryopithecus* (subgenus *Proconsul*). With the discovery that *Pliopithecus* had a tail (Ankel, 1965), there were further defections from the position that *Pliopithecus* was in or near gibbon ancestry (see von Koenigswald, 1969). Nevertheless, the monkey-like features of the skeleton of *Pliopithecus* seem only primitive retentions of what originally characterized the basal Higher Primates. As Le Gros Clark and Thomas (1952) repeatedly point out, there are special postcranial features of resemblance to the modern hylobatids in *Limnopithecus*. Where there is little resemblance to *Hylobates* or *Symphalangus*, there is usually a similarity to *Ateles* or *Alouatta*. Such ties are entirely to be expected because the first of these modern monkeys brachiates and the howler might be said to be a probrachiator as far as locomotor repertoire is concerned. The facial–cranial–dental resemblance to hylobatids seen in the Czechoslovakian material of *Pliopithecus* is quite unmistakable to those who have seen it. The following special features of resemblance among *Pliopithecus*, *Limnopithecus*, and modern hylobatids leave little doubt in my mind that these Miocene forms were in or near the ancestry of the modern gibbons:

1. The snout or muzzle of *Pliopithecus* is extremely short and small when compared with cranial height or length or facial breadth, as is the case in *Hylobates*.
2. Perhaps as a consequence of the foregoing, relative to molar size, facial breadth, and palatal length or breadth, the orbits of *Pliopithecus* are unusually large and encircled by forward-jutting circumorbital ridges; such projecting ridges, encircling the orbits, are not seen in *Dryopithecus* or the living great apes but do occur in the gibbon and siamang.
3. *Pliopithecus*, like hylobatines, shows a depression between the orbits in the glabellar region, and the interorbital septum is

narrow relative to orbital breadth. This is part and parcel of the whole reduction of the snout.

4. The mandible is relatively shallower posteriorly and the articular condyle is comparatively low, as in living hylobatids.
5. Canines are long and saber-like, and although apparently still dimorphic in size, the height of upper canine enamel crowns makes up a much greater proportion of the anterior–posterior length of the upper tooth row than is even the case for small dryopithecines with large upper canines such as *D. africanus.*
6. Tooth cusps resemble those of modern hylobatids in being low and rounded. Occurrence of accessory cuspules and distinct crenulations is infrequent compared with dryopithecines.
7. The elongate straight-shafted humerus, especially of *Limnopithecus,* and its high brachial index (104) foreshadow gibbons.
8. *Pliopithecus* shows high phalangeal curvature, as in arboreal arm swingers.
9. The scapula of *Pliopithecus* shows that the glenoid fossa was more cranially than laterally oriented, as in arm swingers and as opposed to quadrupedal monkeys.
10. Lastly, as in gibbons, the ratio of the neck of the radius to the maximum diameter of the radial head is higher in *Pliopithecus* than in quadrupedal monkeys.

In conclusion, the listed features, foreshadowing or the same as special distinctions of modern hylobatids, convince me that *Limnopithecus* and *Pliopithecus* were part of the early adaptive radiation of Hylobatidae, presumably best set off as an extinct subfamily: Pliopithecinae. Of course, these similarities can be written off as being the result of parallelism, especially following the assumption that any small fruit-eating anthropoid would show features of resemblance to modern gibbons on account of ecological, dietary, and size-related factors. This view would be more convincing if *Limnopithecus* and *Pliopithecus* did not themselves differ from each other postcranially. The similar-size *D. africanus* appears even more different in limb skeleton, which demonstrates that there are many kinds of construction a small ape skeleton can have.

European *Dryopithecus*

The first European *Dryopithecus* to be found was recovered in 1856 near the village of Saint Gaudens, France, by the naturalist M. Fontan and was described the following year by Lartet as *D. fontani* (see Figure 97). It consisted of the two horizontal branches of a mandible with some teeth and an associated piece of the symphysis. Incisors, the right canine, and both third molars as well as the upper parts of the ascending rami were missing. From the same site Lartet also described the shaft of an ape humerus, lacking both ends. Because oak leaves had been found in other sites with the same fauna as that of Saint Gaudens, Lartet named the ancient ape after the dryads, or oak nymphs, of Greek mythology. The Saint Gaudens

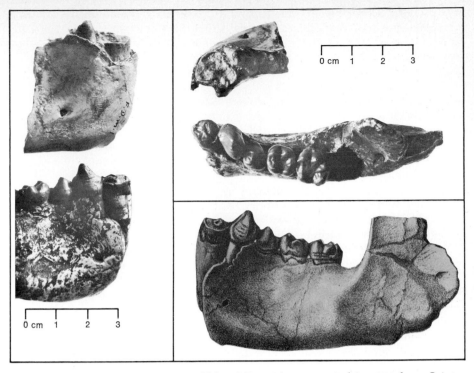

Figure 97 Type mandible of *Dryopithecus* reported in 1856 from Saint Gaudens, France compared with (top left, center top) an East African *Dryopithecus* jaw fragment which has mistakenly been called a human forebear. (Photos of casts courtesy of A. H. Coleman, Yale Peabody Museum.)

locality appears on faunal grounds to be of late Miocene age, perhaps 14 million years old.

Lartet originally recognized the find as that of a great ape—if all body parts were comparable in proportion, about the size of a chimpanzee. He also noted a number of features that later came to be understood as characteristic features of this genus, separating it from the genera represented by the living African and Asian apes.

Although the humeral shaft was about as long as is this part of the same bone in modern *Pan*, the thickness or caliber of the shaft was much less. From this, he hypothesized that *Dryopithecus* was lighter of build and perhaps more adept at leaping than the modern apes. Punctures at the distal end suggested to him that this bone had been chewed by a carnivore. He correctly observed about the first *Dryopithecus* find that although the canines were large and long they were more vertically implanted and less laterally tilted than in modern great apes. The anterior mandibular ramus was comparatively deep, and the incisor sockets in the chin fragment were small. This suggested a deep, but rather narrow, snout in which the incisors were neither as large relatively nor as procumbent as is typical of present-day great apes, particularly *Pan* and *Pongo.* He concluded that canines erupted before third molars. Inasmuch as the root sockets of third molars were not fully formed, it appeared that these teeth had fallen out after death when only their enamel crowns were complete and before the roots had grown to full size.

In a further study of the find, Albert Gaudry noted that the front-to-back length of the lower canines and premolars was less than is typical for these teeth in modern apes. He concluded that the face of *Dryopithecus* was relatively short. This, to him, implied in turn that brain expansion, speech, and perhaps other hominid features could be attributed to *Dryopithecus.* Meanwhile, another more complete mandible of *Dryopithecus* was found at Saint Gaudens. After this jaw became known, Gaudry revised his position (1890) and concluded that the animal was not on the human line but that it was also less evolved than modern apes.

Yet another informative jaw from Saint Gaudens was reported by Harlé (1899) together with other lower teeth (see Figure 98). This left mandibular ramus preserved a complete series of teeth from canine to M_3 showing a high-crowned, vertically oriented, almost recurving canine, a bladelike (or honelike) P_3, and very small P_4. As came to be known at a later date from the much more copious finds of *Dryopithecus* species made in East Africa, all these features, as well as the presence of a distinct external lower molar cingulum and a clear-cut molar size increasing from M_1 to M_3, are apparent in this jaw. These features are confirmed by their presence in the type and second find from the type locality of *Dryopithecus.* It is because of such similarities that we now know

Figure 98   The Bordeaux mandible (inner view) of *Dryopithecus* from the Miocene deposits at Saint Gaudens, France. (Photo courtesy of E. Delson.)

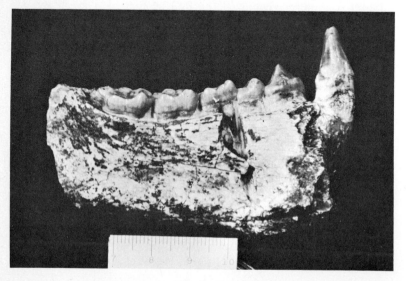

that the name "*Proconsul*," used for East African *Dryopithecus* by those who early studied it, is a synonym.

The seeming paradox as to affinities arose because *Dryopithecus* has a short and comparatively narrow face with almost recurved canines and small, relatively vertically implanted incisors. These characters give plausible resemblances to man of the sort that puzzled Gaudry, but the problem is resolved by our present understanding that these are merely primitive features for the ancestors of great apes. What has happened is that with the modern great apes the canines, especially in males, tend to be more everted and also may sometimes be relatively larger. In all three present-day genera the anterior end of the jaw has been enlarged or spread out to accommodate more procumbent lower incisors. These are, comparatively speaking, either much larger (*Pan* and *Pongo*) or are typically more spaced apart with intervening gaps (*Gorilla*) than is the case in Miocene species of *Dryopithecus*. The enlarged front end of the lower jaw in modern great apes correlates with an enlarged muzzle, and this in turn apparently relates to an evolutionary trend originating in *Dryopithecus* and leading toward a greater emphasis on use of the front teeth in front-of-the-mouth feeding. Probably the large and mobile lips of the modern apes correlate with the relative increase of the muzzle size seen in the present-day forms. It seems likely that *Dryopithecus*, in showing less development of procumbent, enlarged incisors along with a less-expanded muzzle, was more of a general herbivore, less well-adapted to stripping, husking, or shelling fruits and berries than are the modern apes. As is discussed elsewhere in this book, the feeding mechanism of the hominids shows an entirely different trend in which large grinding molars are coupled with small, vertically implanted front teeth set in a face or muzzle comparatively shorter than in any Miocene ape known. In sum, the smaller snout and deep, rounded chin of *Dryopithecus* do not show resemblance to, or foreshadowing of, the hominid condition, but are simply the typical primitive condition of pongids. Some gorillas (among which incisors are often not relatively enlarged compared with Miocene apes) retain the closest approximation to the facial proportions of *Dryopithecus*. Like Gaudry, but much more recently, Leakey was misled into thinking that the primitive suite of facial–dental features of this Miocene ape resembled hominids when, as will be discussed below, he tried to make the species of *Dryopithecus* that he has called "*Sivapithecus*" or "*Kenyapithecus*" *africanus* into the oldest hominid.

In sum, the French mandibles of *Dryopithecus* resemble closely those of the modern great apes, except for expected primitive features, and do not resemble those of hominids in that they have large, interlocking canines—the upper honed against elongate lower front premolars. The mandibles show a fairly rapid eruption sequence of the molars (where the wear differential in succeeding molars decreases but slightly from M_1 to M_3). *Dryopithecus* had relatively thin enamel on the molars—indicated by the fact that the tips of the principal cusps were perforated into the dentine by attritional wear in the early phases of tooth-crown abrasion.

All these features of similarity between ancient and modern apes suggest that *Dryopithecus* particularly resembled the African apes, and not hominids, in two important respects. Because full eruption of third molars roughly correlates with attainment of skeletal maturity in both man and apes, the lack of a marked wear differential on the molars, seen particularly in the mandibles of *Dryopithecus* from Saint Gaudens, means that, like the African apes, *Dryopithecus* probably had a much shorter childhood than has characterized hominids for a very long time. The second important feature of resemblance to the African apes is seen in the similarities of the shared interlocking canine system, coupled with relatively thin enamel capping the molars. The molars in both are also typically long from front to back and successively larger in the gorilla and the Miocene forms. It therefore seems very plausible to me that the modern species of great apes are descended from some one or another of the Miocene pongids we refer to the genus *Dryopithecus*. Apart from the differences between the Miocene and modern forms already discussed, it should be added that none of the three French mandibles from the type locality of *Dryopithecus* at Saint Gaudens give evidence that the type species of the genus possessed a simian shelf, although some later species assigned to the genus do show this structure. Thus the argument that *"Proconsul"* is a genus distinct from *Dryopithecus* because it is characterized by species that lacked simian shelves is unsound.

The second French mandible of *Dryopithecus* is misleading in another regard. Although some have mistakenly thought that a few showed a foreshadowing of the crescentic dental arcades of hominids, we now know that the vast majority, probably all, of fossil ape jaws that go around the midline, showing the arrangement of the arcade, diverge to the rear. This divergence is usually such that the space between the insides of the canines is only about 50 to 60 per cent of the space between the second molars in *Dryopithecus*, whereas in modern apes it is typically 80 to 95 per cent because of the expansion of the front of the jaw discussed above. This gives the arcades of the modern apes the so-called U-shaped arrangement. The second French mandible of *Dryopithecus* has such an arrangement, but this is apparent and not real, because direct examination shows that the two rami have been crushed together posteriorly and that there is extensive fracturing in the symphyseal region, particularly ventrally. When these distortions are corrected, it is clear that, as in other fossil apes later discovered in Asia and Africa, the type species of *Dryopithecus* had jaws that diverged posteriorly.

It should be stressed that such divergence does not foreshadow and is not an indication of a special relationship between earlier Miocene species and hominids, as some authors have concluded. To have cheek-tooth rows converging anteriorly is a characteristic of all Miocene apes.

Other finds of *Dryopithecus* from Europe have, in general, been less informative than those from the type site because they are less complete. They come from scattered localities. In 1911, Depéret described an upper third molar, presumably of *Dryopithecus fontani*, from a locality equivalent in age to Saint Gaudens—the only upper molar found so far in France. In Central Europe (Germany, Austria, and Czechoslovakia) isolated teeth, a series of associated teeth from one lower jaw, and three limb bones that are thought to belong to *Dryopithecus* have been found. Because some of these finds were made many years ago, according to the common practice of those days numerous names that can no longer be justified were coined for them. In fact, with only one or two possible exceptions, there is no way of showing that the bulk of these finds from Central Europe belong to something other than *Dryopithecus fontani*. Some might be a different species, because some of the isolated teeth come from faunas younger than that recovered at Saint Gaudens, but the samples from Germany (isolated teeth) are too scanty to justify separation.

Perhaps the most interesting of these Central European finds is a very well-preserved femur from a site near Eppelsheim, Germany, which was originally found in 1820 (see Figure 99). This femur has been much discussed by paleontologists—debate alternating

Figure 99 *Dryopithecus* humerus (*A*) from Maboko Island, Kenya, compared with that of a chimpanzee (*B*) *Dryopithecus* femur from Eppelsheim, Germany (*C*), compared with that from Maboko Island, Kenya (*D*), and with a chimpanzee femur (*E*). (After Le Gros Clark and Leakey, 1951.)

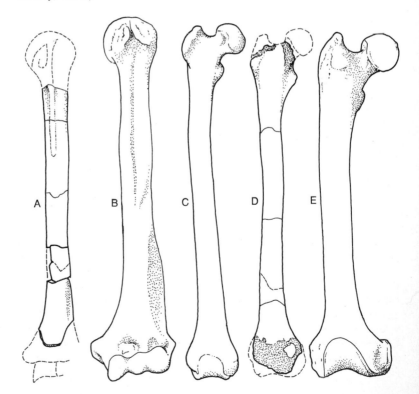

between whether the femur belonged to a gibbon-like animal or whether it should be assigned to *Dryopithecus* on grounds of its large size (it is as long as a *Pan troglodytes* femur). In 1895, this femur was unfortunately named "*Paidopithex rhenanus*" by Pohlig and a little later in the same year was termed "*Pliohylobates eppelsheimensis*" by DuBois. These names should not have been given, because isolated limb bones of mammals—lacking direct association with skulls or dentitions—are inadequate to serve as the basis for Linnean binomina. The question of what this femur is can, I believe, now be resolved.

In 1933, on Maboko Island in Lake Victoria, Kenya, Archdeacon Owen recovered an associated clavicle, fragmentary humerus, and nearly complete femur. Plausible reconstruction of the missing tips of clavicle and humerus, taken together with the absolute length of the femur, shows that these bones are as long as those of a chimpanzee but the shafts are not as thick—just as was observed for the fragmentary humerus collected with the type specimen of *Dryopithecus* (see Figure 99). The femora from Eppelsheim and Maboko are essentially identical in length, caliber of the shaft, and morphology of proximal and distal ends. Moreover, the humerus resembles closely that associated with cranial parts, a mandible, and most of the forelimb of *Dryopithecus africanus* found by Whitworth near Gumba on Rusinga Island and later described by Napier and Davis (1959). These two humeri in turn resemble a third humeral fragment found in Austria, which will be mentioned further below. All three humeri show a significant feature not present in the modern apes or in hominids. That is that the shaft of the humerus is bent backward or retroflexed at a point about one third of the way down from the proximal end. From the evidence of the Gumba specimen (definitely associated with a *Dryopithecus* partial skull and lower and upper teeth), this humeral retroflection must be taken as a characteristic of *Dryopithecus* that apparently does not occur in any other known hominoid genus, including such Miocene contemporaries of *Dryopithecus* as *Oreopithecus*, *Limnopithecus*, and *Pliopithecus*. Napier and Davis have shown that flexed humeri of this sort occur principally in primates that have a quadrupedal locomotor pattern, regardless of whether they are terrestrial or arboreal. It would thus seem that Lartet was probably right in saying that *Dryopithecus* (even with limb bones as long as those of a chimpanzee) was a much lighter form, adept at springing and quadrupedal running. We might expect that, except in the largest species of *Dryopithecus*, we would not be likely to find evidence of structures specifically developed to enhance the weight support and locomotor repertoire of much heavier-bodied animals like the modern great apes. However, these differences do not seem to me to segregate *Dryopithecus* from the modern apes, because the knuckle-walking adaptation of the modern African apes is easily derived from arboreal quadrupedalism where both wrist and elbow joints have developed locking flanges on certain bones, together with robust phalanges adapted to supporting the compressive forces produced by the weight of a comparatively larger forebody. The humerus in the ancestors of the orangutan could also have straightened out during the Pliocene for a different reason—because *Pongo* is a specialized, heavily built, hanging feeder in which tensile stresses on the forelimb would oppose retention of any flexures that might have been present in the forelimb bones of its ancestors. Thus "*Paidopithex*" plausibly represents a member of European *Dryopithecus* species and not some other type of ape.

In the 1930s, in Vindobonian age Miocene deposits of the Vienna Basin, Austria, a large humeral fragment and a nearly complete ulna of a great ape were found at nearby, but separate, sites. These were given the name "*Austriacopithecus.*" They are both chimpanzee size. The humeral shaft is retroflexed, and the ulna resembles ulna fragments of East African *Dryopithecus*. There seems little doubt that these two bones also represent *Dryopithecus*. From another place in the Vienna Basin, a dentist discovered an associated row of lower teeth in a lump of coal that he was about to toss on the fire. Mottl has described and figured this find. She considers it inseparable from *Dryopithecus fontani.*

Bone concentrations discovered around 1900 in deposits of early Pliocene age in the mountains of the Swabian Jura in Southern Germany contained isolated *Dryopithecus* teeth. These sites were near Ebingen, Melchingen, Salmendingen, and Trochtelfingen. Too much was made of these isolated teeth, and several genera and species were coined for them (see Simons and Pilbeam, 1965). At least one of the teeth, an upper molar, resembles those of *Ramapithecus*. Another, smaller than the rest, consists of a third lower molar, which was named *Anthropodus brancoi* by Schlosser in 1901. This same find was placed in a new genus, *Neopithecus*, in 1902 by Abel because the name *Anthropodus* was preoccupied. It seems to me that *Neopithecus* is most probably a species of European *Dryopithecus* of smaller average size than *D. fontani*. If so, it probably will prove to preoccupy the name for the medium-sized European ape found in Miocene–Pliocene deposits of Northern Spain.

Knowledge of *Dryopithecus* from Spain began with the description of a left mandible assignable to this genus that was recovered from a site near Seo de Urgel in the center of Northern Spain. This was descriptively analyzed by Smith-Woodward in 1914. He concluded that the jaw belonged to *D. fontani*, but this is probably not the case. The site is younger than Saint Gaudens, the teeth are narrower and smaller than those of *D. fontani*, and the internal molar cusps are flatter and less distinctly rounded. Moreover, the mandible shows a well-developed simian shelf. It seems more probable that this find, like that of "*Neopithecus*," belongs with the Spanish ape species originally described by de Villalta and Crusafont Pairo (1944) as belonging to two species, "*Hispanopithecus*" *laietanus* and "*Sivapithecus occidentalis*." More recent studies indicate that these are one species of *Dryopithecus*, *D. laietanus* (see Simons and Pilbeam, 1965)—unless, of course, *N. brancoi* preoccupies it in turn. Recent excavations in Spain supervised by Crusafont Pairo have yielded nearly four dozen other finds of Spanish *Dryopithecus*, mostly jaw fragments with one or two teeth or isolated teeth. These are currently being studied by Johannes Hürzeler at Basel.

Asian *Dryopithecus*

As has been the case for other regions where *Dryopithecus* occurs, the materials of Asian *Dryopithecus* that were early found in North India and West Pakistan were given numerous unnecessary names. The first find and species to be described from this area was a palate with the canine through M³ of the right side that lacked the incisors and left teeth. It was recovered near Jabbi, West Pakistan, in Miocene–Pliocene deposits of the Siwalik Hills and named by Lydekker "*Paleopithecus*" *sivalensis*. The exact age and locality of this specimen are unknown, but it may come from the Dhok Pathan level. It was found out later that "*Paleopithecus*" was a name previously applied to fossil footprints of reptiles. Simons and Pilbeam (1965) referred this find to *Dryopithecus* as the type of *D. sivalensis*. Pilgrim (1910) proposed two new species names for Siwalik hominoid primates but gave no descriptions for them; hence the concepts of these two species actually date from 1915, when he discussed the two forms earlier named, *D. punjabicus* and "*Sivapithecus*" *indicus*, and coined names for three further species, *D. chinjiensis*, *D. giganteus*, and *Paleosimia rugosidens*. These three species were considered invalid synonyms at a later date (Simons and Pilbeam, 1965).

It emerges from Pilgrim's (1915) discussion that he had no clear understanding of the three *Dryopithecus* jaws from the type locality at Saint Gaudens, France, which were of crucial importance to understanding the nature of the European fossil ape. Moreover, he could not have known what upper teeth of European *Dryopithecus* were like, because only one tooth—to which he made no reference—had by then been found in France. In his 1915 paper he did make reference to the cast of isolated M_3 of *Dryopithecus darwini* from the Vienna Basin that had been sent him by Abel. Pilgrim also showed limited knowledge of the dental characteristics or the range of variation in tooth morphology of the living great apes. Apparently, only very few specimens of such apes were then available to him for comparative study in India. Granting these limitations to his work, one should add that he was a careful worker, but it would have been quite impossible at that time for anyone to have understood accurately the interrelationships of fossil hominoids without much more direct comparative study of all finds made up to the year 1915. It would also have been necessary to have much more extensive schooling in the anatomy of the teeth of living great apes than was then possible. Consequently, as is discussed here in connection with *Ramapithecus*, he considered a small species, of which he had both upper and lower jaw fragments, to belong to *Dryopithecus* and discussed it under the name of *Dryopithecus punjabicus*. Actually, the material did not belong to *Dryopithecus* but to *Ramapithecus*, which was named much later by Lewis (1934) on the basis of a different find. Acting because he considered *D. punjabicus* definitive of genus *Dryopithecus*, Pilgrim proposed a new name, "*Sivapithecus*," as well as a second species with large teeth and jaws, "*S.*" *indicus.* As Simons and Pilbeam (1965) discussed, the large Indian hominoid species cannot be separated generically from European *Dryopithecus,* and they consequently referred them to the latter genus. Direct studies of all relevant material of "*Siva-pithecus*" to date suggest that all the species and individual specimens that have formerly been referred to "*Sivapithecus*" show no distinct generic characters. Use of this genus should therefore be dropped, even though it has been continued by a few uncritical workers since the revision of 1965. During the 1920s and 1930s, a considerable number of additional species based on finds in the Siwalik Hills were named as belonging to either *Dryopithecus* or "*Sivapithecus*" or alternatively to a new genus coined by Lewis (1934), "*Bramapithecus.*" Species of the latter belong in *Ramapithecus* (see Simons, 1964a), whereas the various proposed species of the former two "genera" all belong either to *Dryopithecus sivalensis* or to *Dryopithecus indicus.* In 1934, Lewis also named "*Sugrivapithecus salmontanus.*" Although this type is relatively small and somewhat divergent, having transversely very narrow cheek teeth, we decided that it would best be considered a female *D. sivalensis.* Nevertheless, in some ways this mandible resembles *D. laietanus* from Spain, but not nearly so much as does another jaw found near Kundal Nala, West Pakistan, that was referred by Simons and Pilbeam (1965) to the Spanish species *D. laietanus.* Recently, Prasad (1969) has attempted to resurrect Pilgrim's genus "*Sivapithecus*" and to restore his name "*S.*" *chinjiensis* for small Siwalik dryopithecines such as are putatively represented by the Kundal Nala jaw. His conclusions are not based on new material, and he does not give adequate reason for sustaining either the genus "*Sivapithecus*" or the species "*S. chinjiensis.*"

A much more extensive discussion of why the surplus of species mentioned here (as well as others named from the Indian subcontinent) are not valid is covered in Simons and Pilbeam (1965). Material found in the years since their publication only strengthens the taxonomic conclusions they drew. In sum, then, the more than one hundred specimens of fossil hominoid primates that have been recovered from Asia to date can conveniently be placed in two species of *Dryopithecus, D. indicus* and *D. sivalensis,* and in one of *Ramapithecus, R. punjabicus.* To these must be added the new species of *Gigantopithecus,* discovered in April 1968, near Haritalyangar, India, but in a horizon hundreds of feet higher than any of the finds of primates previously recorded in that area.

In general, the Indian specimens of *Dryopithecus* resemble closely those of Europe and East Africa. Most of the finds of *D. indicus* are comparable in size with the same parts of lowland gorillas, but some are a bit larger, implying the existence of very large apes south of the Himalayas at the close of the Miocene and the beginning of Pliocene times (Figure 100). The anatomy of all these jaws and teeth when considered in relation to modern forms seems much closer to that of the African apes than it does to that of the orangu-

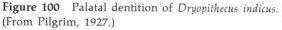

Figure 100 Palatal dentition of *Dryopithecus indicus*.
(From Pilgrim, 1927.)

tan. This is true even though a number of authors have considered
that they ought to resemble orangutan jaws and teeth for zoo-
geographic reasons. The crenulate ridges on M³ of Pilgrim's *Paleosimia* that he took to indicate a resemblance to modern *Pongo* are
actually more like those seen in M³ of *Pan*. In addition, a great
many animals that occur in association with *Dryopithecus* have their
nearest living relatives surviving only in Africa. Examples of such
include some of the extinct Siwalik giraffids, bovids, and suids, an
extinct species of *Gazella*, the Tertiary river hogs, and the aardvarks
of that region. There is thus no reason why the Siwalik apes need
not have been more closely related to the African apes than to the
Asian. Because of the very large size of some of the specimens
of *Dryopithecus indicus* (which also occur at a time much earlier than
any known *Gigantopithecus*), it seems plausible that this species might
have been ancestral to *Gigantopithecus*, as is discussed elsewhere in
this book. In old age, specimens of *Dryopithecus indicus* show considerable interstitial wear between adjacent cheek teeth, as is the case
also in the chimpanzee and in *Gigantopithecus*. Because no limb bones
of *Dryopithecus* have ever been identified from the Siwalik Hills,
little can be said about the habits of the Asian species except that
they appear to be associated in nearly all cases with forest faunas.
In addition, *D. indicus* and *D. sivalensis* ofen occur at the same specific
sites. This has raised the question of whether or not they might
be sexually dimorphic members of one species that also varied in
size through time. However, such a conclusion will have to await
further statistical studies of the size differences concerned, or the
recovery of a larger sample of material. Finally, it should be mentioned that two specimens of fossil apes each consisting of several
associated teeth have been reported from lignites in Keiyuan,

Yunnan, China, in association with animals that also occur in the Siwalik Hill deposits. According to Chow (1958), one of these dental series looks most like *Ramapithecus punjabicus*. The other resembles *D. indicus*. These discoveries thus may constitute an interesting extension of range of the two species.

African *Dryopithecus*

Analysis of the fossil great apes from the Miocene of East Africa (Uganda and Kenya) is more complex than the study of the Eurasian finds because more specimens have been found. Fortunately, however, understanding them is easier because several detailed monographs dealing with the taxonomy and anatomy of these species have been published (Le Gros Clark and Leakey, 1951; Napier and Davis, 1959; Simons and Pilbeam, 1965; Pilbeam, 1970). The East African great apes have been referred to three well-known species, which differ in increasing size, along with a fourth doubtful species to which only one or two individual finds may belong. The three well-understood species were assigned to *Dryopithecus* by Simons and Pilbeam, who discussed extensively their reasons for considering the genus *"Proconsul"* no more than a subgenus at best, and their reasons will again be summarized later in this chapter.

The first finds of fossil apes were made in Miocene deposits at Koru, Kenya, in the 1920s and were forwarded to the British Museum by Wayland, Director of the Uganda Geological Survey. The best of these, a left maxilla with well-preserved canine through M^3, was made the type of a new genus and species by Hopwood (1933). As is discussed in more detail in the section on *Ramapithecus*, Hopwood uncritically accepted Pilgrim's assignment of the maxilla of what later came to be known as *Ramapithecus* (see Simons, 1963b) as typifying the upper dentition of *Dryopithecus*, which in fact it does not resemble. As his published discussion describing genus *"Proconsul"* contrasted it with a maxilla that was not of *Dryopithecus*, one can see why he concluded that he had a genus different from *Dryopithecus*. Actually, we now know that he had a maxilla and mandibles close to European *Dryopithecus*, but not of the same species. Had maxillae of Asian *Dryopithecus* then been known, this mix-up would have been avoidable at the outset. Actually, one such maxilla had been described by Pilgrim in 1928 as *"Sivapithecus orientalis"* (now referred to *D. indicus*, Figure 100), but Hopwood seems not to have been aware of Pilgrim's paper. Even so, because Pilgrim's maxilla was hidden under the guise of yet another invalid generic synonym for *Dryopithecus*, Hopwood might not have realized the pertinence of comparing his Koru maxilla with that reported in 1928 by Pilgrim. Another factor that made the East African fossil apes a group seemingly to be considered apart from those of the Siwalik Hills was that faunal correlations earlier appeared to indicate that none of those Asian apes were older than early Pliocene (12 million years or less), whereas the East African apes were always spoken of as being early Miocene in age (20 million to 25 million years). Recent geochemical dating summarized by Pilbeam (1970) shows that almost all the East

African fossil apes lived between 16 million and 20 million years ago, in middle Miocene times. The absence of an important index fossil, the equid *Hipparion,* from the Siwalik sites that have yielded apes of Kamlial and Chinji ages admits the possibility at least that the Eurasian finds may spread from about 17 million or 18 million to 12 million or 14 million years in age and thus belong in late Miocene times. In all probability, then, at least some of the Siwalik apes are the same age as the specimens reported from Maboko Island and Fort Ternan, Kenya (dated at 14 million years), which Leakey (1965) would still assign to a separate genus, "*Proconsul.*" Thus, neither the age nor the morphological spread between Eurasian and African forms requires continued use of two different genera.

Returning to Hopwood's original description of "*Proconsul*" *africanus,* we can easily see that he rested his characters of difference for the genus on five principal features—its small size, the pronounced upper molar internal shelves or cingula, the large hypocones, the large lateral premolar cusps, and the shortness of the upper molars from front to back. When comparison is made with isolated upper teeth of *Dryopithecus* from Eurasia or with the most complete maxillary dentition of Pilgrim's "*Sivapithecus orientalis,*" which we now refer to *D. indicus,* the size factor must be eliminated, because upper teeth of *D. laietanus* from Spain are no larger than those of Hopwood's Koru maxilla, and, to quote Leakey, "size is not a generic character." In fact, even were "*Proconsul*" accepted as a distinct genus, the work of later authors shows that this group in East Africa contains specimens of jaws of radically different sizes, ranging from mandibular fragments the same absolute size as similar parts in siamang gibbons to other jaw fragments as large as jaw parts of male gorillas. Molars in the "*S. orientalis*" maxilla, just as in that from Koru, show large hypocones, long lateral premolar cusps, and cheek teeth that are similarly short from front to back. Although East African *Dryopithecus* molars typically show rather more pronounced lingual cingula than those of Eurasia, there are exceptions, for several Eurasian *Dryopithecus* upper molars with cingular shelves are known (see Figure 101). We also know that variation in the expression of lingual cingula, from fully present to absent, is common among many mammalian genera. Thus, high frequency of expression (as contrasted with low expression levels) among mammals seems usually to indicate what are no more than racial or subgeneric degrees of difference. In view of this, I should not wish personally to make a generic distinction between the two kinds of apes that rested on different average degrees of expression or development of the shelf. Studies indicate that there is a correlation between distinctly developed internal upper molar cingula and well-developed lower lateral molar cingula, and when upper internal cingula are entirely lacking in apes such as *Pongo* lower lateral cingula are typically lacking as well. Because fully expressed lateral lower molar cingula are present in all three jaws of *Dryopithecus* from the type site in France, this provides clear presumptive evidence that when and if a maxillary dentition from

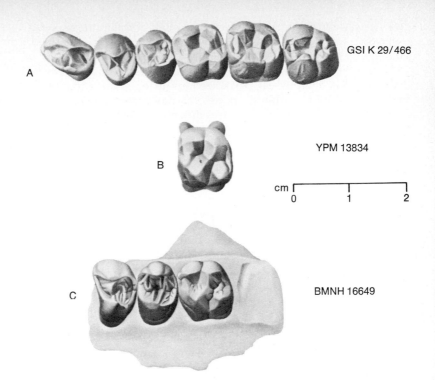

A

B

YPM 13834

cm |‾‾‾‾‾‾‾‾‾‾‾‾|‾‾‾‾‾‾‾‾‾‾‾‾|
    0   1   2

C

BMNH 16649

Figure 101 Comparison of specimens of *Dryopithecus sivalensis* (*A* and *B*), the latter of which also shows Carabelli's groove. *C* is a maxillary fragment of the type of *"Sivapithecus africanus."* This species is also sometimes called *"Kenyapithecus africanus."* (Drawing by Carl Wester, Yale Peabody Museum.)

the type species of *Dryopithecus* is found at Saint Gaudens its upper molars should show distinct lingual cingula.

That the principal defining character supposed to differentiate *"Proconsul"* rests tenuously on the presence of upper molar cingula (reputedly not seen elsewhere) was admitted by Le Gros Clark and Leakey (1951) when they observed that "the distinctive features of the dentition of *Proconsul* are to be found in the maxillary rather than in the mandibular teeth, and the main characteristic of the former is undoubtedly the strong development in the molars of the internal cingulum . . . ."

In fact, had Hopwood (1933) restricted his discussion to the lower jaw of *"Proconsul" africanus*, which in tooth and mandibular morphology constituted the only portion of the animal that could then be compared with the three jaws from the type site of *Dryopithecus*, he might have come to quite different conclusions, for he remarked that "indeed, if this species were represented only by the lower jaw, to separate it from *Dryopithecus* would be difficult."

Another feature of distinction for *"Proconsul"* used in justifying it as a valid genus and frequently cited in the literature is that these

East African forms lack a distinct simian shelf and that the superior transverse torus or shelf above the genial fossa is much enlarged, thus giving the symphysis a triangular cross section.

A number of points about this supposed distinction should be made: Firstly, symphyseal cross sections in apes are notoriously variable in outline within a species, as has recently been reconfirmed by unpublished work of Goodman at Yale (see Figure 102). Secondly, it is not true that symphyseal cross sections of specimens belonging to the type species of supposed *"Proconsul" africanus* actually possess triangular symphyses. The well-preserved *D. afri-*

Figure 102 Tracings of symphyseal cross sections of various individual gorillas showing that the outline of symphyseal sections in apes is highly variable and is unreliable as a taxonomic indicator. *AMNH* = American Museum of Natural History, YPM = Peabody Museum, Yale University. (After M. Goodman.)

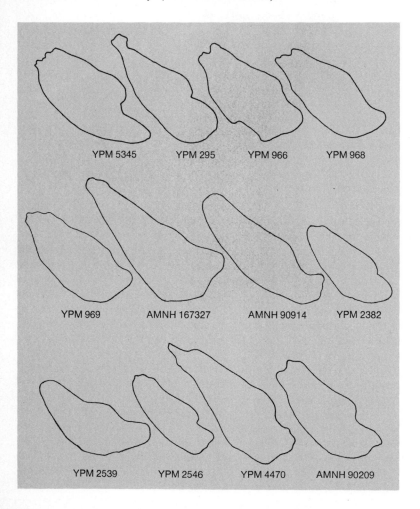

canus from Gumba, Rusinga, which was associated as a single individual with the forelimb skeleton of this species described by Napier and Davis (1959), actually lacks a triangular symphyseal cross section. That is, the superior transverse torus at the back of the symphysis is not swollen out as is frequently the case in the two later-described and much larger species that were referred to "*Proconsul*" by Le Gros Clark and Leakey (1951). Whatever may be the reason for the difference in symphyseal cross section between *D. africanus* and the larger East African middle Miocene fossil apes of the species *Dryopithecus nyanzae* and *Dryopithecus major*, this construction, seen only in the latter two species, cannot be made part of the diagnosis of "*Proconsul*" as a valid genus. We know this sort of cross section is not typical of the type species of the supposed genus, *D.* (= *P.*) *africanus*. Now that it is well established that the size of the simian shelf, its thickness at the superior transverse torus, and even its presence or absence vary widely within a given species of modern great apes, it seems inadvisable to give differences in such structures among fossils much taxonomic weight (see Figure 102). Again, until there is evidence to believe otherwise, it would seem preferable to adopt the position that variations in the outline of the symphyseal cross section are in general due to individual or racial distinctions. Much more must be known about the factors of mechanical function and stress in this part of the mandible before too much can be made of the variation in minor features seen there.

Following the initial studies of Hopwood, MacInnes (1943) described a number of Tertiary apes found subsequently in the Rusinga area as additional specimens of "*Proconsul*" *africanus*. In 1950, Le Gros Clark and Leakey proposed two additional species of Hopwood's genus on the basis of extensive new materials recovered principally at the Rusinga and Songhor localities in East Africa during the 1940s. For one seemingly aberrant maxillary fragment alone, they also proposed another new species, "*Sivapithecus africanus*." These diagnoses were followed in the next year by publication of a detailed monograph that dealt with dental, facial, and postcranial anatomy of the forms concerned. As has already been mentioned above, Napier and Davis (1959) discussed the structure and function of the postcranial skeleton of *D.* (= *P.*) *africanus*. In 1965, Simons and Pilbeam transferred the three species of "*Proconsul*" to genus *Dryopithecus* and the sole maxillary fragment of "*Sivapithecus africanus*" to the species *D. sivalensis*, from which it cannot be distinguished. Leakey (1968a) reasserted the validity of genus "*Proconsul*" for his East African *Dryopithecus* finds without providing any real reasons for such a distinction. He further transferred "*Sivapithecus africanus*" to a genus he had coined for an entirely different species, "*Kenyapithecus*." As is discussed below and on page 268, the type species of genus "*Kenyapithecus*" is a synonym of *Ramapithecus punjabicus* and the type maxilla of "*Sivapithecus africanus*" actually belongs in *Dryopithecus* and bears no significant relationship to *Ramapithecus* or to the type of "*Kenyapithecus*" if considered as a separate entity. As Le Gros Clark and Leakey (1951) correctly noted, the type and name-bearing maxillary fragment of *"Sivapithecus africanus"* has a large anteriorly curved and anterolateral expanded front premolar (see Figure 101). This, as they originally wrote, indicated that the individual concerned possessed a large upper canine of the sort typical among apes, a feature confirmed by Simons and Pilbeam (1965), who noted that on the dorsal surface of this particular maxillary fragment part of the trough or alveolus for a relatively very large upper canine root is preserved. If the outline of the cross section of this trough is produced beyond the broken margin at a right angle to the long axis of the canine root and if this is projected as a circle, then the diameter of the cross section of the canine root would be about 2 centimeters. A canine with a root so large would be fully as large as those that typify males among the modern great apes. The animal can therefore hardly have been a hominid, as Leakey has endeavored to make it (see below).

Meanwhile, Allbrook and Bishop (1963) discovered at the Moroto II site in Northeast Uganda a large palate that they considered referable to *Dryopithecus major.* As mentioned already, this species had previously been known principally from mandibular specimens and isolated teeth recovered at Songhor in Kenya, East Africa. During the 1960s further collecting at Moroto as well as at a site of similar age about 70 miles to the southeast at Napak, Uganda, produced many more teeth and facial fragments as well as a partial mandible apparently associated with the original palate from Moroto and several other *D. major* specimens as well. These numerous specimens served as the basis for the revision of the Tertiary apes of East Africa recently published by Pilbeam (1970).

Dryopithecus africanus

Although postcranial bones representing the three species sizes of East African *Dryopithecus* are scanty in number compared with what we know of most other groups of later Tertiary fossil mammals, we have some knowledge of each of the three commonest *Dryopithecus* species that occur in the middle Miocene of East Africa. The best association of such bones constitutes most of a subadult left forelimb of *Dryopithecus africanus* (see Figure 103) from near Gumba on Rusinga Island, Lake Victoria, Kenya. This limb was associated with part of a basicranium, a snout with upper dentition, and a mandible with all lower teeth except the third molars, which had apparently not yet been fully formed. These cranial, facial, and dental fragments closely correspond with those of a nearly complete skull of the same species found at a different locality on Rusinga Island by Mary Leakey in 1948 (see Figure 104). Considered together, the two finds represent the fullest skeletal knowledge of any known extinct ape species. Some of the more salient features and functional interpretations of the anatomy of this species are as follows: Firstly, the 1948 Rusinga skull, although the most complete of any known Miocene ape, betrays many evidences of crushing and distortion.

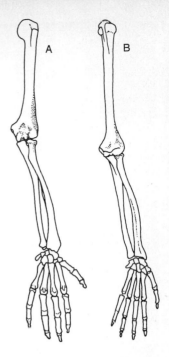

Figure 103 Comparison of the forelimb of a chimpanzee (A) with the associated subadult forelimb of *Dryopithecus africanus* (B). (After Le Gros Clark, 1959.)

Napier and others have pointed out that these disturbances to the natural form have probably exaggerated the apparent length of the snout, and the roof of the cranium also seems to have been wracked upward and slightly forward to such an extent that the projected plane of the basicranium would have tilted obliquely upward from front to back at an angle to the horizontal axis of the tooth row, rather than being approximately parallel to it as is the case in undistorted hominoid crania (see Figure 104, page 248).

Compared with earlier primates, the premaxillae (particularly their ascending branches) are much reduced and the nasal opening has retreated posteriorly, as in the living hominoids. The canines are large relative to the size of the dentition as a whole, and the incisors are procumbent. Although adults of this species were probably not much larger than siamangs, the absolute height of upper and lower incisor crowns was distinctly greater compared with the length of the molar series than is the case for the archaic hominids of genus *Ramapithecus*. Presumably because of the small size and general gracility of the species, no evidence of a brow ridge or superorbital torus is present in the 1948 skull. This is an aspect of the animal that Leakey has more than once proffered as a significant resemblance to modern man. Inasmuch as all middle and early Pleistocene hominids known—and there are dozens of them—show heavy brow ridges and inasmuch as all students agree that modern man is derived from such forms, the lack of brow ridges in some *Homo sapiens* and in *Dryopithecus africanus* cannot be more than a coincidence. The facial fragment from Gumba, Rusinga,

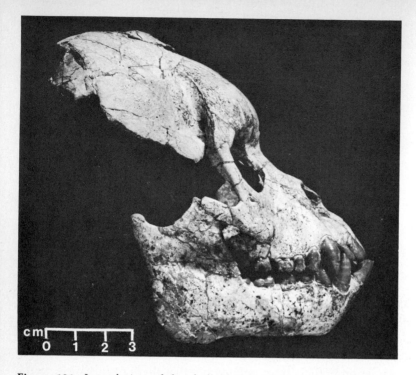

Figure 104 Lateral view of the skull of *Dryopithecus africanus* from Miocene deposits on Rusinga Island, Kenya. (Courtesy of the Trustees of the British Museum [Natural History].)

is less distorted than the same portion of the 1948 skull. It shows that, as in the type species of the genus from France, the snout (or face) was relatively narrow, short, and deep compared with that of most modern apes.

Napier and Davis (1959) were somewhat hampered in their comparative description of the forelimb skeleton of this species because the individual concerned was not adult. Nevertheless, it is possible to show that the humerus, for instance, is, in the proximal half, intermediate in structure between the primates that are thought to have been arboreal quadrupeds, or quadrupedal semi-brachiators, and the chimpanzee. The distal portion of this bone is even more like that of *Pan*. The resemblances extend to several different aspects of the distal humeral structure that appear to characterize present-day chimpanzees and are thought to indicate an elbow joint that allowed both for freedom of movement and stability during suspensory pronation and supination of the limb. The radius resembles those of arboreal quadrupeds but with a lateral curvature of the shaft as in *Pan*. The distal end of the ulna appears to be more "monkey-like." The forearm, relative to the upper arm, is only slightly shorter than in chimpanzees.

The hand appears to be comparatively shorter than in *Pan* and the thumb perhaps relatively longer. The set of the wrist bones indicates that there were large, powerful flexor tendons, a resemblance to the most versatile of the arboreal semibrachiators among the New World monkeys such as *Ateles* and *Alouatta*. In fact, these modern forms make good models for the sort of locomotor behavior postulated for Miocene apes from what is known of their skeleton. Well-developed flexor tendons are also characteristic of the present-day apes. The finger bones of *D. africanus* seem also to resemble most closely those of arboreal quadrupeds and *Pan*, as is also the case for the few known toe bones.

It seems that the forelimb of *Dryopithecus africanus* would have suited it for arm swinging, hanging, and active clambering in the trees. The principal gait was probably quadrupedal. Walker sees evidence in the limb skeleton that *D. africanus* had some terrestrial adaptations—a point of view earlier advocated by Whitworth (1958) and others because of the relatively open–country lowland fauna at Rusinga where *D. africanus* is abundant.

Pilbeam (1970) has emphasized that where there are specific resemblances to a modern species they are more often with *Pan*, which suggests the possibility that this Miocene ape species may lie in or near the ancestry of the modern form.

Dryopithecus nyanzae

Dryopithecus nyanzae was somewhat larger than *D. africanus*—at least in jaws and face about the size of small *Pan troglodytes*. However, relative to the chimpanzee, there are a number of proportionate differences similar in character to those seen in other *Dryopithecus* species. For instance, the incisors are small, the snout was not large and there was relatively little prognathism. The type specimen of *D. nyanzae* consists of a somewhat crushed palate with most of the teeth except for the incisors, which had fallen out. Like other Miocene apes, it shows a distinct canine fossa above the premolars. A traditional dogma of anthropology has been that the canine fossa is a special feature of hominids, but actually it occurs with some frequency in living apes and this pit seems to be present in every known *Dryopithecus*. Some have even gone so far as to suggest that the canine fossa is an exclusive attribute of hominids and that it houses muscles associated with speech. Such is certainly not the case. Presence, absence, or degree of development of the canine fossa is of no use whatever in determining whether an animal has pongid or hominid affinities.

In certain dental features *D. nyanzae* can perhaps be considered primitive. It resembles Oligocene *Aegyptopithecus* more than do its contemporaries in having molars that are comparatively broad from inside to out and short anteroposteriorly. The first molars are quite small relative to the second. This possibly means that $M_{\overline{1}}^{1}$ erupted when the animal was comparatively young and small, when the jaws could not house a larger tooth. This in turn might possibly mean that the animal grew up somewhat faster than modern apes do. The teeth are otherwise similar to those of the two other species of subgenus *Proconsul*—perhaps a little closer to *Dryopithecus major*. The molars have the characteristic internal beaded cingulum of subgenus *Proconsul*. The canines in presumed males are large and long, but the canine roots are not nearly so thick or barrel-like as those typical of *Dryopithecus major*. As in *D. major*, the anterior insertion of the cheek bones in mainly above M^2. In general, the face would have been slightly narrower and less prognathous than was that of *Dryopithecus major*. In this, it resembles the similar-sized *Dryopithecus fontani* from France as well as *Dryopithecus indicus* from Haritalyangar, India. The best maxilla of the latter also preserves evidence of a canine fossa and shows that, as in *D. nyanzae* and *D. africanus*, the external cusp of P^3 is distinctly longer than the internal.

The postcranial remains found in 1933 by Archdeacon Owen on Maboko Island that have been provisionally referred to *D. nyanzae* on grounds of size have already been mentioned here. This associated individual constitutes a nearly complete right femur, the proximal end of the left femur, the shaft of the left humerus, and part of the right clavicle. In addition, from Rusinga Island there are two unassociated tali or astragali and two clavicular fragments from different sites that are thought to belong to this species.

As has been mentioned in the discussion of European *Dryopithecus*, the remains suggest a lightly built, arboreal quadruped, whereas the tali, in the canonical analysis of Day and Wood (1968), have been shown to lie about two standard deviations from the mean of modern *Pan* (a talus from Songhor presumably of *D. major* lies within the range of a sample of gorillas). On the posterior face of the neck of the femur in *D. nyanzae* is a prominence commonly seen in lemurs and monkeys that has been lost in all living hominoids. The prominence apparently transmits a tendon utilized during leaping or springing motions that was probably lost due to the heavier builds of the modern forms.

Dryopithecus major

In 1950, Le Gros Clark and Leakey described (and the following year fully discussed) the species *Dryopithecus major*, which occurs only at Songhor, Kenya, except for an odd, large half-symphysis fragment from Rusinga that lacks teeth and that was recently transferred by Leakey (1967) to *"Kenyapithecus" africanus*, where it is certainly much too large to belong.

In 1952, Le Gros Clark discussed additional finds of this large species—also collected principally from the Songhor site. The most complete mandible from Songhor has an interesting history of recovery that is instructive in regard to the persistence sometimes needed to collect relatively complete specimens of fossil mammals. In 1932, the central portion of a large, lower right canine crown was discovered at Songhor. Much later, in 1947, the symphyseal region onto which this canine fit was discovered. It preserved all tooth roots from left canine to right M_1. In 1948, the missing tip of the right canine turned up, and finally, in 1962—more than a generation after the first part was found—most of the left horizontal ramus with P_4 through M_3 was recovered.

The degree of divergence posteriorly of the tooth rows of this *D. major* mandible can easily be calculated by superimposing on a photographic print of the jaw (taken from directly above) a mirror image of the same made by reversing the negative. When this is done, it is clear that the tooth rows diverge posteriorly just as in all other species of fossil apes known, including not only those of *Dryopithecus* but also Oligocene *Aeolopithecus* and *Aegyptopithecus*, Miocene *Limnopithecus* and *Pliopithecus,* and Pliocene–Pleistocene *Gigantopithecus.* In several cases, the angles of posterior divergence in these jaws are higher than in the new mandible from Rusinga that Leakey (1968b) recently tried unsuccessfully to prove was a hominid. Consequently, having a high angle of posterior tooth-row divergence is not a hominid feature but is merely the primitive or basal condition for hominoids. From the rather V-shaped or parabolic arcade outline, the hominids have developed an almost semicircular arcade, whereas, in a reverse trend, in the lines leading to modern great apes the symphyseal region has broadened, causing the long axes of the lower cheek teeth to come into almost parallel lines. Study of this, the best Songhor mandible of *Dryopithecus major,* as well as the others has produced several interesting observations which Pilbeam (1970) covers in detail.

Firstly, *D. major* shows internally a longer, gently dropping surface behind the lower incisors. This is known as the planum alveolare. In some Miocene *Dryopithecus* species the plane drops away at a steeper angle, as it does also in the modern apes other than the gorilla. Both gorilla and *D. major* tend to share unusually thick symphyses and a long planum alveolare. Another feature of this region of interest is the angle between the plane of the anterior face of the mandible and the line of the base of the horizontal jaw ramus when viewed from the side. In *D. major* there is a sharp angle where the two outlines meet, whereas in the other species of *Dryopithecus* the same region is rounded. Leakey (1968a) tried to pass off all fossil apes as having such a sharp angle at the base of the symphyseal cross section and to argue that in hominids this contour is rounded. Among all species of the Hominoidea only *D. major* typically possesses the pronounced ventral symphyseal angle. It is therefore of some interest that this angle can occasionally be found in jaws of mountain gorillas. It is possible that the angular ventral symphysis is a correlate of the general robusticity of these two large species.

By far the most complete facial, palatal, and upper dental information we have about *D. major* is based on the excellently preserved palate and partial face of this species from Moroto II, Uganda, found by Bishop and White in August 1961 (Figure 105). In December 1961, Allbrook had led a group of students to the same area, and they recovered the right maxilla and two other fragments that fit together with the first finds. In this state of discovery the palate had lost all but one tooth. In any case, it was described by Allbrook

Figure 105 View of the palate of *Dryopithecus major* from Moroto, Uganda. (Photo courtesy of John Howard.)

cm
0   1   2

and Bishop (1963). These authors correctly considered the specimen referable to *D.* (= *P.*) *major.* Another visit to the site, led by Bishop in December 1963, was for purposes of screening scree downslope from the spot of recovery. This work produced three dozen other fragments with most of the missing teeth and parts of two different mandibles as well. The latter jaws had apparently weathered out from the same horizon on the other side of the gully. The more complete one probably belongs with the same individual, as the palate for it is of appropriate size to fit. This fossil is close in both absolute size and overall shape to a lightly built female lowland gorilla, but in canine size and a few other dimensions the proportions suggest a male. As in other species of *Dryopithecus,* the external border of the upper jaw is shallow below the floor of the nasal aperture. The incisors are rather small and are rooted closer to the nasal opening itself than in the modern apes.

Few postcranials have been described for this species, but the astragalus or talus from Songhor that has been assigned to this species is not monkey-like but is specifically like modern *Gorilla* and falls within the range of variation of this living species (see Day and Wood, 1968). A lumbar vertebra from the above-discussed Moroto II site in Karamoja, Uganda, is probably associated with the palate and face from that spot, and thus must be of *D. major.*

The vertebra has been described by Walker and Rose (1968). It is fully as large as that of an adult male chimpanzee. Moreover, it shows a mosaic of hominoid, not cercopithecoid, features, principally resembling lumbars of *Homo, Pan,* and *Gorilla.* In stoutness of the pedicles and in other details there is close correspondence with the gorilla. Walker and Rose conclude that there is nothing to prevent the animal's having been in or near the ancestry of the modern gorilla.

The ecological relationships of East African *Dryopithecus,* particularly of *D. major,* have been reviewed by Pilbeam (1970). Basically, the environment in middle Miocene times appears to have been much as it is today in East Africa, but a little wetter. There were then rainforests on the slopes of large volcanoes, and these highlands were surrounded by savanna woodlands at lower elevations. It is thus most significant that *D. major* is either the predominant or the only ape that occurs at the sites deposited high on the slopes of volcanoes, such as those of Koru, Songhor, Napak, and Moroto. At the lower sites on Rusinga Island, *D. nyanzae* and *D. africanus* are common, and there is no indisputable evidence of the presence there of the large species. This provides good inferential evidence that the ecological preferences of these East African Miocene ape species had by then already diverged.

Gigantopithecus

In 1935, Professor G. H. R. von Koenigswald purchased in a Hong Kong drugstore a huge, fossilized molar of a primate that had previously been unknown to science. He named it *Gigantopithecus blacki* in honor of Davidson Black, a medical missionary in Peking who had been instrumental in initiating and pursuing the excavations of *Homo erectus* (= *Sinanthropus*) at Choukoutien, near Peking. For over 20 years after that, all that was known of *Gigantopithecus* was determined from isolated teeth purchased in the drugstores of Hong Kong and Canton, where, along with other types of fossils, they were sold as medicine. The age and locality of the fossils were in doubt.

Between 1956 and 1960, Chinese scientists recovered from caves in the Tahsin and Liuchang Districts of Kwangsi Province, South China, three fairly complete mandibles and over a thousand teeth of this animal. The associated faunas found with the specimens indicated a Pleistocene age. In the spring of 1968, my Yale group, working in the Siwalik foothills of the Himalayas, recovered from sediments between 3 million and 7 million years old a nearly complete mandible bearing striking resemblances to Chinese *Gigantopithecus.* The age of the Chinese *Gigantopithecus* is between $\frac{1}{2}$ million and 1 million years. The Indian find almost certainly represents a species in or near the ancestry of *Gigantopithecus blacki,* and because it is clearly intermediate between *G. blacki* and the yet older fossil apes of the late Miocene (about 12 million or 14 million years), it provides important new information concerning the evolutionary history of *Gigantopithecus.*

In some dimensions *Gigantopithecus blacki* is twice the size of a male mountain gorilla, and is larger than gorillas in nearly all comparable measurements. Assuming that proportions of tooth and jaw relative to body size were the same as in *Gorilla*, adult males of *Gigantopithecus* probably had an upright standing height of nearly 8 feet and weighed as much as 600 pounds. The large size, the fact that it was poorly known, and the dental resemblances to hominids allowed considerable differences of opinion about *Gigantopithecus* to flourish. Some authors considered it to be a giant ape; others concluded that it was more-or-less closely related to the ancestry of man.

Several recent developments in paleontology and in the study of functional anatomy now permit more soundly based inter-pretations of *Gigantopithecus*. Studies by Jolly (1970), Pilbeam (1970), and Simons and Ettel (1970) strongly suggest that the anatomical features of the jaws and teeth of primates analyzed as functional complexes often permit useful speculation about diet and manner of feeding of such species. This speculation is also enhanced by finding analogies with living forms. On what, and in what manner, an animal feeds is an important component of its behavior and obviously has far-reaching implications for understanding other aspects of its life habit.

According to von Koenigswald, the curious practice of selling fossil bones and teeth (known as dragon bones, "lung ku," and dragon teeth, "lung ch'ih") as medicine is an ancient tradition in China, going back at least to the Han and T'ang Dynasties. By the middle of the nineteenth century, western scientists had begun to purchase small collections of fossils from Chinese druggists. One such tooth, which had been regarded as of Pliocene age, was an upper human molar purchased in Peking. It was this tooth that caused Davidson Black and others to concentrate their searches for early man in the neighborhood of Peking. Their work eventually led to the discovery of Chinese *Homo erectus*, the celebrated Peking man or "Sinanthropus."

Von Koenigswald, who was familiar with such collections of fossil teeth from China, went to Java in 1931 to join the Geological Survey and there began a search for fossils. However, his initial inquiries at drugstores were thwarted because he did not know how to ask for "dragon teeth" and did not have a prescription. Once armed with a proper prescription and the appropriate names, he was able to find fossil teeth in almost every Chinese community throughout Southeast Asia and even as far away as New York City. The first tooth of this animal that he recovered in 1935 was a right lower M_3 with a crown length (front to back) of nearly 1 inch. By 1939, von Koenigswald had acquired three additional molars. Even without knowledge of where the drugstore teeth came from, their stain-ing, and the characteristics of the matrix gave evidence that they belonged to the *Stegodon–Ailuropoda* fauna of South China.

After von Koenigswald's initial description in 1935, another sci-entist, Weidenreich, decided that the enormous M_3 represented no more than the tooth of a giant orangutan. However, soon afterward he came around to the view that this huge animal had hominid affinities and should be referred to as *"Gigantanthropus."* Even were this so, according to the rules of taxonomy no such change of name is allowable—even if the original designation does imply incorrect taxonomic affinities. During the war, when communication with von Koenigswald was impossible, Weidenreich (1945) published a detailed analysis of the first four *Gigantopithecus* molars recovered and argued that they were of a hominid. He maintained that they were larger and perhaps older than those of *"Meganthropus"* and *"Pithecanthropus,"* which in turn were successive in time. From this he concluded that men had been derived by diminution from gigantic forms. Von Koenigswald considered this opinion unjustifiable, on both morphological and geological grounds. Remane (1950) further stressed the view that the *Gigantopithecus* teeth could only have belonged to a giant ape. Actually, both of these alternative positions were premature, because both were based on study of only four teeth. Von Koenigswald (1952) undertook a more elaborate study of the eight teeth that had by then been purchased in drugstores. He concluded that the creature had affinities with the "human group," was of early middle Pleistocene age, and was thus contemporary with undoubted hominids of the *Homo erectus* stage. As a consequence of these studies, several major questions about *Gigantopithecus* were raised that for the most part remained unanswered. Was the creature an ape or from a semihuman stock? What was its age? Whence did it come?

In the early 1950s, the central pharmaceutical house in Peking, in cooperation with W. C. Pei of the Academia Sinica, and others, began to look over incoming collections of "dragon teeth" with an eye to identifying localities of new or unusual fossil mammals, such as *Gigantopithecus*. In 1955, Pei was able to identify 47 teeth of *Gigantopithecus* from collections of "dragon teeth" made in Kwangsi and Kwangtung Provinces, and in the spring of 1956 a field party of the Academia Sinica discovered three teeth of the animal in place in a cave in the Tahsin district of Southern Kwangsi. While this was going on, Chin Hsiu-huai, a farmer from the village of Changtsao, when collecting lime phosphate as fertilizer from a cave on Lountsai Mountain in Liucheng District, Kwangsi, recovered a large *Gigantopithecus* jaw, which he gave to the state. Excavations in the *"Gigantopithecus* cave," about 90 meters above the surrounding terrain on Lountsai (or Lengchishan) Mountain, were immediately begun by the field group from the Academia Sinica, and in 1957 and 1958 two more mandibles of *Gigantopithecus* (II and III) were discovered along with over a thousand isolated teeth of the giant primate.

Several new questions about *Gigantopithecus* were raised by the discovery of the three new mandibles with associated animals. First of all, it was noted that there is a marked size dimorphism between the first comparatively small mandible and the enormous third one. Contrasts of either I or III with the second mandible were limited by the fact that *Gigantopithecus* II was not adult at death. The size difference between mandibles I and III could have been the result

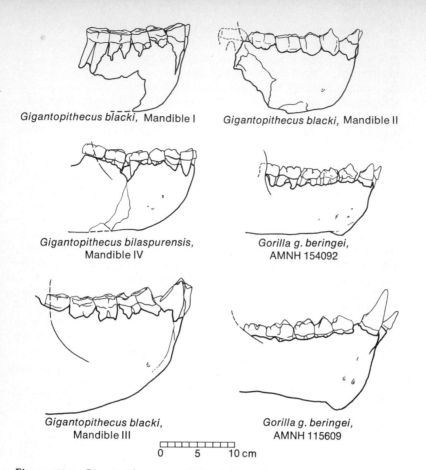

Gigantopithecus blacki, Mandible I   Gigantopithecus blacki, Mandible II

Gigantopithecus bilaspurensis,
Mandible IV

Gorilla g. beringei,
AMNH 154092

Gigantopithecus blacki,
Mandible III

Gorilla g. beringei,
AMNH 115609

0   5   10 cm

Figure 106 *Gigantopithecus* mandibles I, II, and III from Kwangsi, China, and the *Gigantopithecus* mandible IV from Bilaspur, India, compared with those of male and female mountain gorillas. (After Simons and Chopra, 1969; illustration by S. Weeks.)

of rather marked sexual dimorphism, or the jaws may represent two different species that lived at different times (see Figure 106). Opinions also differed as to the interpretation of associated animals. Were the other bones washed into the caves and fissures where they were found along with those of *Gigantopithecus,* or are they the remains of prey of carnivores such as hyenas and red dogs? Could *Gigantopithecus* have been a predator?

It was surprising that not a vestige of any skeletal bones of *Gigantopithecus* other than mandibles came from either excavation. Stone tools were also absent from the caves. These, had they been present, would have been easily identified. Moreover, if the cave deposits had been of late middle Pleistocene age, as Pei (1957) believed, they might well have been inhabited by the tool maker, *Homo erectus.*

Another question arose from the relative size and shapes of the different teeth, associated as individuals for the first time in these three mandibles. In the jaws the incisors are very small, and the canines (although moderately large) have been flattened by canine-to-canine wear in a manner unlike that seen in any living ape. In addition, although the premolars and molars of *Gigantopithecus* resemble those of *Australopithecus* with extensive flat wear on crowns, they differ in being long from front to back and unusually tall. From Figure 106, in which all four *Gigantopithecus* mandibles are compared, the great depth of the jaws is evident. Particularly in the Indian find, discovered in 1968, it can be seen that the anterior root of the ascending ramus is set far forward and the region of the angle is everted. These features, all of which represent clear differences from *Gorilla,* appear to increase the power of chewing. In addition, the jaw rami are relatively thick and the cross sectional area at the symphysis is relatively large, indicating that the mandible of *Gigantopithecus* was adapted to resisting transverse wracking or shearing stresses as opposed to up and down forces alone.

In all the mandibles the incisors (in some cases known only from the space available for them) were comparatively small. This indicates that in *Gigantopithecus* the incisors had a relatively unimportant role in feeding. These ponderous animals may have sat while feeding and garnered out food items with the hands, as do geladas, gorillas, and pandas. If the objects eaten were small or required little preparation by nipping and shredding, they could have been passed directly to the grinding cheek teeth. In the adult male and female jaws from Kwangsi, these teeth show heavy wear. Differences between the very large jaw (supposedly male) and the other two smaller jaws (supposedly female and subadult) in absolute size and especially in relative size of the canines are reasons for concluding that *Gigantopithecus* was characterized by a marked sexual dimorphism. The second Chinese jaw is of a subadult male. The Indian mandible, with its small canines, apparently represents a young adult female, in which wear on the third molar had not yet perforated the enamel. Examination of Figure 107 will show that in both the *Australopithecus* mandible from Omo, Ethiopa, and the *Gigantopithecus* jaw from Bilaspur, India, the crowns of the third molars have been worn almost flat, without perforation through the enamel into the dentine. This indicates that in both species unusually thick enamel was typical. Thick enamel is of course just another adaptation for resisting the abrasive wear generated by long-sustained or powerful chewing. Most of the differences seen here from mandibles of apes are analogous to changes that have occurred in the giant panda because of its adaptation to fully herbivorous ground feeding. The differences are analogous to those seen in the gelada baboon compared with the common baboon (*Papio*). Because the panda (*Ailuropoda*) is a prominent element in the fauna in which *Gigantopithecus* occurs, the similarities in projected feeding habits gain in significance. Nevertheless, should *Gigantopithecus* have made bamboo a dominant element in its diet,

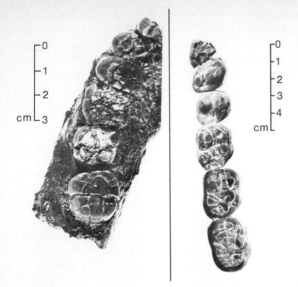

Figure 107 Comparison of the crown views of the teeth in *Australopithecus* (*Paranthropus*) (left) and *Gigantopithecus* mandibles (right). (*Australopithecus* photo courtesy of F. Clark Howell. *Gigantopithecus* photo courtesy of Grant Meyer, Yale Peabody Museum.)

it would presumably have been in strong competition with the contemporary panda, the living species of which has only been seen to feed on bamboo in the wild. Had there been such direct competition for food resources, it seems unlikely that they should have occurred together so often as fossils. A short deep face, a closed and closely packed tooth row, and large flat premolars with small accessory cusps and wrinkles are all features that can be seen in the panda but contrast sharply with other bears (genus *Ursus*) and even more so with less herbivorous carnivores. These structures, both by analogy with living forms and on the basis of functional interpretation, must be considered as adaptations for feeding on tough plant material. A field observer reporting the diet of the giant panda remarked that "the bulk of its nourishment consists . . . of stone-hard bamboo stems larger than a finger." Clearly, the amount of chewing force required to prepare such a rock-hard foodstuff for digestion must be many times greater than that required to prepare a similar amount of animal protein. Jaws of *Gigantopithecus* exhibit broad resemblances to mandibular and dental adaptations of *Ailuropoda*. The similarity even extends to common possession of accessory cuspules on molars and premolars.

Jolly (1970) believes that the first cycle of hominid evolution was precipitated by the shift on the part of a protohominid stock from a forest-arboreal, frugivorus–herbivorus feeding habit typical of many apes to a savanna-woodland graminivorous feeding habit. The shift in choice of environment and feeding behavior then evoked selection pressures that eventually resulted in the specific anatomical changes that distinguish hominids from pongids (apes). Some of these differences include development in hominids of small, vertically implanted incisors, reduced canines, relatively flat occlusal surfaces, closed tooth rows, deep face, and deep, thick (heavily buttressed) mandible with relatively vertically aligned ascending rami. The features of the jaw, face, and dentition that distinguish hominids from pongids are remarkably similar to the complex of features that distinguish geladas from baboons of genus *Papio*. Jolly's hypothesis is that the lineage of man arose because the earliest members became grazers and not, as some have suggested, because the adoption of tools rendered large canines redundant and unnecessary.

Recent work by Pilbeam (1969) and by others on *Ramapithecus* has lent support to and expanded on Jolly's idea. This work has shown that *Ramapithecus* possessed many features of the "*Theropithecus* complex" and that as a result it provides clear-cut fossil evidence of a primate species that had just embarked on the first cycle of hominid evolution. *Ramapithecus* appears to have lived more than 8 million years before the first well-dated stone tools appear in the fossil record. It is thus very unlikely that canine reduction (already evident in *Ramapithecus*) could have any relation to the use of fabricated tools as weapons.

An expression of the "*Theropithecus* complex" in hominids is seen in the degree of molarization of the premolars. That is, the premolars, both P_3 and P_4, have become broad, flat-crowned teeth serving to increase the tooth area available for grinding or milling. This feature is not seen in *Theropithecus* because the principal trend is toward enlargement of molars. In *Gigantopithecus*, on the other hand, we see not only molarization of the premolars but also flattening by crown wear of the canines. This probably indicates that in the evolutionary history of the *Gigantopithecus* line there was selection pressure for increased molar grinding area. Graminivorous feeding habits along with ever-increasing body size are two factors that might very plausibly have constituted, or at least contributed to, this selection pressure.

In hominids the canines have never shown this trend toward molarization, but instead by the late Pliocene (between 2 million to 6 million years ago) the canines had evolved into almost incisor-like teeth. Thus we have a fundamental difference between the teeth of hominids (*Ramapithecus–Australopithecus–Homo*) and those of *Gigantopithecus*. Hominids evolved a rounded (or parabolic) dental arcade with an anterior continuous shearing blade comprised of incisors and canines and a posterior complement of grinding teeth, the premolars and molars. *Gigantopithecus* retained the posteriorly diverging tooth rows typical of apes and incorporated both the premolars and to a lesser extent the canines into the grinding row. The incisors of *Gigantopithecus* are very small, peglike teeth that are generally worn off flat; although their function is still unclear, it is possible that they too were used for grinding. Whether this turns out to be the case or not, it is clear that *Gigantopithecus* possessed some of the specializations of the "*Theropithecus* complex" to a greater degree than the Pleistocene Hominidae did. Both the hominids and *Gigantopithecus* have deep, robust jaws and extensive dental grinding areas, but *Gigantopithecus* jaws are even greater in their depth and robusticity. All the teeth of *Gigantopithecus*, with the possible exception of the incisors, were used for grinding. This huge primate appears to represent an evolutionary side branch of apes that became increasingly adapted to a particular feeding habit (presumably, a specialized form of browsing or grazing). For the first 10 million years or so of its history, the lineage of man apparently independently became adapted to a similar feeding habit with differences that on the one hand permitted the later stages of human evolution and on the other relegated *Gigantopithecus* to ultimate extinction, possibly at the hands of man.

The faunal grouping associated with *Gigantopithecus* includes, among primates, an orangutan; among the rodents, a porcupine; among the carnivores, species of the red dog, the masked palm civet, a common bear (genus *Ursus*), the giant panda (genus *Ailuropoda*), the hog badger, a cat (genus *Felis*), and a variety of the spotted hyena (genus *Crocuta*); among Proboscidea, *Mastodon* and *Stegodon;* among Perissodactyla, horses, a chalicothere,a tapir, and a rhinoceros; and, among Artiodactyla, a boar (genus *Sus*), a deer, a bovid, and a goat. It appears from the preponderance of carnivores in the fauna that these cave deposits represent accumulations in lairs. The larger animals present in the fauna (including particularly Perissodactyla) are represented chiefly by milk teeth. A sampling bias of this sort is often seen in accumulations of bones left by predators. It is to be regretted that more extensive information about actual numbers of specimens and about their state of preservation is not available. The presence of the red dog or Indian dhole (well-enough preserved to admit species identification) is particularly suggestive. This animal hunts in packs, commonly attacking such prey as deer, ibex, wild pigs, wild sheep, antelope, water buffalo, and on occasion tigers, leopards, Himalayan black bears, and sloth bears.

Because its dentition indicates that *Gigantopithecus* had few if any carnivorous tendencies, we must conclude that the fossil accumulations in the Kwangsi Province caves represent finished meals of some former resident to which *Gigantopithecus* was a prey element. The suggestion made by at least one scientist that *Gigantopithecus* was a huge, manlike carnivore that scaled the Kwangsi cliffs dragging animal prey in hand is highly unlikely on biological grounds (discussed above) and on geological grounds as well. That is, what are now caves in high-standing cliffs were probably in middle Pleistocene times sinkholes or potholes in a limestone karst topography.

Another interesting aspect of the *Stegodon–Ailuropoda* fauna is the fact that many of the specimens show evidence of having been gnawed by porcupines, which might explain why so few skeletal parts of *Gigantopithecus* have been recovered. Concerning the surrounding environment at the time of deposition, some reconstruction of plant ecology and prevailing climatic conditions is possible. There are represented animals adapted to woodland or forest environments, along with those adjusted to mixed or more open habitats such as open woodland, savanna woodland, and open grassland. One can conclude then that at the time the remains of these animals were accumulating in the Kwangsi caves, the surrounding countryside was composed of forest, open woodland, and more open areas.

Regarding the age of *Gigantopithecus* in China, we must rely upon a correlation of the *Stegodon–Ailuropoda* fauna with similar faunas elsewhere for which there are absolute dates. It is not ordinarily possible to date limestone cave deposits by absolute means (radiocarbon or K/Ar). Unfortunately, the *Stegodon–Ailuropoda* fauna is what has been called "mixed"; that is, it contains some primitive genera (*Mastodon, Stegodon,* Chalicotheridae) and some advanced, or recent, genera (*Equus, Cuon* [the red dog], *Ailuropoda*). Currently, a middle Pleistocene age (perhaps $\frac{1}{2}$ million to 1 million years old) appears to be favored for the *Stegodon–Ailuropoda* fauna for a variety of reasons, which include occasional presence of *Elephas* sp., the presence of a *Stegodon* species advanced beyond the *Stegodon* typical of the early Pleistocene, and the common presence of several species of modern genera in addition to *Elephas.* The age of this fauna is an open question, with one author having suggested that it may be as old as late Pliocene. Turning to the Yale discovery of a much older species, *Gigantopithecus bilaspurensis* (Figure 107), in India, one can see that its resemblances to *Gigantopithecus blacki* from China are clear. *G. bilaspurensis* shows morphological elements of the "*Theropithecus* complex" and is just as likely to have been a graminivorus feeder as *Gigantopithecus blacki.* It is of some interest to consider the evidence as to the environment of the Indian species. The onset of Dhok Pathan times was marked by an influx of animals adapted to living in drier, grassland environments; these include higher elephantids, equids (i. e., horse relatives, principally *Hipparion*), and antelopes. The appearance of *Gigantopithecus* in the Dhok Pathan is also supportive of the hypothesis that the Indian and Chinese forms represent a lineage that became adapted to the drier conditions of an open grassland environment.

In summary, it appears that *Gigantopithecus blacki* of the Chinese Pleistocene derives directly from *G. bilaspurensis,* which was recently discovered in deposits about 200 miles north of New Delhi, India (Figures 106 and 107). This lineage appears to represent a side branch of gorilla-sized, and possibly rather gorilla-like, Asian apes. An identifiable ancestor of *Gigantopithecus* among the earlier forest-dwelling apes of the genus *Dryopithecus* may well be *Dryopithecus indicus,* which occurred in North India and West Pakistan in late Miocene and/or early Pliocene times. It is found together with *Ramapithecus,* a possibly related, but much more *Australopithecus*-like, form. If *D. indicus* does lie in an ancestral position to *Gigantopithecus,* it had not yet developed many of the most characteristic features of the *Gigantopithecus* dental mechanism, inasmuch as its canines were large and overlapping and were separated from adjacent incisors by a gap in the tooth row. *D. indicus* was a much more conventional ape. Its similarities to *Gigantopithecus* consists principally of its large size (the jaws were almost as large as those of lowland gorilla males) and that the broad, relatively flat-crowned cheek teeth do exhibit considerable wear between adjacent teeth—a feature otherwise uncommon among Tertiary fossil apes. It is also possible that *D. indicus* represents a northeastern extension of races (or species) closely related to the ancestors of the modern African gorilla. Many mammals that inhabited the foothills of the Himalayas at the close of Miocene times have modern African relatives or descendants. These include such forms as the giraffe, the aardvark, the pangolin, and the buffalo. The adaptive radiation of *Dryopithecus,* in turn, took place much earlier in Africa. As has already been discussed, these are known from a variety of deposits in Uganda and Kenya that represent both upland and lowland habitats. These apes appear to have originated from such forms as the Oligocene Egyptian ape *Aegyptopithecus zeuxis.*

In 1960, I suggested the possibility that the late Miocene primate *Oreopithecus,* which occurs in Tuscany, Italy, and at Fort Ternan, Kenya, might have an ancestral relationship to *Gigantopithecus.* I did so because both forms exhibit extremely deep jaws in relation to absolute size of cheek teeth and because both share a tendency to have accessory small cusps on the molars. In addition, the front two cusps of the lower molars are separated slightly from the back three by vertical internal and external grooves, so that these teeth are somewhat "wasp-waisted." However, the newer studies of *Gigantopithecus* show that acquisition of extra cuspules and central pinching of the molars must have been relatively recent acquisitions in the ancestry of *Gigantopithecus blacki* because they are absent in the North Indian Pliocene species *G. bilaspurensis.* In consequence, the probability of descent from *D. indicus,* rather than from *Oreopithecus,* is enhanced.

OREOPITHECUS

Oreopithecus bambolii was originally described in 1872 by Gervais on the basis of a nearly complete lower subadult dentition from Pontian lignites of Monte Bamboli, in the province of Grossetto, Tuscany, Italy (Figure 108). There has not been general agreement about its classification. Gervais initially noted certain features of *Oreopithecus* separating it from most monkeys and apes—the symphysis is deep and vertically oriented, the mental foramina are located high on the horizontal ramus, and the anterior premolar is bicuspid. He also noted that P_3 and P_4 are more homomorphic than in the apes or the cercopithecoid monkeys. Both Gervais and, later, Schlosser (1887) considered the molars to be baboon- or macaque-like. A different point of view was expressed by Forsyth-Major (1880) when he remarked (translated from the German): "*Oreopithecus* from the Miocene lignite of Monte Bamboli and Casteani of whose dentition ample material is before me and is shortly to be published, shows in the appearance of its anterior premolars an analogy to man." Schwalbe (1915) concluded that *Oreopithecus* represents a distinct family of the Hominoidea. Al-

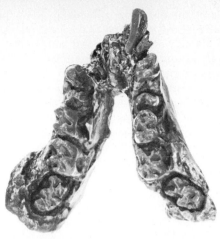

Figure 108 The mandibular dentition of the type of *Oreopithecus*. (Photo of cast courtesy of A. H. Coleman, Yale Peabody Museum.)

0   1   2 cm

though that is the conclusion supported here, Schwalbe's observations were based on casts only and his findings do not contribute greatly to understanding of this primate. It would seem that most of the early students, quite a few of whom did not have access to the original specimens, considered the creature to be intermediate between the cercopithecoids and the hominoids. Whereas Gregory 1922, 1951) supported the latter view, Hürzeler (1954, 1958, 1968) developed the idea that the affinities of *Oreopithecus* were as an ancestor of Hominidae, or at least that it was a hominid. Hürzeler's extensively illustrated studies have done a great deal to bring before the scientific public awareness of this primate, even though hominid placement has not been generally accepted. In the last of these papers he retreats somewhat from his earlier position but still indicates in his Figure 27 that *Oreopithecus* is a side branch closer to the ancestry of man than to the ancestry of any of the apes. It would appear from his studies as well as those of Straus (1963) that the affinities of this genus are probably somewhat closer to those of the hominoids than to those of the cercopithecoids. Such features as do resemble cercopithecoids are the pronounced mid-sagittal keel on the centra of the lumbar vertebrae and a large talonid basin on the lower molars. Like *Homo* and *Australopithecus*, the pelvis is different from that of the apes in that the ilium is broad from front to back and not particularly high. There is a manlike anterior inferior iliac spine. Nevertheless, the joints of the hips, shoulders, arms, and legs appear to be constructed for mobility rather than for stability. The arms are distinctly longer than the hindlimbs, and the phalanges of the hands are definitely curved. These features suggest an arm-swinging or hanging-feeding adaptation. This is also indicated by its occurrence as a fossil, for the Monte Bamboli lignites presumably accumulated in swamp forests. Fully terrestrial mammals such as horses are rare in these deposits, but animals related to forms that presently enter swamps such as the Okefino-kee Swamp of Southern Georgia are abundant. These include a presumably swamp-dwelling rabbit and bear, as well as various rodents and antelope. Along with these extinct species, remains of a variety of fishes, amphibians, snakes, crocodiles, turtles, and birds are abundant. By far the most abundant mammal in these deposits is *Oreopithecus*. Hürzeler was able to catalogue almost two hundred different specimens, mostly consisting of isolated bones or teeth. But there were several excellent finds including foot and limb bones. These collections were topped off by the discovery in 1958 of a nearly entire skeleton of *Oreopithecus*. This find was made by Hürzeler himself (see Figure 10). The skeleton was first exposed on the ceiling of a mine excavation about 300 feet below the surface of the ground. Working under trying circumstances, Hürzeler was able to save most of this remarkable specimen, which (apart from the skeleton of *Procolobus* discovered in the Pliocene of Kenya in 1966) is at present the most complete skeleton of a higher primate of pre-Pleistocene age known. The femoral–humeral and intermembral indexes derived from this skeleton are a bit lower than those of the orangutan, but nevertheless the character of the distal end of the humerus as well as the construction of the head and the distal condyles of the femur of *Oreopithecus* show definite resemblance to the orangutan.

It may prove preferable to consider that *Oreopithecus* is a derivative of an early cercopithecoid stock that converged in the direction of the apes. Now that we know that this happened in the case of species of the extinct Malagasay lemur genus *Palaeopropithecus*, it would not be entirely out of the question that the Cercopithecoidea could also have produced an apelike form. It would seem that the hominid resemblances, which include a steep symphysis, a hypoconulid on the molars, no precanine diastema, and a deep, rounded chin with vertically implanted incisors, along with a few other features, are structures that have arisen is parallel to similar conditions in hominids. Hürzeler has stressed that the canines are small and, although they are, there is still a marked sexual dimorphism, with the canines of the males being long enough to overlap and interlock. *Gigantopithecus* canines were probably even shorter crowned and may have been relatively smaller than in *Oreopithecus*, (for instance, see Remane, 1960; Woo, 1962). This establishes that hominoids other than undoubted hominids can show crown shortening in the canines, but this point was not dealt with by Hürzeler (1968).

Certainly, the deep, foreshortened face with approximately equal-sized premolars is reminiscent of the hominid face, but these characters are not so different from what is seen among some colobines, which show deep jaws and deep faces as well as relatively small canines and less heteromorphic premolars. In addition, the upper central incisors are like nothing else among primates in that they show a heavy, folded, polycuspidate, and high-cusped internal cingulum. Moreover, both *Pongo* and *Gigantopithecus* typically show deep faces and deep jaws. Hürzeler failed to compare *Oreopithecus* with colobines. In any case, the dentition of *Oreopithecus* could be explained were it an arboreal browser in which selection for canine dimorphism had been dampened for one or all of several reasons. These could have included the following: (1) Predation pressures were relaxed because of the comparative large size and arboreal swamp habitat of *Oreopithecus*. (2) Group social structure obviated intragroup disciplining by dominant males (which at least among many cercopithecoids involves slashing with canines) in the dominance hierarchy. The large size of the molars of *Oreopithecus* and their marked increased size gradient posteriorly, although differing in detail from other primate species, broadly suggests a forest-dwelling herbivore, which correlates well with the environment of preservation of the fossils in swamp-accumulated lignites.

The age of *Oreopithecus* has also been uncertain, but Hürzeler (1968) cites the work of Lorenz (1968) that the *Oreopithecus* fauna of Tuscany, Italy, antedates the arrival of *Hipparion* in Europe. This would suggest a late Miocene date, which in turn agrees well with the occurrence of *Oreopithecus* in an allied form at Fort Ternan, Kenya—a site that has been dated (repeatedly) by the K/Ar method to 14 million ± 300 thousand years. This is an age that would be universally considered late Miocene.

MABOKOPITHECUS

The primate *Mabokopithecus clarki* was recently named by von Koenigswald from a single left third molar that has lost the hypoconulid. Primate taxa based on single teeth are hardly to be desired, but this tooth is fairly complex in structure and is distinctive from *Oreopithecus*. Von Koenigswald (1969) conjectured that *Mabokopithecus* in the late Miocene could "be ancestral to *Oreopithecus* from the Pliocene." The evidence that all *Oreopithecus* are of Miocene age is growing, on the basis of the work of Gillet, Lorenz, and Waltersdorf (1965) on the Tuscan sediments and fauna and on the fact of its occurrence at Fort Ternan, Kenya, at a K/Ar Miocene age date of 14 million years. My comparisons of the Fort Ternan teeth with casts of *Oreopithecus* at the British Museum suggested to me that the Fort Ternan teeth are referable to genus *Oreopithecus* sp. cf. *bambolii*. To me, it seems unsustained at present that these teeth are either older or taxonomically distinct from *Oreopithecus*. The fauna from Maboko Island is usually considered contemporary with that of Fort Ternan.

The first find of *Ramapithecus* was not recognized as being that of a new genus, but was described by Pilgrim (1910, 1915) as belonging to a then-new species of *Dryopithecus*, *D. punjabicus*. In the second of the two papers, Pilgrim gave a full description of two specimens from different localities that he believed could be assigned to this species. One of them consisted of posterior fragments of the horizontal ramus of both sides of what had once been a single mandible, preserving on one side M_2 and on the other M_3. The find was made prior to 1910 by Vinayak Rao at a site at the top of or just above the Chinji Zone near the village of Chinji, West Pakistan. To the same species, Pilgrim (1915) allocated the left maxilla from Haritalyangar, Himachal Pradesh, North India. This paratype maxilla has P^3–M^2, and on the back of M^2 is a small contact facet indicating that the specimen was an adult with M^3 fully erupted. At the front of the maxillary fragment the cross section of an extremely small and short canine alveolus is preserved. This is a distinctly nonpongid feature of the maxillary dentition, which, however, was never recognized by any who studied it until 1963. This maxilla is more complete than any remains of upper teeth of *Dryopithecus* from Europe, which for more than 60 years consisted of finds of single upper teeth alone. Because Pilgrim mistakenly concluded that it belonged to the previously European genus, the Haritalyangar maxilla was frequently figured in the early part of this century as that of *Dryopithecus*, which in turn is responsible for the creation of the genus *Proconsul* (Hopwood, 1933), as has been discussed. Tooth proportions in it are not those of a female ape.

Later, other specimens of what was to become *Ramapithecus* were also discovered in the Siwalik Hills, but their distinctiveness from *Dryopithecus* at the generic level remained unrecognized. Neither Pilgrim (1915) nor any other person acquainted with the anatomy of the Haritalyangar maxilla found by Vinayak Rao noticed that the cross section of the canine root at the front showed it to have been an exceedingly small canine, the root having been shorter from alveolar border to tip and narrower from inside to out than is the case in many individuals of modern man, with P^3–M^2 of the same approximate size. This, along with a lateral margin of the nasal aperture close to the level of the tooth row, indicated that the lower face was diminutive and the canine small, as I pointed out (Simons, 1963a). In March 1969, I had the further opportunity of confirming the very small size of the socket by cleaning out the remaining matrix, and it is relatively shorter than in female pongids.

In August 1932, Dr. G. E. Lewis of the Geology Department at Yale University, while participating in the first Yale North India Expedition, obtained from a villager a second left maxilla that he had found near Haritalyangar. The maxilla preserved P^3 through M^2, a longitudinal cross section of the central incisor root, the lateral incisor root, and a small canine alveolus of the left side. M^2 shows a posterior contact facet for M^3, which means that the individual was fully adult. Lewis was initially dissatisfied with the local man's account of the site from which this find had come, but petrographic studies carried out later by Krynine (1937) indicated that in all probability the find was made at the cuesta scarp at Haritalyangar from which the vast majority of other fossil hominoid finds from North India were recovered.

Lewis initially recognized that this was a new and more manlike genus of primate than had been known before. In 1934, he named *Ramapithecus brevirostris*, in translation meaning "Rama's short-faced ape." Meanwhile, other finds of Indian fossil hominoids by Lewis, DeTerra, and others were made during the 1930's. Some of these ultimately proved to belong to *Ramapithecus*, but their proper association with Lewis's 1934 maxilla remained unrecognized for more than two decades. Gregory, Hellman, and Lewis (1938) discussed a mandible that they considered to be cf. *Ramapithecus*. The specimen they had under consideration had been found during the course of the second Yale North India Expedition at Kundal Nala in the Salt Range, West Pakistan.

Although Lewis (personal communication) was somewhat dissatisfied with their collective decision to allocate this jaw to *Ramapithecus*, according to size it seemed appropriate to occlude with the maxilla. Much new knowledge of the dental anatomy of *Dryopithecus* and *Australopithecus* accumulated in the Old World during the decades of the 1930s, 1940s, and 1950s, and by the early 1960s it was possible to see why the Kundal Nala mandible was not of a *Ramapithecus*. Indeed, authorities such as Le Gros Clark (1956) and Piveteau (1957) had by then pointed out that if the Kundal Nala mandible were of *Ramapithecus*, then *Ramapithecus* did not have hominid mandibular features. I (Simons, 1963b, 1964a) pointed out that the mandibles from India that had been assigned to the species *Bramapithecus* (Lewis, 1934) made better functional correlates with the maxillary part of the dental mechanism of *Ramapithecus* and that these mandibles agreed with *Australopithecus* in several important respects not to be found in the Kundal Nala jaw. The latter evidently belongs to a small species of *Dryopithecus*, either D. *laietanus* (see Simons and Pilbeam, 1965) or perhaps D. *chinjiensis*, if this is a valid species (see Prasad, 1969). The differences in the two sets of material can be understood from the contrasts made in Table 4.

Meanwhile, an important discovery had been made in 1960 by the Leakey expedition at Fort Ternan, Kenya. A foreman, Heslon Mukiri, had found two parts of the maxillae of an individual of *Ramapithecus* (Figure 109). A canine was associated with the left-side fragment, and P^4 through M^2 were preserved as well. On the right, only M^{1-2} were preserved. A lower molar (probably M_1) is reputed to come from the same spot, and several feet farther into the cliff at the same horizon a single central incisor was found that has later figured in discussion of this find as possibly being associated with the same individual as the maxillae (see Simons, 1969a). Nevertheless, most paleontologists would not accept material that has

TABLE 4 COMPARISON OF PRIMITIVE HOMINID JAWS FROM THE SIWALIKS (HASNOT, DOMELI, AND HARITALYANGAR) WITH A CONTEMPORARY APE JAW FROM KUNDAL NALA, PAKISTAN

Features typical of *Australopithecus* including (*Paranthropus*)	*Ramapithecus* jaws (= *Bramapithecus*) from Hasnot and Haritalyangar, India, and Domeli, West Pakistan	Typical *Dryopithecus* and Kundal Nala mandible from Salt Range, West Pakistan
1. Molars broad	Same as at left	Molars elongate
2. P_4 broad	Same as at left	P_4 small, narrow
3. P_3^4 short anteroposteriorly	Same as at left	P_3 large, bladelike hone
4. Molars subequal sized (M_{2-3}) with $M_1 \cong$ or $<$ $M_2 \cong M_3$	Same as at left	Molars $M_1 < M_2 < M_3$
5. Ramus broad and shallow under M_{2-3}	Same as at left	Ramus thin and deep under M_{2-3}
6. Much interstitial wear at early age	Same as at left	Little interstitial wear at early age
7. Thick cheek-tooth enamel (molars wear almost flat without exposing dentine)	Same as at left	Relatively thin cheek-tooth enamel (dentine exposed in early wear at apices of cusps)
8. Central fovea of molars broad	Same as at left	Central fovea restricted
9. Long axis of the symphyseal cross section 20 to 40° from vertical	Same as at left	Long axis of symphyseal cross section 50 to 60° from vertical

been found "several feet apart" as associated, because too many cases are known where uncritical acceptance of association has led to wrong conclusions. More recently, Leakey (personal communication) was unable to comment on the probability that the incisor belongs to the same individual, but his own study suggests that it may be a trifle large to belong with the Fort Ternan *Ramapithecus* palate. Recovery of parts of extinct animals several feet apart does not constitute an association unless broken ends from separate spots contact or interlock and can be fitted together, thus proving that they are parts of the same individual animal.

In 1962, Leakey unfortunately coined a new genus and species for the East African primate maxilla, "*Kenyapithecus wickeri.*" His diagnosis and description of this taxon exactly characterize the two Indian maxillae of *Ramapithecus* from Haritalyangar, one of which

Figure 109 The maxillary fragment of *Ramapithecus* from Fort Ternan, Kenya, articulated with the newly described mandibular fragment from the same site. Scale × 1.5 approximately. (Photo courtesy of P. Andrews.)

had been made the prior type of *Ramapithecus brevirostris* by Lewis in 1934. Thus *"Kenyapithecus wickeri"* from the time of initial description could be considered a junior subjective synonym of the prior species. Such a synonymy can be indicated as follows: *Ramapithecus brevirostris* (= *Kenyapithecus wickeri*).

Meanwhile, work at Yale had indicated to me that *Ramapithecus brevirostris* as a species was a synonym of the much earlier described species *Dryopithecus punjabicus*, but that *Ramapithecus* is validly distinct at the generic level, as Lewis initially correctly understood on the basis of the second Haritalyangar specimen. In consequence, the correct name for all these animals became *Ramapithecus punjabicus*. The student may justly be somewhat bored by this type of discussion involving consideration of a long series of different names to remember and the complex reasons for their validity, or lack of validity. Nevertheless, the task of those working on this subject has been unnecessarily complicated by the almost irrepressible tendency for the finders of fossil apes and humans to proliferate unnecessary names for them. This is presumed to be one of the consequences of "discoverer's bias," discussed in Chapter 3. Actually, what one hopes for in the study of an animal like *Ramapithecus* is a construction of what it was when alive, not endless taxonomic discussions. Regrettably, such discussions will go on as long as those principally involved in naming primate fossils do not understand and apply in a balanced manner the rules of taxonomy.

What can be said about the ecology and anatomy of *Ramapithecus*? The paleoenvironment in which it occurs has been studied by several workers such as Lewis (1937), Krynine (1937), and more recently Tattersall (1969a,b), and Simons (1969a).

Tattersall's recent reviews summarize the work of earlier students as far as the *Ramapithecus* remains from the Siwalik Hills of North India and West Pakistan are concerned. His main conclusions have been further confirmed by the findings of the recent Yale–Punjab field program in the Nagri Zone near Haritalyangar, India. The fauna from deposits there contains *Hipparion*, but apparently it is of pre-Pikermian age, which would put it as having been deposited at about the time of the Miocene–Pliocene boundary.

Simons (1969a) discusses the faunal associations so far published for the *Ramapithecus* find recovered from Fort Ternan, Kenya. In the Indian Nagri fauna as a whole, one finds *Ramapithecus* associated with presumably forest-dwelling apes such as *Dryopithecus indicus, D. sivalensis,* and a hylobatid. Nearly every other element of the fauna indicates a predominantly forest ecology for at least the major part of the time of deposition of the Nagri sediments; a similar environment is indicated by the fauna so far reported from Fort Ternan, Kenya (see Simons, 1969a). What these faunas do not indicate is how open the forests may have been, but the rarity of *Gazella* in the Nagri fauna would suggest that there were few if any patches of savanna.

In the Nagri Zone, the fauna is a variety of bush or forest-dwelling mammals, including an okapi-like giraffid, a great variety of different genera of suids (none of which resemble the only living suid with savanna-dwelling adaptations), and *Phacochoerus,* the wart hogs. Predominant among the suids is *Propotamochoerus,* which appears to be related to the modern African *Potamochoerus,* the river or water hogs, which are forest-dwelling animals never found today far from water. The Nagri also contains species of the modern genus *Sus,* present-day species of which inhabit forests and, in the north, open woodlands. The primitive forest-adapted equid species *Hipparion nagriensis* occurs along with viverrid, felid, and procyonid carnivores. Finds of *Crocuta* species are rare in the Nagri but may suggest the occurrence of occasional tree savannas. Nevertheless, a forested, well-watered environment is suggested by the frequency of recovery of crocodilian scutes and bones, by abundant palm fossils, and by the frequent recovery of deinotheres, tragulids, anthracotheres, and rhinocerotids. Toward the end of Nagri times, there is evidence of the development of drier conditions, and Higher Primates are much less abundant in the ensuing Indian Dhok Pathan fauna. In West Pakistan they do continue on in Dhok Pathan times in some abundance.

In Kenya at Fort Ternan the faunal situation of *Ramapithecus* is broadly similar to that in India. There are lesser apes, either *Pliopithecus* or *Limnopithecus,* and *Oreopithecus* cf. *bambolii,* a distinctly forest-dwelling form (see Hürzeler, 1958). *Dryopithecus* (probably more advanced than the subgenus *Proconsul*) is also present as well as at least two kinds of monkeys. There are rhinocerotids, giraffids, and several bovids present as well as incursive cricetid and sciurid rodents, but no *Hipparion* and no anthracotheres are known from

Fort Ternan. This association containing many different kinds of forest-dwelling animals along with more open-country forms such as some of the bovids suggests a well-watered forest, perhaps adjacent to savanna areas and not inconsistent with what is known of prior faunal environments in the East African middle Miocene at Rusinga Island, Songhor, or Koru.

The course of study of *Ramapithecus* has been fraught with misunderstandings. First it was unclear what kind of lower jaws should be grouped with the upper. When more about this was known (Simons, 1964a), scholars generally failed to learn the extent and nature of the known material. Although the general consensus ever since the 1930s was that *Ramapithecus* probably stood in or near the ancestry of *Australopithecus*, various objections to this have been raised. These have tended to be critiques focused on one feature or another of partial resemblance to apes of the sort that neglect consideration of the entire complex of features of the dental mechanism that resemble *Australopithecus* and later hominids. The resemblances to *Australopithecus* pervade the whole face and dentition of *Ramapithecus*. Together these features combine to indicate increased power of the grinding cheek teeth and a decrease in the size of front teeth, presumably as a result of a de-emphasis on the juicing and shredding function of the procumbent incisors and large interlocking canines of typical apes. The mechanical efficiency of the chewing muscles has been increased by a shifting forward of their location. This is indicated by the fact that, relative to apes such as the similar-sized pygmy chimpanzee, the maxillary base of the cheek bone is moved slightly forward over the M^1, which allows for a more frontal location of the masseter muscle. In correlation with this, the coronoid process of the mandible is placed somewhat forward so as to allow for a more anterior location of the ventral insertion of the temporal muscle. This is indicated on the referred mandibles of *Ramapithecus* by a forward location of the anterior edge of the base of the coronoid process. The British Museum mandible of *Ramapithecus* shows that the lever arm of the mandible and the effectiveness of the anterior lower teeth in cutting were increased by the shortened length of the lower tooth row. In this specimen the anterior face of the symphyseal region begins to turn upward, to the point where it is broken, at a much higher angle to the horizontal than in apes such as the pygmy chimpanzee. This presumably indicates that the lower incisors cut along a more vertically oriented axis than in the apes and that they were less procumbent than is typical, for instance, in the chimpanzee. Reduction in the relative size of the upper incisors, indicated in the Yale specimen by the short roots that are clearly small (relative to the female pygmy chimpanzee in transverse breadth and length at the alveolar border), correlates well with the indication in the British Museum mandible that the teeth were compressed from front to back.

Another sign that the teeth were powerfully stressed during chewing is the rapidly accumulating wear between cheek teeth to

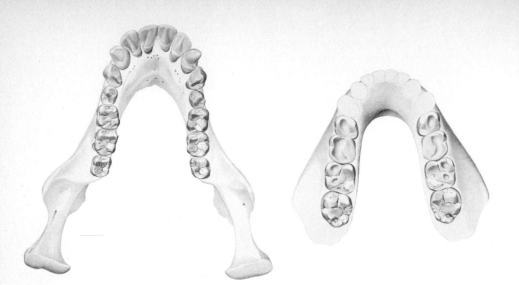

Figure 110 Comparison of the mandibular dentition of a pygmy chimpanzee (left) and of *Ramapithecus* (right), the latter reconstructed from the Calcutta and Hasnot jaw fragments. The angle of posterior divergence of the horizontal rami and detailed anatomy of the front of the jaw are not known in *Ramapithecus*. Both brought to same approximate tooth-row length, showing relatively larger cheek teeth and thicker rami in the latter. (Drawings by C. Wester, Yale Peabody Museum.)

be noted on all specimens of *Ramapithecus* (see Figure 110). This is called by dentists "interproximal" or "interstitial" wear—in contrast with abrasive or grinding wear, which is manifested on tooth crowns. In terms of the degree of abrasion on their tooth crowns, apes in old age often show interstitial wear. In *Ramapithecus* such wear advanced more rapidly, even in juvenile stages, as can be seen in the Fort Ternan, Kenya, find of *Ramapithecus*. This individual shows marked interstitial wear, even though its last molars or wisdom teeth had not fully erupted. In addition with an improvement in the grinding efficiency of the cheek teeth, individual premolar and molar cusps in *Ramapithecus* were thickly enveloped with enamel. That the thickness of enamel in *Ramapithecus* was greater than is typical of apes, even such ancient apes as *Aegyptopithecus* and *Propliopithecus,* is clearly indicated by the differential manner in which these cusps wore. In *Ramapithecus* the principal cusps of the molar crowns could be truncated by abrasive wear to the point where the occlusal face was almost flat before there were perforations in the four or five principal cusps into the dentine (Figure 110). In typical apes, on the other hand, the apices of molar cusps are divested of enamel at an early dental age, with the result that perforations into the softer dentine, which wears more rapidly, form tiny volcano-like tips to all the principal cusps long before the entire occlusal face, through abrasion, reaches anything like a flattened surface. Thick enamel producing the *Ramapithecus* type of molar crown wear is often seen in *Australopithecus*, both in the gracile varieties as well as in subgenus *Paranthropus*.

Mann (1968) has recently shown that *Australopithecus* typically shares, together with modern and paleolithic human populations who eat (or ate) coarse diets, a distinct wear differential on successive molars. In *Australopithecus* the first molars may have the entire enamel cap together with all cusps completely eroded away, so that only a basin excavated in the dentin and surrounded by a raised rim of enamel survives in the first molars, when there has been hardly any penetration through the enamel in the third molars. This can be termed a high differential of decreasing wear posteriorly. Mann has further shown that both modern humans and the African apes reach approximate skeletal maturity at about the same time as the full emplacement of the last (third) molars. Fossil apes share with their modern descendants similar degrees of wear in the three successively erupting molar sets due to the facts that M_2^2 and M_3^3 follow the M_1^1 more rapidly in a shorter period of time and that in these apes skeletal and sexual maturity is reached in little more than half the time this process takes in modern human. In other words, modern humans take much longer to grow up than do apes. What Mann was able to show by analogy was that, indicated by the decreasing wear differential on the molars, *Australopithecus* also appears to have had a long childhood relative to the apes—regardless of the absolute length of time concerned. The relevance of the foregoing discussion to *Ramapithecus* is that the Calcutta mandible of *Ramapithecus* (Figure 111) distinctly shows this type of staged-out wear on the molars. Thus this find provides presumptive evidence that, like species of *Australopithecus* and *Homo*, *Ramapithecus* individuals had staged-out eruption of the successive molars and may consequently have had a childhood learning period relatively longer than do the apes. This would be entirely consistent with the idea that the earlier genus *Ramapithecus*

Figure 111 The Calcutta mandible of *Ramapithecus*, showing a differential wear gradient on the molars. (Photo courtesy of D. Pilbeam.)

0 cm   1   2

may lie in or near the ancestry of *Australopithecus* and subsequent hominids. It should be stressed that this developmental resemblance of the ancient to more modern forms is entirely independent of the broad structural resemblances between jaws and teeth of *Ramapithecus* and *Australopithecus*. The probability that these similarities are due not to convergent feeding but to true phyletic relatedness is thereby increased.

What should be concluded as to the meaning of the changes in the dental mechanism of *Ramapithecus* away from that typical of living and fossil apes? Clearly, this animal was adapting toward a diet different from that preferred by the typically forest-dwelling apes. Actually, the exact diet of *Ramapithecus* is more obscure and perhaps not so important as the fact that its dental anatomy reflects a definite change in the character of foodstuff ingested. Presumably, the greater grinding efficiency and the larger, broader, and more durable cheek teeth indicate adaptation for a tougher, coarser diet—just the sort of diet that might more easily be found on the ground in the form of seeds, roots, and perhaps even raw meat and bones.

The dryopithecines spread widely throughout Eurasia in middle Miocene times. It seems likely that in Eurasia as well as in Africa they encountered a great variety of environments. Clearly, in the northernmost and southernmost parts of their range a principally frugivorous diet could not have been maintained the year round as in the tropics, where there are successively fruiting trees. In more temperate climates the fruiting is seasonal, and large apes would have had to turn increasingly to other food sources as they ranged toward the poles. Factors such as this may have been instrumental in shifting feeding and foraging habits more and more toward the ground. In any case, by the end of the Miocene, *Ramapithecus*, with an *Australopithecus*-like dental mechanism, had already appeared, and the stage was set for increasingly successful ground living and the growing acculturation of hominids.

What Made Man?

Psalm 8: "What is man that thou art mindful of him . . ."

With the acquisition of more and more new evidence about the structure of earliest hominids it is becoming clearer that there were several important stages or cycles between the first decisive commitment to a different feeding habit for hominids, indicated by *Ramapithecus*, and the full development of culture-bearing man of genus *Homo*. In addition, there has not been general agreement as to what basically characterizes man or the taxonomic family, Hominidae, to which he belongs. Part of the reason that there is disagreement about how man arose is the hazy distinction generally made between what it is to be a hominid—a taxonomic category— and what it is to be "Man" with a capital M, or human. As has been discussed earlier in this book, mammalian families are usually defined as groups because the members share the same broad tendencies in locomotor and feeding habits. Because these will have been of long-standing duration, together the limbs, the jaws, and teeth should show the structural distinctions of the group. In this regard, there is now no longer any doubt that *Australopithecus* had both a dental mechanism and a locomotor mechanism of the hindlimb that broadly agree with those of modern man in the manner in which these differ from pongid mechanisms. Therefore, *Australopithecus* can definitely be considered a hominid, but whether it should also be considered a "Man" or human is a different question.

For me, what it is to be human is to be more than just a toolmaker. It is to be a perfected, large-brained hunter. The brain volume of the earliest humans should, at least at its upper extremes, come within the lower end of the brain-volume range of normal *Homo sapiens*. For the first humans, defined in this manner, postcranial distinctions from modern man should be almost negligible, as is commonly the case for different species of mammals that belong in one genus. The Java and Peking men fulfill all these requirements; thus for me middle Pleistocene *Homo erectus* is the oldest man. In turn, the creatures from Africa (and possibly Southeast Asia) that are older than around 1 to $1\frac{1}{2}$ million years, whether called *Australopithecus africanus*, *Australopithecus habilis*, *Paranthropus robustus*, or *Zinjanthropus boisei* and whether tool manufacturers or not, can be styled adequately by the popular term "near-men."

There are several principal theories concerning the fundamental process or the basic reason why mankind arose. These theories will be discussed below under separate, successive headings:

INVENTION OF TOOLS

That man began with the invention of tools is a very ancient idea. Even Lucretius wrote that the first men used tools of stone. The more specific concept—that man can be defined as a toolmaker—is apparently traceable to Benjamin Franklin, although there is no surviving document on the subject in his handwriting. Authority for this is James Boswell, who, when attending the Royal Society dining club in London with Samuel Johnson, had ample opportunity to learn his opinions. In his *Life of Johnson* he recorded the following conversation. Boswell remarked, "I think Dr. Franklin's definition of Man a good one—'a tool-making animal'." Dr. Johnson was apparently in an overly wry or literal mood, for he replied, "But many a man never made a tool and suppose a man without arms, he could never make a tool." In a further note in the *Journal of a Tour to the Hebrides*, which was probably added in 1785 or 1786, Boswell observes, "Dr. Franklin said Man was a 'tool animal', which is very well; for no animal but man makes a thing, by means of which he can make another thing. But this applies to very few of the species. My definition of *Man* is, 'a cooking animal'." Another aspect of the idea that "tools made man" is the widespread view that somehow the invention of tools, particularly their use as weapons, substituted for the large canines of our earlier ape ancestors. This has frequently been used as an explanation for the small canines of male hominids. This interpretation is one of the common dogmas of physical anthropology, but it overlooks several alternative possibilities, among which are

1. Canines of ancestral hominids have always been small.
2. Hominid canines are small in order to facilitate a changed mechanical function in chewing.
3. Canine reduction is a morphological change paralleling the evolution of appeasment behavior. The first succinct expression of this possibility is apparently traceable to Charles Darwin (1871), who wrote as follows.

He who rejects with scorn the belief that the shape of his own canines, and their occasional great development in other men, are due to our early forefathers having been provided with these formidable weapons, will probably reveal by sneering the line of his descent. (2d ed., p. 122)

The early male forefathers of man were probably furnished with great canine teeth; but as they gradually acquired the habit of using stones, clubs, or other weapons, for fighting with their enemies or rivals, they would use their jaws and teeth less and less. In this case, the jaws, together with the teeth, would become reduced in size. (2d ed., p. 53)

For this theory to be proved correct it would be necessary to show that stone tools are at least as old as any hominid with canines reduced relative to those of apes and with large molars. Howell and Richard Leakey believe that the oldest tools go back approximately 2.6 million years. We have evidence of *Australopithecus* at least twice as old, and *Ramapithecus* jaws are about four times as old, yet all the specimens of both these genera from between 2.6 million years and 10 million or 14 million years ago show reduced, noninterlocking canines. Clearly, then, the canine size reduction predated the invention of tools. This has led to one of the principal confusions about the nature of early Pleistocene hominids, which emerges from most of the reports of findings by the Leakeys at Olduvai and East Rudolf—the idea that a tool maker must resemble *Homo* more than *Australopithecus* does. First, the finding of a robust *Australopithecus*, "Zinj," on a living floor associated with stone tools led the Leakeys to suggest that this was the tool maker. The later discovery of a more gracile type at about the same level, the "pre-Zinj juvenile," which turned out to be more than one individual, brought about transfer of the tool-making abilities to this form, called by the Leakeys "*Homo habilis*" because of its ascribed tool-making capacities. Since the original discovery of the latter, two more skulls of delicate build have been found in East Africa, both of them from Olduvai in Tanzania. But they along with the type of "*habilis*," resemble *Australopithecus africanus* both in all relevant details of the type mandible and in small brain size, indicated by the two new crania. This has lead some to the speculation that there was another, a third kind of hominid still entirely undiscovered in the late Pliocene or early Pleistocene of East Africa. Because, by now, hundreds of australopithecine finds have been made in Africa, the existence of this supposed contemporary of theirs is improbable. How much easier to accept is the idea (compatible with all the finds made to date) that in East and South Africa *Australopithecus* was the tool maker, even if not yet human in the sense that any of its early Pleistocene forms should be considered species of genus *Homo*.

The proposition that Kinzey (1969) espouses—that canines were small in the ancestors of hominids even before they ceased being apes in other respects—requires two assumptions I now think unlikely. These are (1) that every one of all the many dozens of middle and early Miocene apes known that preserve canines show large ones; this would in turn mean that species *with small canines* posited as ancestors of hominids are not yet known in the Miocene; and (2) that *Propliopithecus* from the Fayum Oligocene (with its small lower canines) does document a separate stock for hominids in the Oligocene. Even the most liberal interpretation of the extremely close biochemical similarities between man and chimpanzees would require a split of their common stock well after the 30 million year date of *Propliopithecus*.

As a sort of variant on substitution of tools for bladelike canines, Hutchinson (1963) suggested the intriguing possibility that, with the evolution of hairlessness and increasing socialization, appeasment behavior would be advantageous, particularly for the young, and canine biting and slashing would no longer be of value. The skin of "naked apes" would be relatively vulnerable to the effects of even mild biting. It would therefore be selectively advantageous for the stability of the group that either antagonistic behavior among individuals or length of the canines should change.

BRAIN ENLARGEMENT

The hypothesis that brain enlargement marked the beginning of man was long popular, but went out of fashion with the discovery that the endocranial volumes of the *Australopithecus* group were not larger than those of gorillas. There was also always the problem of why, among all the hominoids, the brains of humans got larger first, unless the impetus for larger brains derived from some other factor than the size increase itself. In any case, this theory was well expressed by Elliot-Smith, speaking before the British Association for the Advancement of Science in September 1912:

If all the factors in his [man's] emergence are not yet known, there is one unquestionable, tangible factor that we can sieze hold of and examine—the steady and uniform development of the brain along a well-defined course throughout the primates right up to man—which must give us the fundamental reason for "man's emergence and ascent," whatever other factors may contribute toward that consummation.

The idea that big brains preceded reduction of the apelike canines as well as came before the loss of other apelike features is of some historical interest, because this is what the Piltdown forgery was intended to prove by its perpetrator. It is interesting that the find, which purportedly associated an apelike jaw and canine with a brain case of modern size, was also made in 1912. In the same presentation, Elliot-Smith wrote further:

> Long ages ago, possibly in the Miocene the ancestors common to man, the gorilla, and the chimpanzee became separated into groups and the different conditions to which they became exposed after they parted company were in the main responsible for the contrasts in their fate. In one group the distinctively primate process of growth and specialization of the brain . . . reached a stage where the more venturesome members of the group, stimulated perhaps by some local failure of the customary food . . . were impelled to issue forth from their forests, and seek new sources of food and new surroundings on hill and plain . . . . The other group, perhaps because they happened to be more favorably situated or attuned to their surroundings, living in a land of plenty which encouraged indolence in habit and stagnation of effort and growth . . . remained apes.

In the foregoing passage a reason other than simple or orthogenetic trends toward brain enlargement with time (supposed somehow to be inherent in primates) is actually provided—the suggestion that failure of a particular food supply would provide the impetus for a change in feeding habits and choice of environment. In sum, the theories that mankind arose when large brain size had evolved basically fail because there would always have been a prior cause for which the larger brain or greater ingenuity was needed selectively.

UPRIGHT WALKING

A few writers have postulated that perhaps the turning point that led basal hominids away from the habits and habitus of their ape forebears was the development of habitual, terrestrial bipedal walking. The French paleoanthropologist Marcelin Boule suggested that the change came about so that our forebears, presumed to have moved out onto the savannas, could see further over the savanna grasses by standing upright and thus avoid approaching predators more successfully. Kurtén (1966) has recently pointed out that this argument, a favorite among paleoanthropologists, may be specious, because he doubts that there were large open-country predators among the Carnivora in Miocene–Pliocene times when this transition is supposed to have happened. Several other theories have also been propounded for the origin of habitual bipedal walking. Among these are the following:

1. In order to carry food or young.
2. As an outgrowth of bipedal charging during fighting, as seen in bears, chimpanzees, and gorillas.
3. As a result of the acrobatic abilities involved in order to balance and walk bipedally on tree branches or vines, seen in gibbons.
4. In order to pursue small animal prey more rapidly.

EVOLUTION OF LANGUAGE

The theory that man began with the evolution of language has perhaps more historical interest than present-day relevance. We still have no idea when speech began among hominids, but linguists suggest that no more than 50,000 years would be needed to produce all the present-day languages of the world from a common stock or root language. Perhaps language as complex as we know it today is the hallmark of *Homo sapiens* alone, the earliest fully modern-seeming populations of which were spreading into Europe at about the same time.

One of the early proponents that "speech makes man" was Sir James Burnett, Lord Monbodo, who in 1773, in a work entitled *"Of the origin and progress of language,"* speculated that orangutans and chimpanzees were only varieties of men that had never discovered how to talk to each other.

In the nineteenth century both Karl Ernst von Baer and Ernst Haeckel came to the conclusion that the property of speech appeared to be directly related to the unusually large brain of modern man. They therefore reasoned that after speech and brain enlargement came development of upright posture. Haeckel, in his *"History of natural creation,"* also advocated the view that "speech makes man" and concluded that the immediate forebears of the earliest humans were the "Pithecanthropi alali"—speechless ape-men.

After considering all these possible hypotheses, those who have read earlier chapters of this book will know that the analogy with the terrestrially foraging baboon *Theropithecus* recently worked out by Jolly explains what seems to be the most probable impetus for the separation of man's earliest forerunners from the apes. Almost all the distinctive groups, or higher categories, of mammals have arisen when a given stock has spread into a new adaptive niche and developed the ability to exploit it. The morphological and behavioral distinctions that come to characterize a distinct group of mammals, such as a family, develop or become easier to discern the more permanent and the more extensive the adaptive shift. Probably, initial phases of such a change are behavioral readjustments that would not at first be reflected in changes in skeletal form.

In consequence, of all the above hypotheses, we may feel fairly safe in concluding that the first cycle in hominid evolution was determined not by the invention of tools or complex culture, nor by the development of large brains and language, nor, necessarily, through acquisition of upright stature, but much more likely was a terrestrial dietary adaptation, increasingly effective in open country. In the absence of known postcranial bones of *Ramapithecus*, its general type of locomotion can only be speculated about. Nevertheless, there are real considerations relevant to the question. We know that the living lesser apes—gibbon and siamang—in their rare excursions to the ground walk bipedally. Palatal, facial, and mandibular measurements of *Ramapithecus* are most comparable in absolute size with those of pygmy chimpanzees. If its body size was also comparable with *Pan paniscus*, then the weight-support problems during bipedal locomotion would have been about the

Figure 112 The different times of acquisition of the principal characteristics associated with man, and illustrating the degree of uncertainty about some of them. (Chart by R. Rowen, Yale Peabody Museum.)

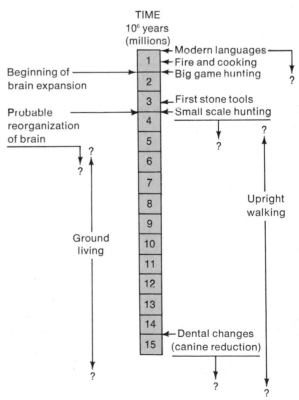

TIMES OF APPEARANCE OF THE MAJOR ATTRIBUTES OF MAN AND HIS ANCESTORS

same for the Miocene–Pliocene form. It is therefore interesting that the few accounts we have of the pygmy chimpanzee in the wild (Rahm, personal communication) indicate that one of the most striking things to be noticed about it is the tendency toward terrestrial, bipedal flight with the arms held upward and outward in a manner reminiscent of the siamang.

Our forebears could thus have been bipedal from the moment they left the trees! Figure 112 (page 281) shows the various times when features generally associated with man may have arisen. It should be clear from this figure how enormous is the scope of our uncertainty about the time of appearance of almost all of the basic features that we associate with being human. Perhaps these uncertainties lie at the heart of the well-known controversies that have marked the study of human evolution. There is still no real agreement on the definition of early man, on the first hominids, or on what is to be considered human. Nevertheless, these very uncertainties should serve as a clarion-call to all those interested in unravelling the tangled skein of man's prehistory. Even the times of the most important advances in this story are still unknown. Until now, it has never been such an important or exciting prospect to contribute, perhaps more soberly and more scientifically, to shedding light on the details of man's still largely unknown past. We stand on the brink of great discoveries.

Indeed, progress during the next decade or two may well be as illuminating as that of the past century.

Appendixes

**APPENDIX 1: A CLASSIFICATION OF PRIMATES,
LIVING AND FOSSIL**

I have tried to determine the number (in parentheses behind each generic name) of seemingly valid species included in the described genera of primates, but as is well known, many fossil and some living species are based on very trivial distinctions, so that the recognized number of valid primate binomina is likely to decrease rather than to increase in the future. As far as the tabulation following is concerned, there appear to be a total of 148 currently accepted primate genera of which 52 are now living and 96 are extinct. Contained within these genera are 360 species of which 206 are extinct and 154 extant. The common opinion that primates are rare as fossils would seem to be somewhat uninformed in view of such high numbers or fossil forms, many of which are admittedly known from one or a few individuals. In any case, their occurrence is different in character from that of such orders as Tubuludentata, which has probably never been diversified, and from Chiroptera, which has long been diversified, but both of which are poorly known as fossils.

ORDER PRIMATES

Suborder Prosimii

INFRAORDER PLESIADAPIFORMES*   Simons and Tattersall 1972[1]

Superfamily Plesiadapoidea*   Trouessart 1879 (Pal.–Eoc.)

Family Plesiadapidae*   Trouessart, 1879 (Pal.–Eoc.)

Subfamily Plesiadapinae*   Trouessart, 1879 (Pal.–Eoc.)
*Platychaerops[2] (3)   Charlesworth, 1854 (Eoc.)
*Plesiadapis (13)   Gervais, 1877 (Pal.–Eoc.)
*Chiromyoides (1)   Stehlin, 1916 (Pal.)
*Pronothodectes (3)   Gidley, 1917 (Pal.)

Subfamily Saxonellinae*   Russell, 1964
*Saxonella (1)   Russell, 1964 (Pal.)

Family Carpolestidae*   Simpson, 1935 (Pal.–Eoc.)
*Elphidotarsius (2)   Gidley, 1923 (Pal.)
*Carpodaptes (3)   Matthew and Granger, 1921 (Pal.)
*Carpolestes (4)   Simpson, 1928 (Pal.–Eoc.)

Superfamily Plesiadapoidea*   incertae sedis

Family Paromomyidae*   Simpson, 1940 (Cret.–Pal.)

Subfamily Paromomyinae*   Simpson, 1940 (Cret.–Pal.)
*Paramomys (2)   Gidley, 1923 (Pal.)
*Palaechthon (2)   Gidley, 1923 (Pal.)
*Plesiolestes (1)   Jepsen, 1930 (Pal.)
*Palenochtha (1)   Simpson, 1934 (Pal.)
*Purgatorius (2)   Van Valen and Sloan, 1965 (Cret.–Pal.)

Subfamily Phenacolemurinae*   Simpson, 1958 (Pal.–Eoc.)
*Phenacolemur (5)   Matthew, 1915 (Pal.–Eoc.)

Family Picrodontidae*   Simpson, 1937 (Pal.)
*Picrodus (1)   Douglass, 1908 (Pal.)
*Zanycteris (1)   Matthew, 1917 (Pal.)

---

*Group or genus extinct.

[1] Most but not all of the authors cited here can be found in the Bibliography. The remainder are either in Simpson (1945) or in Hill's series (1953 *et seq.*).

[2] Although several authors have spelled this *Platychoerops,* Charlesworth's original form was *Platychaerops.*

INFRAORDER LEMURIFORMES

Superfamily Adapoidea*[3]   Trouessart, 1879 (Eoc.)

Family Adapidae*   Trouessart, 1879 (Eoc.)

Subfamily Adapinae*   Trouessart, 1879 (Eoc.)
Adapis (3)   Cuvier, 1821 (Eoc.–Olig.)
Pronycticebus (1)   Grandidier, 1904 (Eoc.–?Olig.)
Protoadapis (3)   Lemoine, 1878 (Eoc.)
Anchomomys (4)   Stehlin, 1916 (Eoc.)
Caenopithecus (1)   Rütimeyer, 1862 (Eoc.)
Lantianius (1)   Chow, 1964 (Eoc.)
Agerina (1)   Crusafont Pairo, 1967 (Eoc.)

Subfamily Notharctinae*   Trouessart, 1879 (Eoc.)
Notharctus (7)   Leidy, 1870 (Eoc.)
Pelycodus (4)   Cope, 1875 (Eoc.)
Smilodectes (1)   Wortman, 1903 (Eoc.)

Superfamily Lemuroidea   Gray, 1821 (Subrec.–Rec.)

Family Lemuridae   Gray, 1821 (Subrec.–Rec.)

Subfamily Lemurinae   Gray, 1821 (Subrec.–Rec.)
Lemur (5) (*2)[4]   Linnaeus, 1758 (Subrec.–Rec.)
Hapalemur (3)   Geoffroy, 1851 (Subrec.–Rec.)
Lepilemur (1)   Geoffroy, 1851 (Subrec.–Rec.)

Subfamily Cheirogaleinae   Gray, 1870 (Subrec.–Rec.)
Cheirogaleus (2) (*1)   Geoffroy, 1812 (Subrec.–Rec.)
Microcebus (2)   Geoffroy, 1828 (Rec.)
Phaner (1)   Gray, 1870 (Rec.)
?Allocebus (1)   Petter and Petter, 1967 (Rec.)

Family Indriidae   Burnett, 1828 (Subrec.–Rec.)

Subfamily Indriinae   Burnett 1828 (Subrec.–Rec.)
Palaeopropithecus (1)   Grandidier, 1899 (Subrec.–Rec.)
Mesopropithecus (2)   Standing, 1908 (Subrec.–Rec.)
Propithecus (2) (*1)   Bennett, 1832 (Subrec.–Rec.)
Archaeoindris (1)   Lamberton, 1939 (Subrec.–Rec.)
Indri (1)   Geoffroy, 1795 (Subrec.–Rec.)
Avahi (1)   Jourdan, 1834 (Subrec.–Rec.)

Subfamily Hadropithecinae*   Abel, 1931 (Subrec.–Rec.)
Hadropithecus (1)   Lorenz, 1900 (Subrec.–Rec.)

---

[3] Article 36 of the Code of Zoological Nomenclature gives authorship of all categories from subfamily through superfamily to the first proposer of any of the three.

[4] Number following asterisk denotes the number of extinct species known in addition to the number of living species entered on the left.

Subfamily Archaeolemurinae*   Forsyth-Major, 1896 (Pleist.)
Archaeolemur (2)   Filhol, 1895 (Pleist.)

Family Daubentoniidae   Gray, 1821 (Subrec.–Rec.)
Daubentonia (1) (*1)   Geoffroy, 1795 (Subrec.–Rec.)

Family Megaladapidae*   Forsyth-Major, 1893 (Pleist.)
Megaladapis (3)   Forsyth-Major, 1893 (Pleist.)

INFRAORDER LORISIFORMES
Superfamily Lorisoidea   Gray, 1821 (Mio.–Rec.)

Family Lorisidae   Gray, 1821 (Mio.–Rec.)

Subfamily Lorisidae   Gray, 1821 (Plio.–Rec.)
Indraloris (1)   Lewis, 1933 (Plio.)
Loris (1)   Geoffroy, 1796 (Rec.)
Nycticebus (2)   Geoffroy, 1812 (Rec.)
Arctocebus (1)   Gray, 1863 (Rec.)
Perodicticus (1)   Bennett, 1831 (Rec.)

Subfamily Galaginae   Gray, 1825 (Rec.)
Galago (6)   Geoffroy, 1796 (Rec.)

Family Lorisidae   *incertae sedis*
Progalago (3)   MacInnes, 1943 (Mio.)
Komba (2)   Simpson, 1967 (Mio.)

INFRAORDER TARSIIFORMES
Superfamily Tarsiioidea   Gray, 1825 (L. Eoc.–Rec.)

Family Tarsiidae   Gray, 1825 (M. Eoc.–Rec.)

Subfamily Tarsiinae   Gray, 1825 (Rec.)
Tarsius (3)   Starr, 1870 (Rec.)

Subfamily Microchoerinae*   Lydekker, 1887 (M.–U. Eoc.)
Nannopithex (2)   Stehlin, 1916 (M. Eoc.)
Necrolemur (2)   Filhol, 1873 (M.–U. Eoc.)
Microchoerus (3)   Wood, 1846 (U. Eoc.)
Pseudoloris (1)   Stehlin, 1916 (U. Eoc.)

Superfamily Tarsioidea   *incertae sedis*

Family Anaptomorphidae*   Cope, 1883 (L.–M. Eoc.)

Subfamily Anaptomorphinae   Simpson, 1940
Absarokius (3)   Matthew, 1915 (L. Eoc.)
Tetonius (2)   Matthew, 1915 (L. Eoc.)
Tetonoides (2)   Gazin, 1962 (L. Eoc.)
Uintalacus (1)   Gazin, 1958 (L. Eoc.)
Anemorhysis (2)   Gazin, 1958 (L. Eoc.)
Trogolemur (1)   Matthew, 1909 (L.–M. Eoc.)

Anaptomorphus (2)   Cope, 1872 (M. Eoc.)
Uintanius (1)   Matthew, 1915 (M. Eoc.)

Subfamily Omomyinae*   Wortman, 1904 (L. Eoc.–Mio.)
Omomys (4)   Leidy, 1869 (Eoc.)
Loveina (1)   Simpson, 1940 (Eoc.)
Hemiacodon (1)   Marsh, 1872 (Eoc.)
Washakius (2)   Leidy, 1873 (Eoc.)
Shoshonius (1)   Granger, 1910 (Eoc.)
Macrotarsius (2)   Clark, 1941 (Olig.)
Teilhardina (1)   Simpson, 1940 (Eoc.)
Utahia (1)   Gazin, 1958 (Eoc.)
Stockia (1)   Gazin, 1958 (Eoc.)
Ourayia (2)   Gazin, 1958 (Eoc.)
Rooneyia (1)   Wilson, 1966 (Olig.)
Ekgmowechashala (1)   MacDonald, 1963 (Mioc.)

Family Omomyidae?   *incertae sedis*
Periconodon (1)   Stehlin, 1916 (Eoc.)
Hoanghonius (1)   Zdansky, 1930 (Eoc.)
Lushius (1)   Chow, 1961 (Eoc.)

Suborder Anthropoidea   Mivart, 1864 (E. Olig.–Rec.)
INFRAORDER PLATYRRHINI
Superfamily Ceboidea   Simpson, 1931 (E. Olig.–Rec.)

Family Cebidae   Swainson, 1835 (E. Olig.–Rec.)

Subfamily Aotinae   Elliot, 1913 (Mio.–Rec.)
Homunculus (3)   Ameghino, 1891 (Mio.)
Aotus (1)   Humboldt, 1811 (Rec.)
Callicebus (3)   Thomas, 1903 (Pleist.–Rec.)
Dolichocebus (1)   Kraglievich, 1951 (Olig.)

Subfamily Pithecinae   Mivart, 1865 (Rec.)
Cacajao (3)   Lesson, 1840 (Rec.)
Pithecia (2)   Desmarest, 1804 (Rec.)
Chiropotes (2)   Lesson, 1840 (Rec.)

Subfamily Alouattinae   Elliot, 1904 (Pleist.–Rec.)
Alouatta (5)   Lacépède, 1799 (Pleist.–Rec.)

Subfamily Cebinae   Mivart, 1865 (Mioc.–Rec.)
Cebus (4)   Erxleben, 1777 (Pleist.–Rec.)
Saimiri (2)   Voigt, 1831 (Rec.)
Neosaimiri (1)   Stirton, 1951 (Mio.)
Stirtonia (1)   Hershkovitz, 1969 (Mio.)

Subfamily Cebupithecinae*   Hershkovitz, 1969 (Mio.)
Cebupithecia (1)   Stirton and Savage, 1951 (Mio.)

Subfamily Atelinae   Miller, 1924 (Rec.)
Ateles (4)   Geoffroy, 1806 (Rec.)

Brachyteles (1)   Spix, 1823 (Rec.)
Lagothrix (2)   Geoffroy, 1812 (Rec.)

Subfamily Callimiconinae   Thomas, 1913 (Rec.)
Callimico (1)   Ribeiro, 1911 (Rec.)

Family Callithricidae   Thomas, 1903 (Rec.)
Callithrix (3)   Erxleben, 1777 (Rec.)
Saguinus (16)   Hoffmannsegg, 1807 (Rec.)

Family Xenothricidae*   Hershkovitz, 1969 (Pleist.)
Xenothrix (1)   Williams and Coopman, 1952 (Pleist.)

Superfamily Ceboidea?   Simpson, 1931

Branisella (1)   Hoffstetter, 1969 (Olig.)

INFRAORDER CATARRHINI
Superfamily Cercopithecoidea   Gray, 1821 (Olig., Plio.–Rec.)

Family Cercopithecidae   Gray, 1821 (Olig., Plio.–Rec.)

Subfamily Cercopithecinae   Blanford, 1888 (Plio.–Rec.)
Macaca (13) (*4)   Lacépède, 1799 (Rec.)
Libypithecus (1)   Stromer, 1913 (M. Plio.)
Cercocebus (4)   Geoffroy, 1812 (Pleist.–Rec.)
Parapapio (4)   Jones, 1937 (Pleist.)
Dinopithecus (2)   Broom, 1936 (Pleist.)
Gorgopithecus (1)   Broom and Robinson, 1949 (Pleist.)
Papio (7) (*4)   Erxleben, 1777 (Pleist.–Rec.)
Procynocephalus (2)   Schlosser, 1922 (Pleist.)
Theropithecus (1) (*2)   Geoffroy, 1843 (Pleist.–Rec.)
Cercopithecus (17)   Brünnich, 1772 (M. Plio.–Rec.)
Allenopithecus (1)   Lang, 1923 (Rec.)
Erythrocebus (1)   Trouessart, 1897 (Rec.)
Miopithecus (1)   Geoffroy, 1842 (Rec.)

Subfamily Parapithecinae*   Schlosser, 1911 (L. Olig.)
Parapithecus (2)   Schlosser, 1910 (L. Olig.)
Apidium (2)   Osborn, 1908 (L. Olig.)

Subfamily Colobinae   Elliot, 1913 (Plio.–Rec.)
Mesopithecus (1)   Wagner, 1839 (L. Plio.)
Dolichopithecus (1)   Depéret, 1889 (Plio.)
Presbytis (13)   Eschscholtz, 1821 (L. Pleist.–Rec.)
Pygathrix (1)   Geoffroy, 1812 (Rec.)
Rhinopithecus (2)   Milne-Edwards, 1872 (Subfossil–Rec.)
Simias (1)   Miller, 1902 (Rec.)
Nasalis (1)   Geoffroy, 1812 (Rec.)
Colobus (4)   Illiger, 1811 (Rec.)
Procolobus (1)   Rochebrune, 1887 (Rec.)

*Family Cercopithecidae   *incertae sedis*
*Cercopithecoides (2)   Mollett, 1947 (Pleist.)
*Paracolobus (1)   R. Leakey, 1969 (Plio.)
*Prohylobates (1)   Fourtau, 1918 (Mio.)
*Victoriapithecus (2)   von Koenigswald, 1969 (Mio.)

Superfamily Oreopithecoidea*

Family Oreopithecidae*   Schwalbe, 1915 (Mio.–L. Plio.)
*Oreopithecus (1)   Gervais, 1872 (L. Plio.)
*Mobokopithecus (1)   von Koenigswald, 1969 (Mio.)

Superfamily Hominoidea   Simpson, 1931

Family Hylobatidae   Gill, 1872 (Olig.–Rec.)

Subfamily Pliopithecinae*   Zapfe, 1961 (Olig.–L. Plio., ?Pleist.)
*Pliopithecus (5)   Gervais, 1849 (L. Mio.–L. Plio., ?Pleist.)
*Limnopithecus (2)   Hopwood, 1933 (L. Mio.)
*Aeolopithecus (1)   Simons, 1965 (Olig.)

Subfamily Hylobatinae   Gill, 1872 (Pleist.–Rec.)
Hylobates (7)   Illiger, 1811 (Pleist.–Rec.)
Symphalangus (1)   Gloger, 1841 (Rec.)

Family Pongidae   Elliot, 1913 (Mio.–Rec.)

Subfamily Dryopithecinae*   Gregory and Hellman,
                    1939 (M. Mio.–Plio.)
*Dryopithecus (7)   Lartet, 1856 (M. Mio.–Plio.)
*Aegyptopithecus (1)   Simons, 1965 (E. Olig.)
*Propliopithecus (2)   Schlosser, 1910 (L. Olig.)

Subfamily ?Dryopithecinae   *incertae sedis*
*Oligopithecus (1)   Simons, 1962 (E. Olig.)

Subfamily Ponginae   Allen, 1925 (Pleist.–Rec.)
Pongo (1)   Lacépède, 1799 (L. Pleist.–Rec.)
Pan (2)   Oken, 1816 (Rec.)
Gorilla (1)   Geoffroy, 1852 (Rec.)

Subfamily Gigantopithecinae*   Gremiatskij, 1961 (Plio.–Pleist.)
*Gigantopithecus (2)   von Koenigswald, 1935 (Plio.–Pleist.)

Family Hominidae   Gray, 1825 (Mio.–Rec.)
*Ramapithecus (1)   Lewis, 1934 (Mio.–Plio.)
*Australopithecus (4)   Dart, 1925 (Pleist.)
Homo (1) (*1)   Linnaeus, 1758 (Pleist.–Rec.)

Superfamily Hominoidea?

Amphipithecus (1)   Colbert, 1937 (Eoc.)
Pondaungia (1)   Pilgrim, 1927 (Eoc.)

APPENDIX 2: A LIST OF GENERIC SYNONYMS

For convenience of students reading the older literature, the follow-ing list of generic synonyms is provided. However, it must not be considered exhaustive. In order to avoid overcomplication, only strict generic synonyms are tabulated. "Partem" cases, where some but not all of the referred material or hypodigm has been trans-ferred from one genus to another, are not included. Instead only genera that have been dropped, as being fully synonymous with another, by the International Commission of Nomenclature or that have a type specimen of the type species of the supposed genus assignable to a prior genus are listed. Generic proliferation has long been a propensity of students of the primates—of both living and fossil forms. The genera here considered synonyms are indented below the generic name to which their types have been transferred by various revisors and competent first-hand observers. Further details on such synonyms can be found in Hill's series on Primates, in various papers by Hershkovitz on New World monkeys, on Hominoidea in Simons and Pilbeam (1965), and on Hominidae in Campbell (1966). In most cases, and unless they have been widely used, generic synonyms that are only spelling variants of the ac-cepted genera are not included either, but can be found in the above-listed references. A few generic names such as *Simia* and *Pithecus* have been broadly applied to several different primate genera. Such overextended synonyms are also not listed here. Known material of some proposed genera such as *Brachygnatho-pithecus* has been parceled out to two or more genera. In these cases, multiple synonyms have not been included.

ADAPIS
  APHELOTHERIUM
  LEPTADAPIS
  PALEOLEMUR
ALLENOPITHECUS
  LASIOPYGA
ALOUATTA
  MYCETES
AOTUS
  AOTES
  NOCTHORA
  NYCTIPITHECUS
ARCHAEOLEMUR
  LOPHIOLEMUR
  NESOPITHECUS
  GLOBILEMUR
  BRADYLEMUR
  PROTOINDRIS
ATELES
  ATELEUS
  PANISCUS

ATHELES
  ATELOCHIRUS
  MAMATELESUS
  MONTANEIA
  AMERANTHROPOIDES
AUSTRALOPITHECUS
  PARANTHROPUS
  PLESIANTHROPUS
  MEGANTHROPUS
  ZINJANTHROPUS
  ?TCHADANTHROPUS
  ?AFRICANTHROPUS
  PRAANTHROPUS
  PARAUSTRALOPITHECUS
  HEMANTHROPUS
BRACHYTELES
  EROIDES
  PROTOPITHECUS
  BRACHYTELEUS
CACAJAO
  BRACHYURUS

CERCOPTOCHUS
OUKARIA
UAKERIA
COTHURUS
NEOCOTHURUS
CALLITHRIX
　HAPALE
　MICO
　JACCUS
　SYLVANUS
　ARCTOPITHECUS
　OUISTITIS
　LIOCEPHALUS
　MICOELLA
　JACCHUS
　SAGOINUS
　SAGOUIN
CEBUS
　AEGIPAN
　PSEUDOCEBUS
　CALIPTROCEBUS
　OTOCEBUS
　EUCEBUS
CERCOCEBUS
　CERCOLOPHOCEBUS
　LEPTOCEBUS
CERCOPITHECUS
　RHINOSTIGMA
　ALLOCHROCEBUS
CHEIROGALEUS
　CEBUGALE
　MYXOCEBUS
　OPOLEMUR
　ALTILILEMUR
　ALTILEMUR
　MIOXICEBUS
CHIROPOTES
　BRACHYURUS
COLOBUS
　PILIOCOLOBUS
　PROCOLOBUS
　PTERYCOLOBUS
　LOPHOCOLOBUS
　COLOBOLUS
DAUBENTONIA
　SCOLECOPHAGUS
　AYE-AYE
　CHEIROMYS
　PSILODACTYLUS
　MYSLEMUR
DRYOPITHECUS
　PALEOPITHECUS
　ANTHROPODUS
　PAIDOPITHEX
　PLIOHYLOBATES

NEOPITHECUS
GRIPHOPITHECUS
SIVAPITHECUS
PALEOSIMIA
HYLOPITHECUS
XENOPITHECUS
PROCONSUL
SUGRIVAPITHECUS
?ADAETONTHERIUM
HISPANOPITHECUS
INDOPITHECUS
UDABNOPITHECUS
RHENOPITHECUS
ANKARAPITHECUS
RAHONOPITHECUS
GALAGO
　OTOLICNUS
　MACROPUS
　HEMIGALAGO
　CHIROSCIURUS
　OTOLEMUR
　OTOGALE
　CALLOTUS
　SCIUROCHEIRUS
　GALAGOIDES
　EUOTICUS
GORILLA
　PSEUDOGORILLA
HADROPITHECUS
　PITHECODON
HAPALEMUR
　HAPALOLEMUR
　PROLEMUR
　MYOXICEBUS
HOMO
　PITHECANTHROPUS
　EOANTHROPUS
　ATLANTHROPUS
　CYPHANTHROPUS
　SINANTHROPUS
　NIPPONANTHROPUS
　PALAEANTHROPUS
　PSEUDHOMO
　PROTANTHROPUS
　TELANTHROPUS
　PRAEHOMO
　ANTHROPUS
　MAURANTHROPUS
　EUROPANTHROPUS
　EURANTHROPUS
　HEMIANTHROPUS
　PROANTHROPUS
HOMUNCULUS
　?ECPHANTODON
　?ANTHROPOPS

?PITHECULUS
HYLOBATES
  NOMASCUS
  BUNOPITHECUS
  BRACHYTANYTES
INDRI
  INDRIS
  INDRIUM
  LICHANOTES
  PITHELEMUR
LAGOTHRIX
  GASTRIMARGUS
  OREONAX
LEMUR
  PROSIMIA
  PROCEBUS
  CATTA
  MAKI
  VARECIA
  MOCOCO
  ODORLEMUR
  EULEMUR
  PALAEOCHIROGALUS
LEONTOPITHECUS
  LEONTIDEUS
LEPILEMUR
  GALEOCEBUS
  MIXOCEBUS
  LEPIDOLEMUR
LICHANOTUS
  AVAHI
  MICRORYNCHUS
  AVAHIS
  HABROCEBUS
  SEMNOCEBUS
  IROPOCUS
  HOKUSPOCUS
LORIS
  TARDIGRADUS
  ARACHNOCEBUS
MACACA
  AULAXINUUS
  CYNOPITHECUS
  CYNOMOLGUS
  GYMNOPYGA
  INUUS
  LYSSODES
  MAGOTUS
  MAGUS
  NEMISTRINUS
  DUANDEROU
  RHESUS
  SALMACIS
  SILENUS
  SYLVANUS

  VETULUS
  ZATI
  SIMIA
  PITHEX
  NEOCEBUS
  CYNOMACACA
  PITHECUS
MEGALADAPIS
  THAUMASTOLEMUR
  PELORIADAPIS
  MESOADAPIS
MICROCEBUS
  MYSCEBUS
  GLISCEBUS
  MYOCEBUS
  MIRZA
  AZEMA
  MURILEMUR
  SCARTES
MIOPITHECUS
  CERCOPITHECI
NASALIS
  RHINOCHOPITHECUS
NOTHARCTUS
  LIMNOTHERIUM
  HIPPOSYUS
  TOMITHERIUM
  THINOLESTES
  TELMALESTES
  TELMATOLESTES
  PROSINOPA
NYCTICEBUS
  BRADYCEBUS
  BRADYLEMUR
  TARDIGRADUS
OMOMYS
  EURYACODON
  PALAEACODON
OURAYIA
  MYTONIUS
PALAECHTHON
  TORREJONIA
PALAEOPROPITHECUS
  BRADYTHERIUM
PAN
  CHIMPANSEE
  ANTHROPOPITHECUS
  TROGLODYTES
  BONOBO
  SATYRUS
  ENGECO
  ANDROPITHECUS
  MIMETES
  HYLANTHROPUS
  PSEUDOANTHROPOS

PAPIO
  COMOPITHECUS
  CHAEROPITHECUS
  CHOIROPITHECUS
  CYNOCEPHALUS
  MAIMON
PELYCODUS
  LEMURAVUS
  PROTOTOMUS
PERODICTICUS
  POTTO
PHENACOLEMUR
  IGNACIUS
PITHECIA
  YARKIA
PLATYCHAEROPS
  MIOLOPHUS
PLESIADAPIS
  NOTHODECTES
  MENATOTHERIUM
PONGO
  SIMIA
  PITHECUS
PRESBYTIS
  SEMNOPITHECUS
  TRACHYPITHECUS
  KASI
  PITHECUS
  CORYPITHECUS
  PRESBYPITHECUS
  LOPHOPITHECUS
PROCOLOBUS
  LOPHOCOLOBUS
PROCYNOCEPHALUS
  PARADOLICHOPITHECUS
PROGALAGO
  MIOEUOTICUS
PRONYCTICEBUS
  AGERINA
PROPITHECUS
  MACROMERUS
PROPLIOPITHECUS
  MOERIPITHECUS
PROTOADAPIS
  MEGATARSIUS
  EUROPOLEMUR
PSEUDOLORIS
  PIVETONIA
RAMAPITHECUS
  BRAMAPITHECUS
  KENYAPITHECUS
RHINOPITHECUS
  PRESBYTISCUS
SAGUINUS
  LEONTOCEBUS

TAMARIN
TAMIRINUS
OEDIPOMIDAS
LEONTIDEUS
MARIKINA
MIDAS
MYSTAX
SAIMIRI
  CHRYSOTHERIX
  PITHESCIURUS
SMILODECTES
  APHANOLEMUR
SYMPHALANGUS
  SYNDACTYLUS
  SIAMANGA
TARSIUS
  MACROTARSUS
  PROSIMIA
  RABIENUS
  CEPHALOPACHUS
  HYPSICEBUS
  RUBIENUS
TETONIUS
  PARATETONIUS
THEROPITHECUS
  SIMOPITHECUS

APPENDIX 3: CHECKLISTS OF LIVING PRIMATES

Allen, G. M., 1939, A checklist of African mammals, *Bull. Mus. Comp. Zool. Harv.* 83, 113–178.

Cabrera, A., 1957, *Catalogo de los mamiferos de America del Sur,* Vol. 4, No. 1, Instituto Nacional de Investigacion de la Ciencias Naturales, Ciencio Zoologica, Buenos Aires y Peru, pp. 133–202.

Chasen, F. N., 1940, A handlist of Malaysian mammals, *Bull. Raffles Mus.,* 15, 60–89.

Ellerman, J. R., and Morrison-Scott, T. C. S., 1951, *Checklist of Palearctic and Indian mammals 1758–1946,* Trustees of the British Museum, London, pp. 189–213.

Ellerman, J. R., Morrison-Scott, T. C. S., and Hayman, R. W., 1953, *Southern African mammals 1758–1951: A reclassification,* Trustees of the British Museum, London, pp. 89–103.

Hall, E. R., and Kelson, K. R., 1959, *The mammals of North America,* Vol. I, Ronald Press, New York, pp. 218–234.

Napier, J. R., and Napier, P. H., 1967, *A handbook of living primates,* Academic Press, London.

Bibliography

Abel, O., 1931, *Die Stellung des Menschen im Rahmen der Wirbeltiere,* Fischer, Jena.

Allbrook, D., and Bishop, W. W., 1963, New fossil hominoid material from Uganda, *Nature,* 197, 1187–1190.

Ameghino, F., 1891, Nuevos restos de mammiferos fossiles descubiertos por Cárlos Ameghino en el Eoceno inferior de la Patagonia austral: Especies nuevas, adiciones y correciones, *Rev. Argent. Hist. Nat.,* 1, 289–328, 383–397.

————, 1892, Énumération synoptique des espèces de mammifères fossiles des formations éocènes de Patagonie, *Bol. Acad. Cienc. Córdoba,* 13, 259–452.

————, 1898, El *Arhinolemur,* genero del Tercario del Paraná que representa un tipo nuevo de la clase de los mamíferos, *An. Soc. Cienc. Argent.,* 46, 376.

————, 1902, Première contribution à la connaissance de la faune mammalogique des couches à *Colpodon, Bol. Acad. Cienc. Córdoba,* 17, 71–141.

————, 1904, Recherches de morphologie phylogénétique sur les molaires supérieurs des ongulés, *Ann. Mus. Nac. Buenos Aires,* 3, 1–541.

Andrews, C. W., 1916, Note on a new baboon (*Simopithecus oswaldi,* gen, et sp. n.) from the (?) Pliocene of British East Africa, *Ann. Mag. Nat. Hist.,* 18, 410–419.

Ankel, F., 1965, Der Canalis sacralis als Indikator für die Länge der Caudalregion der Primaten, *Folia Primat.,* 3, 263–276.

Arambourg, C., 1947, Contribution à l'étude géologique et paléontologique du bassin du Lac Rodolphe et de la basse vallée de l'Omo: Deuxième partie, paléontologie, *Mission Sci. Omo,* 1. (3), 231–562, 1932–1933. *I. Géol. Anth. Paris,* 232–562.

Baker, W. E., and Durand, H. M., 1836, Sub-himalayan fossil remains of the Dadoopoor collection. *J. Asiatic Soc.,* 5, 739.

————, 1959, Vertebrés continentaux du Miocène supérieur de l'Afrique du Nord, *Mem. Serv. Carte Géol. Algérie (n.s.) Pal.,* 4, 1–161.

Bluntschli, H., 1931, *Homunculus patagonicus* und die ihm zugereihten Fossilfunde aus den Santa Cruz-Schichten Patagoniens, *Morph. Jb. Leipzig,* 67, 811–892.

Boule, M., 1921, *Les hommes fossiles: Éléments de paléontologie humaine,* avec 239 figures dans le texte et hors le texte, Masson, Paris, 491 pp.

Brain, C. K., 1967, New light on old bones, *SAMAB,* 9. (1), 22–27.

Branco, W., 1898, Die menschenähnlichen Zähne aus dem Bohnerz der Schwäbischen Alp, *Jh. Ver. Vaterl. Naturkde, Württemberg, Teil I*, 54, 1–144.

Broom, R., 1936, A new fossil anthropoid skull from South Africa, *Nature,* 138, 486–488.

———, 1937, On some new Pleistocene mammals from limestone caves of the Transvaal, *S. Afr. J. Sci.,* 33, 750–768.

———, 1939, The dentition of the Transvaal Pleistocene anthropoids, *Plesianthropus* and *Paranthropus, Ann. Transvaal Mus.,* 19, 303–314.

———, 1940, The South African Pleistocene cercopithecid apes, *Ann. Transvaal Mus.,* 20, 89–100.

———, 1950, The genera and species of the South African fossil ape-men, *Transvaal Mus. Mem.,* 2, 1–153.

———, and Robinson, J. T., 1948, Size of the brain in the ape man, *Plesianthropus, Nature,* 161, 438.

———, 1949, A new type of fossil baboon, *Gorgopithecus major, Proc. Zool. Soc. London,* 119, 379–386.

Buettner-Janusch, J., 1966, *Origin of man,* Wiley, New York.

Butler, P. M., 1963, Tooth morphology and primate evolution, IN *Dental anthropology,* ed. D. R. Brothwell, Pergamon, New York, pp. 1–13.

Burnett, Sir J., Lord Monbodo, 1773–1792, *Of the origin and progress of language,* printed for A. Kinkaid and W. Creech, Edinburgh.

Campbell, B., 1966, *Human evolution: An introduction to man's adaptations,* Cambridge U.P., New York.

Carleton, A., 1936, The limb bones and vertebrae of the extinct lemurs of Madagascar, *Proc. Zool. Soc. London,* 281–307.

Charlesworth, E., 1854, Notice on new vertebrate fossils, *Rep. Brit. Assoc. Adv. Sci. Liverpool,* 25 (trans.), 80.

Chow, M., 1958, Mammalian faunas and correlation of Tertiary and Pleistocene of South China, *J. Pal. Soc. India,* 3, 123–130.

Clark, J., 1941, An anaptomorphid primate from the Oligocene of Montana, *J. Pal.,* 15, 562–563.

Cocci, I., 1872, Su di due Scimmie fossili italiane, *Boll. R. Com. Geol. Ital.,* 3, 59–71.

Cooke, H. B. S., 1963, Pleistocene mammal faunas of Africa with particular reference to South Africa, IN *African ecology and human evolution,* eds. F. C. Howell and F. Bourliére, Aldine, Chicago.

Cope, E. D., 1872a, Third account of new Vertebrata from the Bridger Eocene of Wyoming Territory, *Pal. Bull.,* 3(8), 1.

———, 1872b, An anthropomorphous lemur, *Am. Naturalist,* 16, 73–74.

———, 1873, On the extinct Vertebrata of the Eocene of Wyoming observed by the expedition of 1872, with notes on the geology, *6th Ann. Rep. U.S. Geol. Surv. Terr.,* pp. 545–649.

———, 1875, Systematic catalogue of Vertebrata of the Eocene of New Mexico, collected in 1874, *Geogr. Expl. Surv. West of 100th Meridian (Wheeler),* pp. 5–37.

———, 1881, On the Vertebrata of the Wind River Eocene beds of Wyoming, *Bull. U.S. Geol. Geogr. Surv. Terr. (Hayden),* 6(1), 183–202.

———, 1883, On the mutual relations of the bunotherian Mammalia, *Proc. Acad. Nat. Sci. Phila.,* 20, 139–197.

Crook, J. H., 1966, Gelada baboon herd structure and movement: A comparative report, *Symp. Zool. Soc. London,* 18, 237–258.

Cuvier, G., 1821, *Discours sur la théorie de la terre, servant d'introduction aux recherches sur les ossements fossiles,* Paris (2nd ed. 1823).

Dart, R. A., 1925, *Australopithecus africanus:* The man-ape of South Africa, *Nature,* 115, 195–199.

———, 1926, Taungs and its significance, *Nat. Hist.,* 26, 315–327.

———, 1962, The most complete *Australopithecus* skull from the pink breccia at Makapansgat, *Actes IV Congr. Panafr. Préhist., Étude Quat.,* 40, 337–340.

Darwin, C., 1871, *The descent of man,* John Murray, London.

Day, M. H., 1965, *Guide to fossil man,* World Publ. Co., Cleveland.

———, 1969, Hominoid tali from East Africa, *Nature,* 222, 591–592.

———, and Napier, J. R., 1966, A hominid toe from Bed I, Olduvai Gorge, Tanzania, *Nature,* 211, 929–930.

———, and Wood, B. A., 1968, Functional affinities of the Olduvai Hominid 8 talus, *Man,* 3(3), 440–455.

de Villalta, J. F., and Crusafont Pairo, M., 1944, Dos nuevos Antropomorfos del Mioceno español, y su situación de la moderna sistematica de los Simidos, *Notes y Commun. Inst. Geol. Min. España,* 13, 7–25.

Delfortrie, E., 1873, Un singe de la famille des Lémuriens, *Act. Soc. Linn. Bordeaux,* 24, 87–95.

Depéret, C., 1887, Études paléontologiques dans le bassin du Rhône, Période Miocène. Recherches sur la succession des faunes des vertébrés miocènes de la vallée du Rhône, *Arch. Mus. Sci. Nat. Lyon,* 4, 45–313.

———, 1897, Les animaux pliocène de Roussillon, *Mém. Soc. Géol. France, Pal.,* 3, 1–164.

———, 1929, *Dolichopithecus avernensis* Depéret, nouveau singe du pliocène supérieur de Sénèze (Haute-Loire), *Trav. Lab. Géol. Fac. Sci. Lyon. Mem.,* 12, 5–12.

Dorr, J. A., Jr., 1952, Early Cenozoic stratigraphy and vertebrate paleontology of the Hoback Basin, Wyoming, *Bull. Geol. Soc. Amer.,* 63, 59–93.

Edinger, T., 1938, Mitteilungen über Wirbeltierreste aus dem Mittel-Pliozän des Natrontales (Ägypten). 9. Das Gehirn des *Lybipithecus, Zbl. Min. Geol. Pal. Stuttgart,* 8, 122–128.

Eicher, Don L., 1968, *Geologic time,* Prentice-Hall, Englewood Cliffs, N.J.

Eimerl, S., and De Vore, I., 1965, *The Primates,* "Life Nature Library."

Elliot, D. G., 1913, *A review of the primates, Amer. Mus. Nat. Hist. Monogr.,* pp. 1–1360.

Elliot-Smith, G., 1912, Presidential address to the anthropology section (H) of the 82nd Annual Meeting of the British Association for the Advancement of Science, *Rep. 82nd Meeting Brit. Assoc. Adv. Sci.*

Evernden, J. F., and Curtis, G. H., 1965, The potassium-argon dating of late Cenozoic rocks in East Africa and Italy, *Cur. Anth.,* 6(4), 343–385.

———, Savage, D. E., Curtis, G. H., and James, G. T., 1964, Potassium–argon dates and the Cenozoic mammalian chronology of North America, *Amer. J. Sci.,* 262, 145–198.

Every, R. G., 1970, Sharpness of teeth in man and other primates, *Postilla* (Peabody Museum, Yale University), No. 143, 1–30.

Ferembach, D., 1958, Les Limnopithèques du Kenya, *Ann. Pal., Paris,* 44, 149–249.

Fiedler, W., 1956, Übersicht über das System der Primaten, IN *Primatologia,* Vol. I, eds. H. Hofer, A. H. Schultz, and D. Starck, Karger, Basel, pp. 1–266.

Filhol, H., 1873, Sur un nouveau genre de lémurien fossile: Récemment découvert dans les gisements de phosphate de chaux du Quercy, *C. R. Acad. Sci. Paris,* 77, 1111–1112.

———, 1890, Description d'une nouvelle espèce de lémurien fossile *(Necrolemur parvulus), Bull. Doc. Philom. Paris,* 11, 39–40.

Flacourt, E., 1658, *Histoire de la grande Isle Madagascar,* Paris.

Forsyth-Major, C. I., 1880, Beiträge zur Geschichte der fossilen Pferde, insbesondere Italiens, *Abh. Schweiz. Pal. Ges.,* 7, 1–154.

———, 1894, On *Megaladapis madagascariensis,* an extinct giant lemur from Madagascar, with remarks on the associated fauna and on its geological age, *Philos. Trans. Roy. Soc. London (B),* 185, 15–38.

———, 1900, A summary of our present knowledge of extinct primates from Madagascar, *Geol. Mag.,* 7(4), 492–499.

———, 1901, On some characters of the skull in the lemurs and monkeys, *Proc. Zool. Soc. London,* 129–153.

Fourtau, R., 1918, *Contribution à l'étude des Vertébrés,* Egypt Surv. Dept., Cairo, pp. 195–196.

Freedman, L., 1957, The fossil Cercopithecoidea of South Africa, *Ann. Transvaal Mus.,* 23, 121–262.

———, 1961, New cercopithecoid fossils including a new species, from Taung, Cape Province, South Africa, *Ann. S. Afr. Mus.,* 46, 1–14.

Gaudry, A., 1890, Le dryopithèque, *Mém. Soc. Geol. France, Pal. Mem.,* 1, 1–11.

Gazin, C. L., 1952, The Lower Eocene Knight formation of Western Wyoming and its mammalian faunas, *Smithson. Misc. Coll.,* 117, 1–82.

———, 1958, A review of the Middle and Upper Eocene Primates of North America, *Smithson. Misc. Coll.,* 136, No. 1, 1–112.

———, 1962, A further study of the Lower Eocene mammalian faunas of Southwestern Wyoming, *Smithson. Misc. Coll.,* 144, 1–98.

Genet-Varcin, E., 1963, *Les singes actuels et fossiles,* Boubée, Paris.

———, 1969, *A la recherche du primate ancêtre de l'homme,* Boubée, Paris.

Geoffroy Saint-Hilaire, E., 1812, Tableaux des quadrumanes, ou des animaux composent la première ordre de la classe des mammifères, *Mus. Hist. Nat. Paris,* 19, 156–170.

Gervais, P., 1837, Remarques au sujet du genre Paléolémur, *J. Zool., Paris,* 2, 421–426.

———, 1852, *Zoologie et paléontologie française* (animaux vertébrés), 3 vols.

———, 1872, Sur un singe fossile, d'espèce non encore décrite, qui a été decouvert au Monte-Bamboli (Italie), *C. R. Acad. Sci. Paris*, 74, 1217–1223.

————, **1877,** Énumération de quelques ossements d'animaux vertébrés recueillis aux environs de Reims par M. Lemoine, II, *J. Zool., Paris*, 6, 74–79.

Gidley, J. W., 1923, Paleocene primates of the Fort Union, with discussion of relationships of Eocene primates, *Proc. U.S. Nat. Mus.*, 63, 1–38.

Gillet, S., Lorenz, H. G., and Waltersdorf, F., 1965, Introduction à l'étude du Miocène supérieur de la region de Bacinello (environs de Grosseto, Italie), *Serv. Carte Géol. Alsace, Lorraine, Strasbourg*, 18, 31–42.

Goodman, M., 1967, Deciphering primate phylogeny from macromolecular specificities, *Amer. J. Phys. Anth.*, 26, 255–276.

Grandidier, G., 1904, Un nouveau lémurien fossil de France, le *Pronycticebus gaudryi, Bull. Mus. Hist. Nat. Paris*, 10, 9–13.

Granger, W., 1910, Tertiary faunal horizons in the Wind River Basin, Wyoming, with descriptions of new Eocene mammals, *Bull. Amer. Mus. Nat. Hist.*, 28, 235–251.

————, **and Gregory, W. K., 1917,** A revision of the Eocene Primates of the genus *Notharctus, Bull. Amer. Mus. Nat. Hist.*, 37, 841–859.

Gregory, W. K., 1910, The orders of mammals, *Bull. Amer. Mus. Nat. Hist.*, 27, 1–524.

————, **1915,** I. On the relationship of the Eocene lemur *Notharctus* to the Adapidae and the other primates. II. On the classification and phylogeny of the Lemuroidea, *Bull. Geol. Soc. Amer.*, 26, 419–446.

————, **1916,** Studies on the evolution of Primates, *Bull. Amer. Mus. Nat. Hist.*, 35, 239–355.

————, **1918,** The evolution of orthodonty, *Dental Cosmos*, 60, 417–425.

————, **1920,** On the structure and relations of *Notharctus*, an American Eocene primate, *Mem. Amer. Mus. Nat. Hist. (n.s.)*, 3(2), 49–243.

————, **1922,** *The origin and evolution of the human dentition,* Williams and Wilkins, Baltimore.

————, **1951,** *Evolution emerging*, Macmillan, New York.

————, **and Hellman, M., 1926,** The dentition of *Dryopithecus* and the origin of man, *Anth. Papers Amer. Mus. Nat. Hist.*, 28, 1–123.

————, **and Lewis, G. E., 1938,** Fossil anthropoids of the Yale–Cambridge Indian expedition of 1935, Carnegie Institution, Washington, 495, 1–27.

Guthrie, D. A., 1967, The mammalian fauna of the Lysite member, Wind River Formation (early Eocene) of Wyoming, *Mem. S. Calif. Acad. Sci.*, 5, 1–53.

Harlé, E., 1899, Nouvelle pièces de dryopithèque et quelques coquilles, de Saint-Gaudens (Haute Garonne), *Bull. Soc. Géol. France Ser. 3*, 27, 304–310.

Hay, R., 1963, Stratigraphy of Beds I through IV, Olduvai Gorge, Tanganyika, *Science,* 139, 829–833.

Heberer, G., 1956, Die Fossilgeschichte der Hominoidea, IN *Primatologia*, Vol. I, eds. H. Hofer, A. H. Schultz, and D. Starck, Karger, Basel, pp. 379–560.

Heller, F., 1935, *Amphilemur eocaenicus* n.g. et n. sp., ein primitiver Primate aus dem Mitteleozän des Geiseltales bei Halle an der Saale, *Nov. Acta Leop. Carol. Halle*, 2, 293–300.

Hershkovitz, P., 1970, Notes on Tertiary platyrrhine monkeys and description of a new genus from the late Miocene of Colombia, *Folia Primat.*, 12, 1–37.

Hildebrand, M., 1968, Symmetrical gaits of primates, *Amer. J. Phys. Anth.,* 26, 119–130.

Hill, J. P., 1932, The developmental history of the Primates, *Phil. Trans.*, 221, 45–178.

Hill, W. C. O., 1953–1970, *Primates: Comparative anatomy and taxonomy*, Vols. 1–7, Edinburgh U. P., Edinburgh.

Hofer, H. O., and Wilson, J. A., 1967, An endocranial cast of an early Oligocene Primate, *Folia Primat.*, 5, 148–152.

Hoffstetter, M. R., 1969, Un Primate de l'Oligocène inférieur Sud-Américain: *Branisella boliviana* gen. et sp. nov., *C. R. Acad. Sci. Paris*, 269, 434–437.

Holloway, R. L., 1970, Brain evolution in the Hominodea, Aldine, New York, in press.

Hooijer, D. A., 1963, Miocene Mammalia from Congo, *Ann. Kon. Mus. M.-Afr. Tervueren*, 46(8), 1–77.

Hooton, E. A., 1932, *Up from the ape*, Macmillan, New York.

Hopwood, A. T., 1933, Miocene Primates from Kenya, *J. Linn. Soc. (Zool.),* 38, 437–464.

————, **1934,** New fossil mammals from Olduvai, Tanganyika Territory, *Ann. Mag. Nat. Hist. London*, 10, 546–553.

Howells, W. W., 1965, *Mankind in the making*, 2nd ed., Doubleday, Garden City, N.Y.

Hürzeler, J., 1946, *Gesneropithex peyeri* nov. gen. nov. spec., ein neuer Primate aus dem Ludien von Gösgen (Solothurn), *Ber. Schweiz. Pal. Ges. 25 Jahresvers., Ecl. Geol. Helv.*, 39, 354–361.

————, **1948,** Zur Stammesgeschichte der

Necrolemuriden, *Schweiz. Pal. Abh.*, 66, 1–46.

———, **1949,** Neubeschreibung von *Oreopithecus bambolii* Gervais, *Schweiz. Pal. Abh.*, 66, 1–20.

———, **1954,** Contribution à l'odontologie et à la phylogénèse du genre *Pliopithecus* Gervais, *Ann. Pal.*, 40, 1–63.

———, **1958,** *Oreopithecus bambolii* Gervais: A preliminary report, *Verh. Naturforsch. Ges. Basel*, 69, 1–48.

———, **1968,** Questions et reflexions sur l'histoire des anthropomorphes, *Ann. Pal.*, 54, 195–233.

Hutchinson, G. E., 1963, Natural selection, social organization, hairlessness, and the australopithecine canine, *Evolution*, 17, 588–589.

Imbrie, J., 1957, The species problem with fossil animals, IN *The species problem*, ed. E. Mayr, Amer. Assoc. Adv. Sci., Publ. No. 50, pp. 125–153.

International Code of Zoological Nomenclature, 1961, Fifteenth International Congress of Zoology, *Publ. Internat. Comm. Zool. Nom.*, 1–167.

James, W. W., 1960, *The jaws and teeth of Primates*, Pitman, London.

Jepsen, G. L., 1930a, New vertebrate fossils from the Lower Eocene of the Big Horn Basin, Wyoming, *Proc. Amer. Philos. Soc. Phila.*, 69, 117–131.

———, **1930b,** Stratigraphy and paleontology of the Paleocene of Northeastern Park County, Wyoming, *Proc. Amer. Philos. Soc. Phila.*, 69, 463–528.

———, **1934,** A revision of the American Apatemyidae and the description of a new genus *Sinclairella* from the White River Oligocene of South Dakota, *Proc. Amer. Philos. Soc.*, 74, 287–305.

Jolly, C. J., 1967, Evolution of baboons, IN *The baboon in medical research*, Vol. 2, ed. H. Vagtborg, Proc. 1st Internat. Symp. on the Baboon and Its Uses as an Experimental Animal, 1963, San Antonio, Texas, Texas U.P., Austin, pp. 323–338.

———, **1970,** The seed eaters: A new model of hominid differentiation based on a baboon analogy, *Man*, 5, 5–26.

———, **1972,** The classification and natural history of *Theropithecus (Simopithecus)* baboons of the African Pleistocene, *Bull. Brit. Mus. Nat. Hist. Geol. Ser.*, in press.

Jones, T. R., 1937, A new fossil primate from Sterkfontein, Krugersdorp, Transvaal, *S. Afr. J. Sci.*, 33, 709–728.

Kälin, J., 1961, Über die fossilen Primaten des Fayum (unteres Oligozän) von Ägypten, *Z. Wiss. Zool. Leipzig*, 165, 35–46.

Kermack, K. A., 1954, A biometric study of *Micraster corangium* and *M. (isomicraster) senonensis*, *Roy. Soc. London Ser. B, Biol. Sci.*, 237(649), 375–428.

Kraglievich, J. L., 1951, Contribuciones al conocimiento de los primates fósiles de la superior (Colhushuapiano) de Gaimán, Chubut. Com. Inst. Nac. Invest. Cienc. Nat. (Buenos Aires), *Cienc. Zool.*, 11(5), 55–82.

Krynine, P. D., 1937, Petrography and genesis of the Siwalik series, *Amer. J. Sci.*, 34(203), 422–446.

Kurtén, B., 1966, Comment concerning Hockett's and Ascher's contribution on the Human Revolution, *Curr. Anth.*, 7(2), 199–200.

———, **1968,** *Pleistocene mammals of Europe*, Aldine, Chicago.

Lamberton, C., 1934, Contribution à la connaissance de la faune subfossile Malgache: Lémuriens et Ratites, *Mem. Acad. Malgache, Tananarive*, 17, 1–168.

———, **1937,** Contribution à la connaissance de la faune subfossile de Madagascar. Note 2: Les Hadropithèques, *Bull. Acad. Malgache, Tananarive (n.s.)*, 20, 1–44.

———, **1944,** *Bradytherium* ou *Paléopropithèque?* *Bull. Acad. Malgaches*, 26, 1–52.

Lartet, E., 1837, Note sur la découverte récente d'un mâchoire de singe fossile, *C. R. Acad. Sci. Paris*, 4, 85–93.

———, **1856,** Note sur un grand singe fossile qui se rattache au groupe des singes supérieurs, *C. R. Acad. Sci.*, 43.

LeGros, Clark, W. E., 1934a, On the skull structure of *Pronycticebus gaudryi*, *Proc. Zool. Soc. London*, 1, 19–27.

———, **1934b,** *Early forerunners of man*, Bailliére, London.

———, **1945,** Note on the paleontology of the lemuroid brain, *J. Anat. London*, 79, 123–126.

———, **1946,** Significance of the Australopithecinae, *Nature, London*, 157, 863–865.

———, **1947,** Observations of the anatomy of the fossil Australopithecinae, *J. Anat.*, 81, 1–35.

———, **1950,** New paleontological evidence bearing on the evolution of the Hominoidea, *Quart. J. Geol. Soc. London*, 105, 225–264.

———, **1955,** *The fossil evidence for human evolution*, Chicago U.P., Chicago.

———, **1956,** A Miocene lemuroid skull from East Africa, *Brit. Mus. Nat. Hist. Foss. Mamm. Afr.*, 9, 1–6.

———, **1959,** *The antecedents of man*, Edinburgh U.P., Edinburgh.

———, **1967,** *Man-apes or ape-men?* Holt, New York.

————, and Leakey, L. S. B., 1951, The Miocene Hominoidea of East Africa, *Brit. Mus. Nat. Hist. Foss. Mamm. Afr.,* 1, 1–117.

————, and Thomas, D. P., 1952, The Miocene lemuroids of East Africa, *Brit. Mus. Nat. Hist. Foss. Mamm. Afr.,* 5, 1–20.

Leakey, L. S. B., 1943, A Miocene anthropoid mandible from Rusinga, Kenya, *Nature,* 152(3855), 319–320.

————, 1962, A new Lower Pliocene fossil primate from Kenya, *Ann. Mag. Nat. Hist. Ser. 13,* 4, 689–696.

————, 1965, The origin of man, IN *Wenner-Gren Symposion,* ed. I. DeVore, pp. 1–150.

————, 1967, An early Miocene member of Hominidae, *Nature,* 213(5072), 155–163.

————, 1968a, Upper Miocene Primates from Kenya, *Nature,* 218, 527–528.

————, 1968b, Notes on the mammalian faunas from the Miocene and Pleistocene of East Africa, IN *Background to evolution in Africa,* eds. W. W. Bishop and D. Clark, Chicago U.P., Chicago.

Leakey, R. E. F., 1969, New Cercopithecidae from the Chemeron beds of Lake Baringo, Kenya, *Foss. Vert. Afr.,* 1, 53–69.

Leidy, J., 1869, Notice on some extinct vertebrates from Wyoming and Dakota, *Proc. Acad. Nat. Sci. Phila.,* pp. 36–67.

————, 1870, Descriptions of *Paleosyops paludosus, Microsus cuspidatus,* and *Notharctus tenebrosus, Proc. Acad. Nat. Sci. Phila.,* pp. 111–114.

————, 1872, Remarks on some extinct mammals, *Proc. Acad. Nat. Sci. Phila.,* 24, 37–38.

————, 1873, Contributions to the extinct vertebrate fauna of the Western Territories, *Rep. U.S. Geol. Surv. Terr. (Hayden, Washington I),* pp. 14–358.

Lemoine, V., 1878, Communication sur les ossements fossiles des terrains tertiaires inférieurs des environs de Reims faite à la Société d'Histoire Naturelle de Reims, Reims, 2 pts., 1–24, 1–56.

————, 1880, Sur les ossements fossiles des terrains tertiaires inférieurs des environs de Reims, *C. R. Assoc. Fr. Avanc. Sci.,* 8, 585–594.

Lewis, G., 1934, Preliminary notice of new manlike apes from India: Scientific Research of the Yale India expedition, *Amer. J. Sci. Ser. 27,* 5, 161–181.

————, 1937, Taxonomic syllabus of Siwalik fossil anthropoids, *Amer. J. Sci. Ser. 5,* p. 34.

Linnaeus, C., 1758, Systema naturae per regna tria naturae, secundum classes, ordines, genera, species cum characteribus, synonymis, locis, 10th ed., rev., Stockholm, *Laurentii Salvii,* 1(2), 1–824.

Lorenz, G. H., 1968, Stratigraphische und mikropaläontologische Untersuchungen des Braunkohlengebietes von Bacinello, Grosseto (Italien), *Riv. Ital. Pal. Stratig., Milano,* p. 74.

Lydekker, R. 1878, Notices of Siwalik mammals, *Rec. Geol. Surv. India,* 11, 64–104.

————, 1887, Catalogue of the fossil Mammalia in the British Museum (Natural History), Part 5, p. 345.

MacDonald, J. R., 1963, The Miocene faunas from the Wounded Knee area of Western South Dakota, *Bull. Amer. Mus. Nat. Hist.,* 125(3), 141–238.

MacInnes, D. G., 1943, Notes on the East African Miocene primates, *J. E. Afr. Uganda Nat. Hist. Soc.,* 17, 141–181.

Mann, A. E., 1968, The paleodemography of *Australopithecus,* University Microfilms, Ann Arbor, Mich., 1–125.

Marsh, O. C., 1872, Preliminary description of new Tertiary mammals: Parts I–IV, *Amer. J. Sci. and Arts,* 4, 122–128, 202–224.

Matthew, W. D., 1914, A revision of the Lower Eocene Wasatch and Wind River faunas. Part IV: Entelonychia, Primates, Insectivora, *Bull. Amer. Mus. Nat. Hist.,* 34, 429–483.

———— and Granger, W., 1921, New genera of Paleocene mammals, *Amer. Mus. Nov.,* 13, 7.

————, 1923, New fossil mammals from the Pliocene of Sze-Chwan, China, *Amer. Mus. Nat. Hist.,* 48(17), 563–598.

Mayr, E., 1950, Taxonomic categories in fossil hominids, *Symp. Quant. Biol.,* 15, 109–118.

————, 1963, *Animal species and evolution,* Belknap Press, Cambridge, Mass.

————, 1969, The biological meaning of species, *Biol. J. Linn. Soc.,* 1, 311–320.

McAlester, A. L., 1962, Some comments on the species problem, *J. Pal.,* 36(6), 1377–1381.

McKenna, M. C., 1960, Fossil Mammalia from the early Wasatchian Four Mile fauna, Eocene of Northwest Colorado, *Univ. Calif. Publ. Geol. Sci.,* 37, 1.

————, 1963a, The early Tertiary primates and their ancestors, *Proc. 16th Internat. Congr. Zool.,* 4, 69–74.

————, 1963b, New evidence against tupaioid affinities of the mammalian family Anagalidae, *Amer. Mus. Nov.,* 2158, 1–16.

————, 1963c, Primitive Paleocene and

Eocene Apatemyidae (Mammalia, Insectivora) and the primate–insectivore boundary, *Amer. Mus. Nov.,* 2160, 1–39.

————, **1966,** Paleontology and the origin of the primates, *Folia Primat.,* 4(1), 1–25.

————, **1967,** Classification, range, and deployment of the prosimian primates, *Coll. Internat. Cent. Nat. Rech. Sci. Paris,* 163, 603–613.

Mollet, O. D., Van Der Spuy, 1947, Fossil mammals from the Makapan Valley, Potgietersrust. I. Primates. *S. Afr. Journ. Sci.,* 43, 295–303.

Morris, W. J., 1954, An Eocene fauna from the Cathedral Bluffs tongue of the Washakie Basin, Wyoming, *J. Pal.,* 28, 195–203.

Napier, J. R., 1963a, Brachiation and brachiators (with comment by E. H. Ashton), *Symp. Zool. Soc. London,* 10, 183–196.

————, **1963b,** The locomotor functions of hominids, IN *Classification and human evolution,* ed. S. L. Washburn, Aldine, Chicago, pp. 178–189.

————, **1970,** Palooecology and catarrhine evolution, IN *Old World monkeys: Evolution, systematics,* and *behavior,* eds. J. R. Napier and P. H. Napier, Academic Press, New York, pp. 53–96.

————, **and Davis, P. R., 1959,** The forelimb skeleton and associated remains of *Proconsul africanus, Foss. Mamm. Afr.,* Brit. *Mus. Nat. Hist.,* 16, 1–69.

————, **and Napier, P. H., 1967,** *A handbook of living primates,* Academic Press, London.

————, **and Walker, A. C., 1967,** Vertical clinging and leaping: A newly recognised category of locomotor behavior among primates, *Folia Primat.,* 6, 180–203.

Necrasov, O., Samson, P., and Radulesco, C., 1961, Sur un nouveau singe catarrhine fossile, découvert dans un nid fossilifère d'Oltenie (R.P.R.), *An. Stiint. Univ. Al. J. Cuzá, Sect. 2, Stiinte Nat. Jassy (n.s.),* 2(7), 401–416.

Osborn, H. F., 1902, American Eocene Primates and the supposed rodent family Mixodectidae, *Bull. Amer. Mus. Nat. Hist.,* 16, 169–214.

————, **1908,** New fossil mammals from the Fayûm Oligocene, Egypt, *Bull. Amer. Mus. Nat. Hist.,* 24, 265–272.

Owen, R., 1865, On a new genus (*Miolophus*) of mammal from the London Clay, *Geol. Mag.,* 2, 339–341.

Oxnard, C. E., 1967, The functional morphology of the primate shoulder as revealed by comparative anatomical osteometric and discriminant function techniques, *Amer. J. Phys. Anth.,* 26, 219–240.

————, **1968a,** A note on the Olduvai clavicular fragment, *Amer. J. Phys. Anth.,* 29, 429–431.

————, **1968b,** The architecture of the shoulder on some mammals, *J. Morph.,* 126, 249–290.

Patterson, B., 1968, The extinct baboon *Parapapio jonesi* in the early Pleistocene of Northeastern Kenya, *Mus. Comp. Zool.,* 282, 1–4.

————, **Behrensmeyer, A. K., and Sill, W. D., 1970,** Geology and fauna of a new Pliocene locality in Northwestern Kenya, *Nature,* 226, 918–921.

Pei, W. C., 1957, Discovery of *Gigantopithecus* mandibles and other material in Liu-Cheng district of Central Kwangsi in South China, *Vert. Palasiatica,* 1, 65–71.

Pfeiffer, J. E., 1969, *The emergence of man,* Harper, New York.

Pilbeam, D. R., 1967, Man's earliest ancestors, *Sci. J.,* 3, 47–53.

————, **1968,** The earliest hominids, *Nature,* 219, 1335–1338.

————, **1969,** Tertiary Pongidae of East Africa: Evolutionary relationships and taxonomy, *Peabody Mus. Bull.,* 31, 1–185.

————, **1970,** *Human origins,* Thames and Hudson, London.

————, **and Walker, A. C., 1968,** Fossil monkeys from the Miocene of Napak, Northeast Uganda, *Nature,* 220, 657–660.

Pilgrim, G. E., 1910, Notices of new mammalian genera and species from the tertiaries of India, *Rec. Geol. Surv. India,* 40, 63–71.

————, **1915,** New Siwalik Primates and their bearing on the question of the evolution of man and the Anthropoidea, *Rec. Geol. Surv. India,* 45, 1–74.

————, **1927,** A *Sivapithecus* palate and other primate fossils from India, *Pal. Ind. (n.s.),* 14, 1–26.

Piton, L.-E., 1940, Paléontologie du gisement Éocène de Menat (Puy-de-Dôme) (flore et faune), *Mém. Soc. Hist. Nat. Auvergne, Clermont-Ferrand,* 1, 1–103.

Piveteau, J., 1957, *Traité de paléontologie,* Vol. 7, *Primates: Paléontologie humaine,* Masson, Paris.

Pocock, R. I., 1925, Additional notes on the external characters of platyrrhine monkeys, *Proc. Zool. Soc. London,* pp. 27–47.

————, **1926,** The external characters on some platyrrhine monkeys, *Proc. Zool. Soc. London,* pp. 1479–1579.

Prasad, K. N., 1969, Critical observations

on the fossil anthropoids from the Siwalik system of India, *Folia Primat.*, 10, 288–317.

Preuschoft, H., 1970, The posture and mode of locomotion of the subfossil lemurs from Madagascar, Proc. 3rd Internat. Congr. Primatol, Zürich, August 2–5, 1970.

Quinet, G. E., 1966, Sur la formule dentaire de deux primates du Landénien continental belge, *Bull. Inst. Roy. Sci. Nat. Belg., Bruxelles*, 42(38), 1–6.

Radinsky, L. B., 1967, The oldest primate endocast, *Amer. J. Phys. Anth.*, 27, 385–388.

Remane, A., 1921, Zur Beurteilung der fossilen Anthropoiden, *Zbl. Min. Geol. Pal.*, 11, 335–339.

———, 1950, Bemerkungen über *Gigantopithecus blacki*, IN *Über die neuen Vor- und and Frühmenschenfunde aus Afrika, Java, China, und Frankreich*, ed. H. Weinert, *Ztschr. Morph. Anth.*, 42, 113–148.

———, 1956, Paläontologie und Evolution der Primaten: Besonders der Nicht-Hominoiden, IN *Primatologia*, Vol. 1, eds. H. Hofer, A. H. Schultz, and D. Starck, Karger, Basel, pp. 267–378.

———, 1960, Die Stellung von *Gigantopithecus*, Anth. Anz. Stuttgart, 24, 146–159.

———, 1965, Die Geschichte der Menschenaffen, IN *Menschliche Abstammungslehre: Fortschritte der Anthropogenie, 1863–1965*, ed. G. Heberer, Goettingen, pp. 294–303.

Ristori, G., 1890, Le scimmie fossile italien, *Boll. Com. Geol. Italy*, 21, 178–196, 225–237.

Robinson, J. T., 1956, The dentition of the Australopithininae, *Mem. Transvaal Mus.*, 9, 1–179.

———, 1961, The australopithecines and their bearing on the origin of man and of stone tool making, *S. Afr. J. Sci.*, 57, 3–13.

———, 1966, The distinctiveness of *Homo habilis*, *Nature*, 209, 953–960.

Robinson, P., 1957, The species of *Notharctus* from the middle Eocene, *Postilla*, 28, 1–27.

———, 1966, Fossil Mammalia from the Huerfano formation, Eocene of Colorado, *Peabody Mus. Bull.*, 21, 1–95.

———, 1967, The mandibular dentition of ?*Tetonoides* (Primates, Anaptomorphidae), *Ann. Carnegie Mus.*, 39, 187–191.

———, 1968, Paleontology and geology of the Badwater Creek area, Central Wyoming, with a discussion of material from Utah, *Ann. Carnegie Mus.*, 39, 307–326.

Rusconi, C., 1933, Nuevos restos de monos fósiles del terciario antiguo de la Patagonia, *Anal. Soc. Sci. Argent.*, 116, 286–289.

Russell, D. E., 1964, Les mammifères paléocènes d'Europe, *Mem. Mus. National Hist. Nat.*, 13, 1–324.

———, 1967, Sur *Menatotherium* et l'âge Paléocène du gisement de Menat (Puy-de-Dôme), Coll. Internat. Cent. Rech. Sci. Paris, *Probl. Actuels Pal.*, 163, 483–489.

———, Louis, P., and Savage, D. E., 1967, Primates of the French early Eocene, *Univ. Calif. Publ. Geol. Sci.*, 73.

Russell, L. S., 1967, Paleontology of the Swan Hills area, North Central Alberta, Roy. Ontario Mus., Univ. Toronto Contr., *Life Sci.*, 71, 3–31.

Rütimeyer, L., 1862, Die Fauna der Pfahlbauten der Schweiz, *N. Denkschr. Schweiz. Ges. Naturwiss.*, 19(1), 1–248.

———, 1891, Die Eocaene Säugettierwelt von Egerkingen, *Abh. Schweiz. Pal. Ges.*, 18, 1–153.

Sarich, V., 1968, Immunological time scale for hominid evolution, *Science*, 158, 1200.

Schepers, G. W. H., 1946, The South African fossil ape men, Part II, *Transvaal Mus. Mem.*, No. 2, 155–272.

Schlosser, M., 1887, Die Affen, Lemuren, Chiropteren, Insectivoren, Marsupialier, Creodonten, und Carnivoren des europäischen Tertiärs und deren Beziehungen zu ihren lebenden und fossilen aussereuropäischen Verwandten, *Beitr, Pal. Oesterreich-Ungarns und Orients*, 6, 1–227.

———, 1911, Beiträge zur Kenntnis der oligozanen Landsäugetiere aus dem Fayum, Ägypten, *Beitr. Pal. Oesterreich-Ungarns und Orients*, 24, 51–167.

———, 1923, Mammalia (Säugetiere), IN *Grundzüge der Paläontologie (Paläozoologie). II. Abteilung Vertebrata*, 4th ed., ed. K. A. von Zittel, Oldenburg, Munich, pp. 402–689.

Schmerling, P. C., 1833–1834, *Recherches sur ossements fossiles découverts dans les cavernes de la province de Liège*, Liége, 2 vols., pp. 1–167, 1–195.

Schultz, A. H., 1957, Past and recent views of man's specialisation, *Irish J. Med. Science*, 341–356.

———, 1961, Vertebral column and thorax, IN *Primatologia*, eds. H. Hofer, A. H. Schultz and D. Starck, 4, 1–66.

———, 1968, The recent hominoid primates, IN *Perspectives in human evolution*, Vol. 1, eds. S. L. Washburn and P. C. Jay,

Holt, New York, pp. 122–195.

Schwalbe, G., 1915, Über den fossilen Affen *Oreopithecus bambolii:* Zugleich ein Beitrag zur Morphologie der Zähne der Primaten, *Ztschr. Morph. Anth.,* 19, 149–254.

Scott, W. B., 1913, *A history of land mammals in the Western Hemisphere,* Macmillan, New York.

Selenka, E., 1898–1899, *Menschenaffen 1 und 2,* Kreidels, Wiesbaden, pp. 1–160.

Sera, G. L., 1935, I caratteri morfologici di *Paleopropithecus* e l'adattamento acquatico primitivo dei Mammiferi e dei Primati in particolare, *Arch. Ital. Anat. Embriol.,* 35, 229–270.

————, **1938,** Alcuni caratteri scheletrici di importanza ecologia a filetica nei Lemuri fossili et attuali, *Paleontographica Ital., Pisa,* 38(n.s. 8), 1–112.

————, **1950,** Ulteriori osservationi sui lemuri fossili et actuali, *Paleontographica Ital., Pisa,* 47(n.s. 17), 1–113.

Seton, H., 1940, Two new primates from the Lower Eocene of Wyoming, *Proc. New Engl. Zool. Club,* 18, 39–42.

Simons, E. L., 1960, *Apidium* and *Oreopithecus, Nature,* 186, 824–826.

————, **1961a,** Notes on Eocene Tarsioids and a revision of some Necrolemurinae, *Bull. Brit. Mus. Nat. Hist. Geol.,* 5(3), 43–69.

————, **1961b,** The dentition of *Ourayia:* Its bearing on relationships of omomyid prosimians, *Postilla,* 54, 1–20.

————, **1962a,** Two new primate species from the African Oligocene, *Postilla,* 64, 1–12.

————, **1962b,** A new Eocene primate genus, *Cantius,* and a revision of some allied European lemuroids, *Bull. Brit. Mus. Nat. Hist. Geol.,* 7(1), 1–36.

————, **1963a,** A critical reappraisal of Tertiary Primates, IN *Genetic and evolutionary biology of the Primates,* ed. J. Buettner-Janusch, Academic Press, New York, pp. 65–129.

————, **1963b,** Some fallacies in the study of hominid phylogeny, *Proc. 16th Internat. Congr. Zool.,* 4, 25–70.

————, **1964a,** On the mandible of *Ramapithecus, Proc. Nat. Acad. Sci.,* 51(3), 528–535.

————**1964b,** Old World higher Primates: Classification and taxonomy, *Sci. Rev.,* 144, 709–710.

————, **1964c,** The early relatives of man, *Sci. Am.,* 211, 60.

————, **1965a,** Remarks on pongid and hominid evolution: I, IN *The origin of man: A symposion,* ed. P. L. DeVore, The Wenner-Gren Foundation for Anthropological Research, New York, pp. 43–45, 58, 65.

————, **1965b,** New fossil apes from Egypt and the initial differentiation of Hominoidea. *Nature,* 205, 135–139.

————, **1966,** In search of the missing link, *Discovery, Yale Peabody Mus.,* 1(2), 24–30.

————, **1967,** The earliest apes, *Sci. Amer.,* 217(6), 28–35.

————, **1968,** Evolution of the primates, IN *International encyclopedia of the Social Sciences,* Macmillan, New York, pp. 212–214.

————, **1969a,** The late Miocene hominid from Fort Ternan, Kenya, *Nature,* 221, 448–451.

————, **1969b,** A Miocene monkey (*Prohylobates*) from Northern Egypt, *Nature,* 223, 687–689.

————, **1971,** A current review of the interrelationships of Oligocene and Miocene Catarrhini, Papers presented at 2nd Internat. Symp. Dental Morph., 193–208.

————, **1972,** A new species of *Parapithecus* from the Oligocene of Egypt with observations on the initial differentiation of Ceropithecoidea, *Nature,* in press.

————, **and Chopra, S. R. K.,** 1969, A new species of *Gigantopithecus* (Hominoidea, Primates) from north India with some comments on its relationship to earliest hominids, *Postilla* (Peabody Museum, Yale University), 138, 1–18.

————, **and Ettel, P. C.,** 1970, *Gigantopithecus, Sci. Amer.,* 222(1), 76–85.

————, **and Pilbeam, D. R.,** 1965, Preliminary revision of the Dryopithecinae (Pongidae, Antropoidea), *Folia Primat.,* 3, 81–152.

Simpson, G. G., 1928, A new mammalian fauna from the Fort Union of Southern Montana, *Amer. Mus. Nov.,* 279, 1–15.

————, **1929a,** Third contribution to the Fort Union fauna at Bear Creek, Montana, *Amer. Mus. Nov.,* 345, 1–12.

————, **1929b,** Collection of Paleocene mammals from Bear Creek Montana, *Ann. Carnegie Mus.,* 19, 115–122.

————, **1935a,** The Tiffany fauna, Upper Paleocene. II. Structure and relationships of *Plesiadapis, Amer. Mus. Nov.,* 816, 1–30.

————, **1935b,** New Paleocene mammals from the Fort Union of Montana, *Proc. U.S. Nat. Mus.,* 83, 221–244.

————, **1937a,** The Fort Union of the Crazy Mountain field, Montana, and its mammalian faunas, *Bull. U.S. Nat. Mus.,* 169, 1–287.

————, **1937b,** Additions to the Upper Paleocene faunas of the Crazy Mountain field, *Amer. Mus. Nov.,* 940, 1–15.

————, **1937c,** The beginning of the age of mammals, *Biol. Rev.,* 12, 1–47.

————, **1940,** Studies on the earliest primates, *Bull. Amer. Mus. Nat. Hist.,* 77, 185–212.

————, **1945,** The principles of classification and a classification of mammals, *Bull. Amer. Mus. Nat. Hist.,* 85, 1–350.

————, **1953,** Evolution and geography, Condon Lecture, Oregon State System of Higher Education.

————, **1955,** The Phenacolemuridae, a new family of early primates, *Bull. Amer. Mus. Nat. Hist.,* 105, 411–441.

————, **1961,** *Principles of animal taxonomy,* Columbia U.P., New York, pp. 1–247.

————, **1967,** The Tertiary lorisiform primates of Africa, *Bull. Mus. Comp. Zool.,* 136, 39–61.

Standing, H. F., **1908,** On recently discovered subfossil Primates from Madagascar, *Trans. Zool. Soc. London,* 18, 59–162.

————, **1910,** Note sur les ossements subfossiles provenant des fouilles d'Ampasambazimba, *Bull. Acad. Malgache Tananarive (a.s.),* 7, 61–64.

Stehlin, H. G., **1912,** Die Säugetiere des schweizerischen Eocäns. Kritischer Katalog der Materialien, 7ter Theil,erste Hälfte *Adapis, Abh. Schweiz. Pal. Ges.,* 38, 1165–1298.

————, **1916,** Die Säugetiere des schweizerischen Eocäns. Kritischer Katalog der Materialien, 7ter Theil, Zweite Hälfte, *Abh. Schweiz. Pal. Ges.,* 41, 1297–1552.

Stirton, R. A., **1951,** Ceboid monkeys from the Miocene of Colombia, *Univ. Calif. Publ. Geol. Sci.,* 28, 315–356.

————, **and Savage, D. E., 1951,** A new monkey from the La Venta Miocene of Colombia, *Serv. Geol. Nac. Bogota,* 7, 345–356.

Stock, C., **1933,** An Eocene primate from California, *Proc. Nat. Acad. Sci.,* 19, 954–959.

————, **1934,** A second Eocene primate from California, *Proc. Nat. Acad. Sci.,* 20, 150–154.

————, **1938,** A tarsiid primate and a mixodectid from the Poway Eocene, California, *Proc. Nat. Acad. Sci.,* 24, 288–293.

Straus, W. L., Jr., **1963,** The classification of *Oreopithecus,* IN *Classification and human evolution,* ed., S. L. Washburn, Aldine, Chicago, pp. 146–177.

Stromer, E., **1913,** Mitteilungen über Wirbeltierreste aus dem Mittelpliocän des Natrontales (Ägypten), *Ztschr. Deutsch. Geol. Ges.,* 65, 350–372.

Struhsaker, T. T., **1970,** Phylogenetic implications of some vocalizations of *Cercopithecus* monkeys, IN *Old World monkeys,* ed. J. R. Napier and P. H. Napier, Academic Press, New York.

Sylvester-Bradley, P. C., ed., **1956,** The species concept in paleontology, *Syst. Assoc. London,* 2, 1–145.

Szalay, F. S., **1967,** The beginnings of primates, *Evolution,* 22, 19–36.

————, **1968,** Origins of the Apatemyidae (Mammalia, Insectivora), *Amer. Mus. Nov.,* 2352, 1–11.

————, **1969,** Uintasoricinae, a new subfamily of early Tertiary mammals (Primates?), *Amer. Mus. Nov.,* 2363, 1–36.

Tattersall, I. M., **1969a,** Ecology of North Indian *Ramapithecus, Nature,* 221(5179), 451–452.

————, **1969b,** More on the ecology of North Indian *Ramapithecus, Nature,* 224(5221), 821–822.

————, **1970,** *Man's ancestors,* Murray, London.

————, **and Simons, E. L., 1969,** Notes on some little-known primate fossils from India, *Folia Primat.,* 10, 146–153.

Teilhard de Chardin, P., **1916,** Sur quelques primates des phosphorites du Quercy, *Ann. Pal. Paris,* 10, 1–20.

————, **1921,** Les Mammifères de l'Éocène inférieur français et leurs gisements, *Ann. Pal.,* 1916, 10, 171–176; 1921, 11, 108.

————, **1927,** Les Mammifères de l'Éocène inférieur de la Belgique, *Mem. Mus. Roy. Hist. Nat. Belg.,* 36, 1–33.

————, **1938,** The fossils from locality 12 of Choukoutien, *Pal. Sinica, Peking (n.s.),* c5, 1–50.

Thenius, E. **1969,** Stammesgeschichte der Säugetiere (einschliesslich der Hominiden), IN *Handbuch der Zoologie,* Vol. 8(2), Walter de Gruyter, Berlin.

Tobias, P. V., **1964,** The Olduvai Bed I homonine with special references to its cranial capacity, *Nature,* 203, 3.

————, **1965,** Early man in East Africa, *Science,* 149, 22–33.

————, **1966,** On "*Homo habilis*": Reply to comments by T. Bielicki, *Curr. Anth.,* 7(5), 579–580.

————, **1967a,** General questions arising from some Lower and Middle Pleistocene hominids of the Olduvai Gorge, Tanzania, *S. Afr. J. Sci.,* 63, 41–48.

————, **1967b,** *Olduvai Gorge,* vol. 2, ed. L. S. B. Leakey, Cambridge U.P., Cambridge, England.

————, **1968a,** Middle and early Upper Pleistocene members of the genus *Homo* in

Africa, IN *Evolution und Hominisation*, 2nd ed., ed. G. Kurth, Fischer, Stuttgart, pp. 176–194.

———, **1968b,** Cranial capacity in anthropoid apes, *Australopithecus* and *Homo habilis, S. Afr. J. Sci.,* 64, 81–91.

———, **1969,** Bigenic nomina: A proposal for modification of the rules of nomenclature, *Amer. J. Phys. Anth.,* 31(1), 103–106.

Trevor, J. C., 1963, The history of the word "brachiator" and a problem of authorship in primate nomenclature, *Symp. Zool. Soc. London,* 10, 197–198.

Trouessart, E. L., 1879, Catalogue des Mammifères vivants et fossiles, *Rev. Mag. Zool. Ser. 3,* 7, 223–230.

Troxell, E. L., 1926, *Smilodectes* and *Notharctus, Amer. J. Sci.,* 11, 423–428.

van Couvering, J. A., and Miller, J. A., 1969, Miocene stratigraphy and age determinations, Rusinga Island, Kenya, *Nature,* 221, 628–632.

van Valen, L., 1963, The origin and status of the mammalian order Tillodonta, *J. Mamm.,* 44(3), 364–373.

———, **1965,** A Middle Paleocene Primate, *Nature, London,* 207(4995), 435–436.

———, **and Sloan, R. E., 1965,** The earliest Primates, *Science,* 150, 743–745.

Verheyen, W. N., 1962, Contribution à la craniologie comparée des Primates, les genres *Colobus* Illiger 1811 et *Cercopithecus* Linné 1758, *Ann. Mus. Roy. Afr. centr. Tervuren (8) Ser. Sci. Zool.,* 105, 1–255.

Vogel, C., 1968, The phylogenetical evaluation of some characters and some morphological trends in the evaluation of the skull in catarrhine primates, IN *Taxonomy and phylogeny of Old World primates,* ed. B. Chiarelli, Rosenberg and Sellier, Torino, pp. 21–55.

von Koenigswald, G. H. R., 1935, Eine fossile Säugetierfauna mit Simia aus Südchina, *Abst. Wettstein Ber. Wiss. Biol.,* 37, 480.

———, **1940,** Neue Pithecantropusfunde 1936–1938, Batavia, *Wetensch. Meded. Dienst Mijnbouw Nederlandsch-Indië,* 28, 1–232.

———, **1952,** *Gigantopithecus blacki,* a giant fossil hominoid from the Pleistocene of Southern China, *Anth. Papers Amer. Mus. Nat. Hist.,* 43, 295–325.

———, **1969,** Miocene Cercopithecoidea and Oreopithecoidea from Miocene of East Africa, *Foss. Vert. Afr.,* 1, 39–52.

von Lorenz-Liburnau, L., 1905, *Megaladapis edwardsi,* G. Grandidier, *Denkschr. Akad. Wiss. Wien,* 77, 451–490.

Wagner, A., 1839, Fossile Überreste von einem Affenschädel und anderen Säugetieren aus Griechenland, *Gel. Anz. Bayrisch. Acad. Wiss. München,* 8(35), 305–312.

Walker, A., 1967a, Patterns of extinction among the subfossil Madagascan lemuroids, IN *Pleistocene extinctions,* ed. P. S. Martin, Yale U.P., New Haven, Conn., pp. 426–432.

———, **1967b,** Locomotor adaptations in recent and fossil Madagascan lemurs, Dissertation, Univ. London, pp. 1–528.

———, **1969a,** True affinities of *Propotto leakeyi* Simpson 1967, *Nature,* 223(5206), 647–648.

———, **1969b,** The locomotion of lorises with special reference to the Potto, *East African Wildlife J.,* 7, 1–5.

———, **1970,** Postcranial remains of the Miocene Lorisidae of East Africa, *Amer. J. Phys. Anth.,* 33, 249–261.

———, **and Rose, M. D., 1968,** Some hominoid vertebra from the Miocene of Uganda, *Nature,* 217, 980–981.

Weidenreich, F., 1945, Giant early man from Java and South China, *Anth. Papers Amer. Mus. Nat. Hist.,* 40.

———, **1946,** *Apes, giants, and man,* Chicago U.P., Chicago.

Weigelt, I., 1933, Neue Primaten aus der mitteleozänen (oberlutetischen) Braunkohle des Geiseltales, *Nova Acta Leopold. Halle (n.s.),* 1, 97–153.

Weller, J. M., 1961, The species problem, *J. Pal.,* 35, 1181–1192.

Williams, E. E., and Koopman, K. E., 1952, West Indian fossil monkeys, *Amer. Mus. Nov.,* 1546, 1–16.

Wilson, J. A., 1966, A new primate from the earliest Oligocene, West Texas: Preliminary report, *Folia Primat.,* 4, 227–248.

Witworth, T., 1958, Miocene ruminants of East Africa, *Foss. Mamm. Afr. Brit. Mus. Nat. Hist.,* 15, 1–50.

Woo, J.-K., 1962, The mandibles and dentition of *Gigantopithecus, Pal. Sinica, 146 (n.s. D.),* 11, 1–94.

Wood, S., 1846, On the discovery of an alligator and of several new Mammalia in the Hordwell Cliff, with observations on the geological phenomena of that locality, *Geol. J. London,* 1, 1–7.

Wood-Jones, F., 1916, *Arboreal man,* Arnold, London.

Wortman, J. L., 1903, 1904, Studies of Eocene Mammalia in the Marsh collection, *Peabody Mus. Amer. J. Sci.,* 13, 39–448.

Zapfe, H., 1958, The skeleton of Pliopithecus (*Epipliopithecus vindobonensis*) Zapfe and Hürzeler, *Amer. J. Phys. Anth.,* 16, 441–458.

————, **1960,** Die Primatenfunde aus der miozänen Spaltenfüllung von Neudorf an der March (Děvinská Nová Ves), Tschechoslowakei. Mit Anhang: Der Primatenfund aus dem Miozän von Klein Hadersdorf in Niederoesterreich, *Schweiz. Pal. Abh.,* 78, 4–293.

————, **1963,** Lebensbild von *Megaladapis edwardsi* (Grandidier), *Folia. Primat.,* 1, 178–187.

Index

A page number in italics
refers to a figure
or to a figure and the text.

gaudryi, 129
Propithecus, 67, 71, 103, 137, 139
   verreauxi, 66
Propliopithecus, 2, 194, 212, 213, 214, 215,
   216, 218, 272, 278
   haeckeli, 212, 213, 214
Propotamochoerus, 270
Prosimians, 2, 13, 19, 50, 53, 61, 65, 67, 74,
   76, 78, 83, 84, 85, 86, 95, 101, 159,
   160, 162, 166, 169, 174, 175, 177,
   178, 213, 218
   archaic, 21, 105, 106, 111, 158, 160, 169,
   173
   lorisiform, 67
   Malagasy, 109, 114
   recent, 138, 173
   tarsioid, 13
Prosinopa, 2
Protoadapis, 20, 125, 127, 128, 129
   angustidens, 129
   curvicuspidens, 128
Protomomys, 153
Protungulatum, 108
Pseudoloris, 139, 140, 161, 162, 167, 168
   abderhaldini, 163, 168
   parvulus, 166
Pterodon, 21
Pterygoid, 72, 125, 139, 143, 162
   muscle, 114
Ptilocercus, 156
Purgatorius, 108, 109, 120
   ceratops, 108
Purgatorius-Protungulatum molar type, 109
Pygmy chimpanzee, 84, 102. See also
      Chimpanzee; Pan

Quadrupedalism, 54–55, 71, 76, 77, 90, 91,
   102, 236. See also Locomotion
Quarry sites, Fayum Oligocene, 212
Quaternary, 9, 11
Quercy phosphates, France, 124, 127, 129,
   131, 161, 164, 166
Quinet, G. E., 153, 154

Rabbits, 264
Races, 28
Radiation
   basal primate, 104
   of mammals, 13
   placental, 12
Radinsky, L., 142, 143
Radioactive dating, 5, 11
Radioactive decay, asymptotic, 6, 7
Radiocarbon dating, 93
Radius, 76, 198, 248
Rafting, 21, 176
Rahm, U., 282
Ramapithecus, 4, 15, 44, 45, 223, 237, 238,
   239, 247, 259, 266, 268, 269, 270,
   271, 272, 273, 274, 275, 277, 281
   brevirostris, 267, 269

punjabicus, 37, 239, 241, 245, 269
Rao, Vinayak, 266
Remane, A., 2, 3, 229, 255, 264
Reproductive cycle, monkeys and apes, 83
Reproductive periods, 71
Reptiles, 10
   flying, 47
Retinal fovea, 72
Rhinoceratids, 270
Rhinoceros, 13, 260
Rhinoceroses, 14, 45, 95
Rhinopithecus, 195
Rhone Basin, France, 221
Ristori, G., 196
Robinson, J. T., 3, 206
Robinson, P., 122, 138, 139, 144, 145, 152,
   155, 157
Rodents, 12, 13, 14, 32, 103, 110, 169, 186,
   222, 260, 264
   cricetid, 270
   hystricomorph, 176
   phiomyid, 31
Rooneyia, 13, 140, 157, 158, 159, 160, 177,
   178
   viejaensis, 177
Rose, M., 253
rostrum, 85
   foreshortened, 79
   retention of, 72
Rowan, R., 113, 115
Rudolf, East, Kenya, 277
Rusconi, C., 181
Rusinga Island, Kenya, 50, 169, 170, 192,
   217, 224, 225, 236, 245, 246, 248,
   249–251, 253, 270
Russell, D. E., 3, 110–112, 114, 116, 117,
   119, 121, 126, 133–135, 140, 146,
   148, 154, 155, 166
Rütimeyer, L., 2, 131

Saber-toothed cats, 13, 15
Sacrum, 111, 220
Sagittal crest, 85, 207
Saguinus, 180
Saimiri, 180, 183, 212
Saint Gaudens, France, 225, 230, 232, 234,
   235, 243
Saint-Hillaire, G., 174
Salt Range, W. Pakistan, 267
Sansan, France, 216, 223
Santacruzian provincial age, South America,
   179
Sarich, V., 175
Savage, D. E., 3, 121, 126, 133, 135, 140,
   146, 154, 155, 211
Savanna, 207
Saxonella, 115, 116, 117
   crepaturae, 116
Scapula, 58, 76, 90
   of Australopithecus, 58
Scarritt Quarry, Montana, 118

fused, 99
Systema Naturae, 27, 28
Szalay, F. S., 4, 19, 106, 115, 116, 120, 123,
    126, 130, 131, 140, 143, 144, 145,
    146, 147, 149, 154, 157, 162
Szechuan Province, China, 222

Talus, 133, 153, 150, 250
Tapirs, 12, 14, 35, 95, 260
Tarsiers, 16, 17, 60, 64, 72, 78, 86, 131,
    132, 161, 164, 190
Tarsiidae, 53, 67, 140, 161, 168
  European Eocene, 141
Tarsioids, 13, 80, 129, 130, 147
Tarsius, 59, 65, 71, 72, 74, 75, 78, 130, 132,
    140, 143, 147, 149, 150, 151,
    159–166, *167,* 168, 189
  distribution, East Indies, 67
  skeleton of, *67*
Tattersall, I. M., 4, 66, 81, 94, 96, 101, 104,
    111, 270
Taung, South Africa, 18, 205, 207
Taxon, 27, 30, 38
Taxonomic category, 27
  difference, 39
  significance, 39
Taxonomy, 3 *n.,* 4, 27, 29, 30, 36
  animal, 26
  Linnean, 32
Tchadanthropus, 28
Teeth
  anterior, reduction of, 64
  dental designations for, 20 *n.*
  differences in eruption sequence, 44
  hominid, 45
  number of, 60
  reduction and loss, 109
  relative sizes of, 43
Teilhard de Chardin, P., 2, 109, 114, 115,
    131, 153, 161, 166, 168, 199
Teilhardina, 20, 147, *153,* 168
  belgica, 153
  gallica, 154
Telmatolestes, 2, 136
Temporal, 169, 175, 196
Temporo-mandibular joint, 85
Tenrecs, 131
Tertiary, 1, 6, 7, 9, 11, 13, 15, 31, 53, 169
  early, 108, 125, 132, 137, 147, 150, 161,
    162, 164, 192
  primate interrelationships, *107*
  provincial ages:
    Europe, *10*
    North America, *10*
Tetonius, 60, 61, 140, *142,* 144, 145, 146,
    154, 159, 161, 162
  homunculus, 141–143
Tetonoides, 144, 146
Thanatocoenose, 97
Thenius, E., 3, 65

Theropithecus (= Simopithecus), 55, 56, 87,
    91, 103, *202,* 203, 206, 207, 259, 261
  darti, 202
  gelada, 102, 201
  jonathani, 202
  leakeyi, 202
  oswaldi, 202
  waterside habitat of, 204
Thinolestes, 2, 136
Thomas, D. P., 3, 169, 170, 172, 214, 221,
    225, 227, 229
Thoracic flattening, *90*
Tibia, 60, 76, 77
Tibiofibula, 67, 163, 165, 168
Tiffany, Colorado, 110, 117, 118, 121, 122
Tillodonts, 52
Titanotheres, 13
Tobias, P. V., 17, 18, 32
Tomitherium, 2
Tools, 47, 281
  bone, 49
  pseudo-, 49
  use of, 15
Tooth comb, 61, 64, 97, 101, 143, 169, 172,
    173
Tooth structures, terminology, *63*
Torrejonian provincial age, North America,
    112, 114, 117, 120, 121
Tragulids, 270
Tra-tra-tra-tra, 97
Tree shrews, 53, 60, 65, 72–74, 112. *See
    also Tupaia*
Trevor, J. C., 58
Triceratops, 108
Trigon (three cusped tooth), 98
Trogolemur, 14, 145, 146
Trouessart, E. L., 2, 133, 146
Troxell, E. L., 138
Tupaia, 65, 73, 74, 112, 148. *See also* Tree
    shrews
Tupaioidea, 53
Tuscany, Italy, lignites of, 21, 46, 47, 262
Tympanic, 73, 95, 125, 130, 170
  ring, 74, 80, 85, 98, 127, 165, 172, 175
Type, 26, 27, 29–31, 109
  definition of, 29

Uintalacus, 140, 145, 146
Uintanius, 140, 145, 146, 148
Uintasorex, 140
Uintathreres, 12, 13
Ulna, 60, 193, 198, 208, 237, 248
  retroflection of, 55
Ungulates, 12, 109, 132, 143, 151
  even-toed, 13
  odd-toed, 13
Urine washing, 71
Ursids, 185
Ursus, 35, 258, 260
Utahia, 154, 155
  kayi, 155